LEGENDS OF THE GAROU

Krieger Wyrmfoe and the Death Bear

Arne Kleppens — or Wind-Never-Slows to his tribe — sits huddled under a threadbare blanket. His wolf's skin shuts out the cold, but only barely. Soon he will howl to his packmates and they will change places with the other Guardians, and then enjoy a mug of something warm. Arne smiles to himself — one of the Kinfolk brought in chocolate from Italy. That would warm him quite well.

He stands and shakes himself, throwing the blanket into the snow. He paces, trying to limber his body. From the valley in the glacier behind him, he hears howls of approval — Brings-Life-to-the-Old-Tales has finished his story. Arne wonders what it was this time. Perhaps a retelling of the fall of the Thousand Oak Sept? No, too bleak. The winter has already been long and unpleasant. Maybe one of the bawdy tales of Micah Mule-Slayer, the famed Ragabash womanizer? Probably not: the Gaia's Hammer Sept has visitors tonight, and they might not appreciate so risqué a story.

Arne marvels at the skill of the Moon Dancers. Brings-Life is a master storyteller, and younger Garou from septs all over Europe come to tell him stories and hear his advice on re-telling them. But he shares the limelight graciously, and moots often end with the sorrowful howls of the wolf-born Galliard Last Snow-fall, or with the frenzied violin of Dunya Monarch's-Grace. Arne himself is a half-moon, and has no skill for such things. He merely sits and marvels, a weight lifted from his mind, for while a Galliard tells a story, he does not have to worry about truth or falsehood.

He steps forward and howls to the ice and moon-light. He hears four answering howls — his pack, the Ice Runners, coming to join him. From behind him he hears three brief, clipped howls ending in a short bark. On nights as cold as this one, the Guardians change places every hour or so in order to keep from freezing. Arne has heard stories of days past when the sept boasted no fewer than four packs of Guardians. Now his pack and a scattering of Fostern and Adren are the only Garou who take up the Warning Horn and wait in the snow.

Four wolves appear from the ice, and the pack trots towards the fire. Arne lifts his head and smells the hot chocolate waiting for them. The thick syrup of that scent contrasts with the clean bite of the ice and the chalky aroma of the fire. As they near the crude table, Arne sees that the stories have not ended for the night, and that one of the visiting Garou has decided to try her hand at tale-spinning. She does not seem to be well received, however, and her audience appears restless and annoyed. Arne reaches the table and changes to his natural Homid form, pulling his recently-dedicated coat tightly around him. Lena, the Kinfolk woman who brought the chocolate, is already pouring four mugs of it for the Ice Runners (the pack's Ahroun does not indulge in sweets). Arne nudges Lena gently.

"What story is she telling, then?"

She shakes her head. "I don't know. Something about a war and bears, about how the Garou committed some kind of great wrong against Gaia."

Arne nods. While his own knowledge of the War of Rage is sketchy, he has heard that a growing number of cubs feel that it was a mistake, especially with regards to the bear-changers — what were they called? Grizzlies? Gurzzals? An angry growl from one of the sept's Ahroun answers the question.

"The Gurahl were tainted! That is why the war began!" The moot-fire is far enough away that Arne can't tell who says it or even what the reply is. He only hears more growls and sees a burly figure stand in defiance of the speaker. Such a breach of protocol will certainly merit punishment later, perhaps even a censure by Falcon, though Arne admits that the caern's totem doesn't seem as quick to enforce such rules as the stories portray. The booming, yet still calm voice of Brings-Life-to-the-Old-Tales ends the argument.

"You are both wrong," he says, and the wind dies down to hear him. Arne sips his chocolate quietly, straining to hear. "Yes, the Gurahl deserved their fate, but no, they were not tainted. Their story is one I am often called upon to tell to cubs who come seeking the truth behind the War of Rage." He pauses. Arne savors a mouthful of the thick drink, eyes closed, willing the old Galliard to tell the story. He expects that every Garou in the sept is thinking the same thing. "Shall I tell—"

The clamor drowns out the rest of the question. The Garou do not applaud, instead they howl and shout their approval. When Brings-Life-to-the-Old-Tales tells one story in a moot, the sept considers itself fortunate. If he tells two, they feel blessed.

Arne stands and wanders closer to the moot-fire, and sees the old storyteller take up his favorite seat — a rock that sits near the fire and is therefore nicely warmed. He takes on the Crinos form so as to wield the Garou tongue more precisely — some stories, he insists, can only be told properly in this language. He points to the visiting storyteller, nearly in tears of frustration at having her story cut short.

"Just listen, young Moon Dancer, and perhaps you will learn to tell your tale so as not to offend. For now, all of you be quiet and attend. I am not the young Garou once I was, and my voice may not hold out in this chill." Arne smiles. The man's voice would carry through a blizzard. The Galliard arranges himself on the rock, pulls a chunk of wood from the fire, and scratches a glyph into it. Arne squints through the smoke and recognizes the "bear" glyph. He cocks his head in confusion, and then hears a nearby Garou hiss, "Gurahl." He holds the charred wood above his head for the sept to see, and his voice harmonizes with the wind and crackle of the fire: "Let me tell you a story."

• • •

The fire blazed skyward, and Krieger Wyrmfoe saw the moon bathed in its light. *Luna is awash in blood tonight*, he thought, *as am I.* Then he lifted his head towards her and let out a howl of victory. He raised his arms towards the burning glade in triumph. In his right hand, he clutched a handful of teeth. In his left, he hefted the severed head of his foe. Tonight, and from now on, Krieger was immortal. Tonight, he had beaten the Death-Bear.

He strode away from the glade. His weary, bloodied body slowly slipped into its human skin. Krieger found he was limping slightly; the bear's teeth had nearly severed his left leg at the knee, but he was almost completely healed. The minor cuts and bruises over the rest of his body were already closing, but the scar that would form on his leg would win him glory. He would wear it with pride.

He opened his palm and stared down at the still-bloody teeth that lay there. He would string those teeth on a cord and wear them around his neck. Then he would always have the power of the Death-Bear close to him.

Somewhere above him, an owl shrieked. It startled him, and then he chuckled quietly. The battle, the true battle, had also begun with the screech of an owl.

It had happened when Krieger was but a Cliath, a cub just starting out on the warrior's path, that his uncle and mentor died in battle. The great Ahroun's wounds appeared slight, but the beast's claws festered with a strange poison that caused the Garou's muscles to seize and his blood to grow cold even as he tore the beast in two. The poison also preserved the Garou's body in mockery of Gaia's cycle; he lay on the battlefield, unchanging, as though he might sit up at any moment.

How young Krieger had howled when he heard the news! It took four other Garou to restrain him, so great was his rage. As anger turned to grief, he stood by his mentor's body before the Gathering for the Departed and wailed to Luna the unfairness of it all, that the mighty warrior be taken by such an unworthy foe. As the sept left the grave, Krieger heard a Ragabash mention in passing that it was a shame that no bear-changers lived nearby, as they knew the secret of death.

Krieger followed this Ragabash and asked him what he knew of the bear-changers. "Nothing," replied the no-moon, "except what I said. But even that is only a story. I have never met a Gurahl, and it is said they are solitary creatures."

"So who would know of them?" pressed Krieger.

The Ragabash only shrugged and padded off. Krieger sat down against a tree and thought, trying to remember the stories of the Moon Dancers. He wished now that he had listened during the stories, rather than always looking ahead to the revel. He knew he had heard tales of the Fera, but couldn't remember them clearly. He could ask a Galliard, he reasoned, but that would mean explaining what he meant to do.

At that moment, in the tree above him, an owl gave its lonely call, and Krieger thought of the bizarre wolves from the East, who spoke of a land barren and covered in white heat, who followed the night-hunting owl as their patron. These Garou must know something of death, Krieger realized, for their very totem was its harbinger. Though Krieger knew only slightly more of these Garou than he did of the Gurahl, they seemed his best chance for success.

"Very well," growled the young warrior. He stood and peered up into the darkness at the owl. "Hear this," he called to it, "my mentor died honorably in battle, but before his time, and this should not be! If it takes me my entire life, I will find these bear-changers, these Gurahl, and I will have the secret of death from them!" So swearing, he slashed his chest with his claws and flung several drops of blood at the owl. The owl took flight, startled, but now wore a red-brown splatter around its neck. It flew off into the night, and somewhere, great Owl noted Krieger's words and turned his attention back to other matters.

Krieger returned to the sept much changed. No longer was the young Ahroun brash and quick to fight. After the night of his mentor's funeral, he was attentive and thorough. He listened to the elders of the sept when they spoke of ancient lore and traditional wisdom. He sat at the Galliards' feet when they told stories by the moot-fire, and when the time came to join a pack, he declared himself alpha and none thought to challenge the canny warrior.

I could tell you, gathered friends, of Krieger's pack and their exploits. Surely, you have heard the story of their fight with the beast called Hgagogg, the slime-covered monster that flowed without form and caused all who saw it to go mad — all but Krieger's pack, bound together by their totem and their love of Gaia. Perhaps, at another moot, I shall sing the song that the pack's Galliard — called Wind-Carries-Her-Voice — composed on the eve of the pack's victory over the dragon Mazatuk. And surely, no-moons today still recall the night when Stone-Softens earned his name, when the Ragabash talked the very rocks into moving for the pack.

But not tonight. Tonight's story is Krieger's and I mention these other tales only to show you what this pack was capable of. It was a pack composed of Silver Fangs, and it embodied their tribe perfectly: noble, honest, brave, and skillful. In fact, many Garou of the time — and many lore-keepers since, have found it strange that the pack chose not Falcon as their totem, but Owl.

But it isn't strange at all, truly, is it?

After years of glorious deeds, the pack had stopped adventuring. Instead, they chose to become leaders and teachers at various septs, and young Garou — much more populous in those days — challenged each other for the right to study under one of these renowned warriors. Krieger, himself, took on the role of sept leader, at the Sept of Morning's Kill, the very sept in which he had undergone his rite of passage, that same sept that held his mentor's remains. He saw to his duties as leader with the same life and skill with which he'd led his pack, but the other Garou of the sept noticed him take long walks in the forest surrounding the sept. When asked, he said only that he was searching, but would never say what he searched for.

Then came the night of a full moon, and the sept held its moot, told its stories, and danced its revel, as every month. But Krieger was distracted. The night before, he'd seen an owl, and even though many years had passed since his vow, the owl had a splatter of brown around its neck. He allowed a young Ahroun to perform the moot rite — as practice, he said — but all through the moot, Krieger was watching the trees, looking for the owl. During the revel, he saw it again.

The owl perched on a low-hanging branch and stared at Krieger, silently, almost sadly. Krieger reached out and touched the owl's feathers, and found, to his amazement, that the blood around its neck was still wet. "How is this?" he whispered, but the owl did not answer. It simply took to the air, flying like a dying whisper into the forest. And Krieger followed, the blood hot in his veins, his old vow fresh in his soul.

The sounds of the other Garou grew distant. The shadows grew deep and cold as Luna's light struggled to push its way past the leaves. And still the owl flew on.

Krieger glanced around and realized that, although he had grown up here as a cub, he had never been this far into the forest before. The brush here showed no signs of being trampled, not by wolf, man, or any other beast. He heard no rustling from the forest, and could no longer hear his fellow Garou on their revel at all. And still the owl flew on.

Krieger paused to take the wolf's skin, and with the wolf's ears listened for his fellows. With the wolf's nose, he sniffed and found that no predator claimed these woods as territory. And then he ran to catch up to the owl again, for it had not stopped and it flew so silently that if he had not kept his eye on the bird, he surely would have lost it.

He scrambled up a tree to a sturdy branch and watched as his cloud-quiet guide perched on a neighboring limb. The owl regarded him blankly, its honey eyes watching him as though keeping him in place. And then Krieger heard rustlings above him. A slim, dark figure crept down the trunk of the tree and sat next to him.

Krieger sized up the intruder. His skin was mud-brown, his features strange and exaggerated. Even his hair, long and braided, was night-black. Krieger spoke to the foreigner, asking him his business, but the man only laughed and said something quietly, in an odd tongue that Krieger had never before heard. To his shock, he heard laughter from surrounding trees, and found himself out-numbered and cut off from aid, the dupe of an ambush after so many years as a warrior.

Krieger prepared himself to die and reached for his weapon, but the man stopped him, speaking in the Garou tongue. "No need, friend. Forgive us not introducing ourselves to your sept, but Owl told us that the bond we share should be kept to the quiet night. And so here we are."

It never occurred to Krieger to ask by what name these strange Garou were called. He learned only one name — Warning-Spans-Rivers — that of the Garou he spoke with. Now, of course, we know these Garou as the Silent Striders, the noble wanderers who grace us with news of far-off lands. When Krieger met them, they would not yet have suffered their exile — but that is not tonight's story. Krieger eagerly entreated the Garou to continue, to tell him what these foreign wolves knew of the Gurahl.

"The Gurahl?" asked the man. "Why, the bear-changers and my tribe know very little of each other. In fact, the only time we meet is when one of us dies, and —" a sudden shriek from the owl interrupted the man's speech.

"Yes," said Krieger, so eager to hear that he near fell from the tree, "that is what I wish to know. These Gurahl have power over death, I'm told, and —"

"Oh, no." Warning-Spans-Rivers shook his head vigorously. "No, no, brother. Nothing — *nothing* —

holds such power. Death comes to all, call it by what name you choose. The Gurahl simply know how to fight the Death-Bear." Again, the owl called. Warning-Spans-Rivers looked up sharply, and then turned to Krieger. "I would rather thirst forever than that you had asked me this, friend Silver Fang, for I have already said more than is proper. I ask you — seek not to find the Gurahl to ask for resurrections. That is not what Gaia intended." And with that, he and his companions dropped to the ground and ran off.

Krieger was not one to take defeat easily. He knew he could not force the Garou to give up their secrets — not when he faced their entire pack — but he also knew that Warning-Spans-River knew more than he'd said. He did not follow the Garou that night, but the next morning summoned his pack. He told them very little, only that he had discovered a great force for Gaia that had previously been left untapped. If they could harness this force, he said, no Garou need ever fear death again.

The others were skeptical, but followed him. The trail of the strange Garou was cold, but no better tracker has ever walked the earth than White-Fire, the pack's Theurge. She questioned Krieger about what they were tracking, but he answered (somewhat truthfully) that he did not know. The pack pressed on, through the darkest parts of the forest, and then on across the plains.

I could tell you, my friends, of what befell them on their journey, but those are stories in themselves, and already the fire burns low. One important thing, however — throughout the journey, during which they traveled ever East, Krieger searched for the owl. He never saw nor heard the strange messenger. Krieger worried, but put it out of his mind. He would find his answers soon.

The air grew dry and the ground slowly changed to sand beneath the pack's paws. White-Fire used her fetish drum to call up water, and the pack feasted on serpents and lizards and whatever else they could find, and still they pressed on. The trail was even harder to follow here than in the forest, and the Garou were unused to the terrain, but Krieger urged them on, obsessed with finding the answers he had promised himself he would find.

Finally, Stone-Softens, lagging behind as he often did, called out to his pack. Some distance across the sand, they saw one of the strange, black Garou. Krieger recognized him as Warning-Spans-Rivers, and the pack charged.

Warning-Spans-Rivers waited until they arrived, and then greeted them respectfully, each by name. "And to what do we owe this honor, *rhyas*?" he asked.

"Before," growled Krieger, ignoring the Garou's good manners, "you would not tell me of the Gurahl, though you clearly knew more than you said. I could not demand truth from you then, but now my pack is with me."

With a sigh, the desert wolf replied, "You wish to see a Gurahl? There is one nearby. Follow the smell of humans, but hide yourself well. And," he said, trotting away "remember what I told you about meddling with death."

Brushing off his pack's questions about the Garou's cryptic warning, Krieger led them towards a human settlement. It was a longer run than he'd guessed, and by the time they saw the human's tents and smelled their beasts, the sun had set and the moon rose high above the dunes.

White-Fire did not know how to track a Gurahl, since she had never seen or smelled one before. The pack spread out around the village, and waited. Krieger himself lurked near a tent, decorated and obviously meant for someone of importance.

As he watched, a man emerged from the tent and looked around, as though just awakening. He walked towards the edge of the camp, looking over the brush as though waiting. Krieger sniffed; something about the man was wrong. He was old; his hair — what little remained — was gray, but he walked upright and proud. Krieger was still puzzling over this when the

man stumbled forward. The harsh birdcalls of children's taunts echoed from the tents, and Krieger realized that one of them had hit the man with a stone.

The man turned, and spoke with a voice that carried such awful power that even Krieger shrank back. The taunts quieted, then began anew, loud, angry, even desperate. Krieger could see the children now, but could not count them. They stood among the tents, throwing jeers and stones. The man, for his part, didn't seem fazed or afraid, simply annoyed.

Krieger wondered if he should step in and stop this, but before he could decide, the man threw his hands to the sky as if in prayer. Instantly, the ground shifted, and a hideous, pained roar shook the night. What stood up from the ground, sand spilling off it like a robe of glass, was undoubtedly a Gurahl.

The beast stood higher than many of the trees in Krieger's home sept. The children stood, transfixed in fear, the beast's roar flooding their own insults and taunts back at them. The Gurahl's master — for hadn't he summoned up the bear from the sand where it slept? — stood on, smugly, as the beast's paw slashed downward.

By the time Krieger had recovered enough to give the anthem of war, the Gurahl's claws had done their work. Blind with rage, Krieger tore into the bear's flank, just as his packmates appeared from the night to join him. Krieger smelled children's blood from the

sand, Garou blood from the creature's claws as it slashed Stone-Softens' gut open, but something was missing. He released his grip on the bear and jumped back, barking for his pack to do likewise.

He had scarcely begun to give the order when one of the bear's paws swatted him, casually, as one might flick snow off one's shoulder. The mighty Silver Fang Ahroun found himself flung nearly a quarter mile, landing headfirst in a sand dune. Shaking himself, he raced back.

The fight had not gone well. Stone-Softens lay at the bear's feet, lifeless and disemboweled. White-Fire struggled to free herself from a tent, but her struggles were weak, and Krieger saw that her left arm had been torn from its socket. In sick horror, Krieger looked for his other packmates, desperately hoping they were alive and able to fight — or flee! — but then the lifeless corpse of Bryce the Just, the pack's Philodox and beta, landed at his feet. Bryce's body was cold, his skin white… and bloodless.

Recoiling, Krieger realized what had made him uneasy about the man and the Gurahl. When the stones struck the man's bald head, there had been no smell of blood, and likewise, only the taste of dead flesh had greeted Krieger when he bit into the bear.

Its maw stained with Bryce's blood, the Gurahl turned its attention to Krieger. He backed away, looking for a place to run or hide, and tripped over a body in the sand.

As the Gurahl bore down on him, he locked eyes with Wind-Carries-Her-Voice. The Galliard was badly wounded, perhaps dying, but reached out her hand to her alpha and leader and called upon a mighty Gift. Fueling it with the last of her life's blood, she whispered to him to speak of her well at the Gathering for the Departed. The bear charged, moving much too quickly for something so huge. It sank its teeth into Krieger's leg, just above the knee, nearly separating it from his body, but by then they were both engulfed in Luna's light. Krieger and the Gurahl both vanished from the desert…

…and appeared back at the Sept of Morning's Kill, both confused and angry. The beast looked about for her master, but saw only strange trees and the full moon high above. Krieger, though, did not waste time looking. He drew his klaive and howled the Warning of Wyrm's Approach, and leaped at the beast.

The Gurahl was assuredly much stronger than Krieger. Even as the other Garou of the sept arrived, it flung him into a tree so hard that the trunk splintered. And still Krieger fought on. He drove his klaive into the beast's stomach, howling the name of Stone-Softens, and laid the creature open. To his horror, not

blood or viscera came pouring out, but only foul air and black, vicious-looking worms. The beast batted his klaive away and picked him up in a crushing embrace, but Krieger seized its head in his paws and called upon Falcon, squeezing until the bear's skull cracked. It dropped him and ran, and Krieger gave chase.

The other Garou of the sept watched, but could do no more. Just as humans stand immobile or fall into fits when they see us, the noble Garou of the sept were terrified of the Gurahl so that they could not aid their leader, only try and keep up as he chased it into the forest.

Finally, the beast stopped, at bay in a thick glade, and turned to fight. But Krieger was no longer wounded and in mindless rage. He strode into the glade evenly, and the two opponents circled each other. But the bear was weakening. The wound in its stomach had not healed, and it stumbled as though confused. Krieger, however, never faltered once. The moon shone down on him, and just as the bear charged, Luna granted him a great Gift.

The bear hit him with enough force to crush this boulder on which I sit, but Krieger did not budge, for he had become Luna's very avenger, a warrior whose skin, claws, and fangs were made of pure silver. The Gurahl realized its mistake — too late! — and howled, perhaps for its master, perhaps merely in pain. No matter. Krieger tore through its flesh and burst through the monster's back, holding its festering heart.

The Gurahl gave one final lunge, and died.

Krieger looked at his sept, standing awed around him, and spoke. "Hear me, brothers. Tonight I have slain this beast, this Child-Slayer, who has killed my pack." The others growled and gasped at this news. "I must purify this creature's remains with fire, and I would mourn my pack alone. Leave me, but dig in a circle around this glen so that the fire does not spread to the caern." And the Garou ran off to carry out his orders, the Galliards already composing their songs about Krieger Wyrmfoe and his battle with the Child-Slayer.

Krieger did burn the creature's body. He kept the beast's teeth, as I said before, as a trophy. He took the beast's head and burned it at the Gathering for his fallen packmates. But there was something else he kept from that horror, of which he told no one.

After the Gathering, he stole to the Graves of the Hallowed Heroes. He found a grave marking that few of the young Garou at the sept would recognize, and began to dig.

In moments, the body of his mentor lay before him. The poison that killed him still kept him undecayed, and Krieger could barely smell death upon him. He pulled his uncle's corpse from the sacred earth, opened its mouth, and squeezed the Gurahl's heart over it.

The last bit of blood from the heart of the Child-Slayer dripped into his mentor's mouth. Somewhere nearby, the owl screeched. But there was nothing Owl or his servants could do.

• • •

Brings-Life-to-the-Old-Tales paused. The night had become utterly silent. The wind hadn't gusted since he began. The listeners huddled together, some with lips quivering in rage. The Child of Gaia Galliard who had begun the tale of the Gurahl had tears on her cheeks. Arne stared at the fire, without a thought, only the picture in his mind of Krieger trying to raise his mentor from the grave.

"Sadly, Krieger's blasphemy was successful. His mentor did indeed walk again, but not for very long. You see, he — it — returned as a mockery of life, much like the Child-Slayer itself, and this time, Krieger had to sacrifice his life to destroy it.

"Krieger was buried alongside his pack, and the rest of the sept never knew the full story. Only Owl — and perhaps the Silent Striders — knew the truth. How I came to know is a story I'm afraid I must never tell.

"Krieger Wyrmfoe thought that he fought the Death-Bear itself that night. He didn't. He fought a dead creature, raised from its grave by powers beyond itself and enslaved by the man in the desert. It was a powerful foe, to be sure, but not really a Gurahl. Only what a Gurahl can become, for such is the fate of anyone, skin-changer or not, who attempts to reverse Gaia's cycle. The Gurahl were not tainted, but the sept of Morning's Kill did not know the full story. They attempted to find answers, but as Krieger had not told them of his pack's journey, they did not know where to look. They found Gurahl, and demanded answers, but the bear-changers had none to give them. The Garou thought they were lying, and besides, they knew what horrors the Gurahl could wreak. Thus began the War of Rage."

The old Galliard stirred the fire with his staff, sending sparks into the air. The Garou shifted — the revel was coming, and they knew it. Brings-Life stared at the fire, and spoke so softly that the assemblage leaned forward to hear him. "Sometimes," he whispered, "a story doesn't really end." He stepped off of the rock by the fire, and took his place with the other elders.

The silence was broken not by cries of approval, but by Bloody-Snow, the young Ahroun acting as Wyrm Foe, as he darted among the Garou, howling, snarling, and biting. The revel had begun. Arne looked at the elder Moon Dancer, afraid he might be offended by the lack of adulation, but he was not. It wasn't that kind of story, Arne decided.

WEREWOLF
STORYTELLERS HANDBOOK

WEREWOLF CREATED BY MARK REIN•HAGEN

Credits

Authors: Bruce Baugh, Jackie Cassada, Lisa Clark-Fleishman, Geoffrey C. Grabowski, Kylie Greenham, Harry Heckel, Heather Heckel, Shannon Hennessey, Forrest B. Marchinton, Matthew McFarland, Deena McKinney, Nicky Rea, Sean Riley and Adam Tinworth.
Werewolf and the World of Darkness created by Mark Rein•Hagen
Storyteller game system designed by Mark Rein•Hagen
Developer: Ethan Skemp
Editor: Aileen E. Miles
Art Director: Aileen E. Miles
Art: Langdon Foss, Leif Jones, Steve Prescott, Jeff Rebner, Alex Sheikman & Issac Mangold, Ron Spencer, Drew Tucker
Cover Art: Dan Brereton
Layout, Typesetting and Cover Design: Aileen E. Miles

735 PARK NORTH BLVD.
SUITE 128
CLARKSTON, GA 30021
USA

WHITE WOLF
GAME STUDIO

Contents

Introduction

[The art of the novel] happens because the storyteller's own experience of men and things, whether for good or ill — not only what he has passed through himself, but even events which he has only witnessed or been told of — has moved him to an emotion so passionate that he can no longer keep it in his heart.

— Murasaki Shikibu, *The Tale of Genji*

Let's face it: You wouldn't be reading this book unless you had an interest in being a Storyteller and improving your game. Well, you've come to the right place, and players can benefit from reading it too. Though the book points out many of the things Storytellers should or could be doing to enhance play for a troupe, players can learn a few ways they can ensure the Storyteller's fun and help her do her job more easily as well. Ultimately, however, it's the Storyteller who makes or breaks a game, so we address ourselves to you.

The Storyteller has the hardest, yet often most rewarding, job in any troupe. It's similar to being the director and the entire technical crew as well as the supporting actors and extras on a movie set. Players, as the featured actors, can go wild in character creation and development and experience the pleasure of seeing those characters triumph despite overwhelming odds or go down to a noble death in a good cause. But Storytellers create and portray everything that allows the players' characters to do that. Whether coming up with a night's entertainment or devising an entire chronicle, the

Storyteller has to embrace the role of writer, set designer and director to make her tale come alive for the people that experience it. Many become prop masters, lighting technicians and sound engineers. They bring special touches to the game with everything from pictures of notable items to an alarm clock set to ring two hours into a tense mystery, signaling that time's up for those who must solve the puzzle or creating a mood with lighting and appropriate music or sound effects.

As if this weren't enough, the Storyteller must also act out the parts of significant allies and antagonists, insignificant background characters and even entire crowds (such as the other members of the pack's sept). And in **Werewolf**, this may require the flexibility to portray everything from a ravenous wolf to a monstrous corporate CEO, from a sniveling informer to a godlike spirit.

Add to this the job of acting as the interpreter for the rules and the arbitrator for disputes. Even the best-written rules leave room for interpretation and players are creative people who like a lot of license. There will be times when players disagree (sometimes adamantly)

with rulings the Storyteller makes, and such rulings tend to cover things that dice rolls really should not determine. A reputation for being both fair and a good interpreter of the spirit of the game goes a long way. But even that falls by the wayside if players feel their favorite character got the shaft. So let's add a diplomat's credentials to the personas a Storyteller has to take on.

Even after the Storyteller uses meticulous planning and crafts a game to time things to suit the action to a night's play or several intense sessions, the players may miss obvious clues, jump to the wrong conclusion or just plain decide to go the other way. Such is the frustration; such is the challenge. Good Storytellers learn to incorporate the idea of ad-libbing, which can be as intimidating as acting in a live television broadcast when you don't know the lines or even what show you're on. They can adapt to the whims of the troupe and present them with something interesting to do even if it's so far off the planned encounter it takes the troupe into a completely new storyline. No one promised this game came with directions!

Some of the best, most enduring sessions occur when players take an extreme wrong turn in mid-plotline. Fiction writers often speak of their characters rebelling from the writer's plans for them and going off on tangents. Why should Storytellers expect different behavior from live people who are helping to write the story as they go along? You have to be prepared to scrap what doesn't fit and grab onto ideas your players want to experience. If you can change things enough to fit in their pet theories of what's really going on, they'll not only feel smug that they figured it out, but think you're a genius for setting things up so well.

Still, with this incredibly demanding work laid on your doorstep, you might wonder what you get out of all this. After all, Storytellers don't get to be the heroes of their own stories, do have to play the villain (who often gets sliced and diced), don't get paid for all that hard work and don't even get experience points. What could possibly induce an otherwise sane person to do this?

Well, because it's rewarding to see other people respond to the stories you create. It's empowering to be the person others turn to when questions about the game arise. And it's satisfying to know you've done a fantastic job bringing a whole cast of characters to life. But mostly, it's just plain fun! For the person who wants to be the creative force behind the ongoing game, Storytelling is worth every effort expended.

This book is designed with you in mind. We're here to help Storytellers hone their chops. We present a plethora of ideas and advice, a few tips for novices and some thoughts for veteran Storytellers seeking a new direction or touching back on the roots of the game. As an art form, Storytelling is ever evolving, so this book doesn't include lots of heavy-handed rules. We want to help you improve your skills as a Storyteller, not dictate the one-and-only way it should be done. Troupes and Storytellers are individuals, each with their own style and preferences. So don't feel you have to take everything said as gospel. If something from the book works for you, great! Use it with our blessings. If it isn't right for you, don't feel like you have to incorporate it just because we said so. You're the only one who can say what you really need. You're the director. You're the only one entitled to yell, "Cut!" when you capture the scene the way you want it. It's a game. Enjoy it!

The Most Important Aspect…

So, your troupe has gathered to play a session of **Werewolf**. You've all set aside a certain amount of time to play and everyone anticipates having a good time. But why are you playing **Werewolf** and not some other game? Your troupe could be playing badass barbarians or mystical mages instead. They could portray space marines or alien wonder-workers. If the players just wanted to kick out the jams with over-the-top combat, you could run a game of mega-kill robot mechs. But they're investing their time and energy in acting the roles of beast-men instead.

Partly, your troupe comes to play your game because they know they can expect certain things from you (or they *hope* they can count on you, in the case of first timers). Your stories reflect your own personality or your strengths as a Storyteller to some degree. Some Storytellers prefer straight-ahead blitzkrieg action while others specialize in convoluted mysteries the characters must unwind. Many Storytellers rely on a stable of tried-and-true supporting personalities and excel at such portrayals. Others prefer to focus on the troupe and keep outside personnel to a minimum. In most good chronicles, whenever you run a game, your story unfolds around the characters, with them as the central focus. Still, there are exceptions, games that enmesh the characters in situations that seem far too large for them to have any effect on, yet eventually prove to be vulnerable to their efforts.

Regardless of your style and the scope of your game, however, the single most important factor in it is that the characters are werewolves: feared, misunderstood, dedicated to preserving that which daily atrophies or falls prey to the mounting toxins of modern life, a dying breed.

If the players are just portraying characters that are basically human with the occasional foray into berserk battle mode, they're missing the point. While Garou have both human and wolf sides, they're more than the sum of those parts. It's part of your job as the Storyteller to help them find the place where wolf meets man. At one and the same time, you need to help them unleash the wolf while maintaining the human traits that set them apart from normal wolves. Most players have no trouble gleefully grabbing a handful of dice, snarling out a challenge or two and whaling on the opposition while believing they're acting out the wolf's bestial nature. But in actuality, unless they are very sick or injured beyond endurance, wolves don't normally give in to rage. They fight for their food and to preserve themselves and the pack, but it's a rare wolf that is ruled by hatred. Rage is a human emotion. The thing that distinguishes human hatred and fury from that of Garou is that the Garou possess the supernatural ability to become the embodiment of their rage by taking Crinos form and letting their anger overrule their saner selves for a time. In directing your chronicle, you should try to focus on both aspects of the characters, sometimes calling the wolf to the fore, and other times seeking to bring forth the human. Never forget, however, that the characters are first and foremost Garou and the blending together of the two aspects is what drives your stories.

The Most Important Rule

Every book in the Storyteller System invites the Storyteller to change, ignore, improve upon or throw out any rule that doesn't work for her. Most Storytellers find at least a few rules they don't care for and some they feel need tweaking. That's fine with us. We encourage you to think things through and make your game what you want it to be. Use our rules as a starting place, not the final word on the subject. Experiment. Play a game or two without any rules at all, allowing everyone to describe what they're doing and the optimum outcome they'd like to see arising from those actions. You may decide to discard some rules while adhering to others. We've generally found that some rules are needed simply to add dynamic tension. Without any rules at all, there is often a lack of conflict. But, hey, if it works for you, go for it.

The only rule we absolutely want you to follow is one that is ironically absent at times. Picture this: The game bogs down into paging through the book to find out the exact wording for each rule. A beleaguered player insists on knowing precisely how many pounds a werewolf in Crinos form can lift. You find yourself arguing about correct names for Get of Fenris. Someone brings up the idea that wolves need twenty miles of territory to be able to hunt and your sept is located in a fifteen-mile-wide wilderness area, so it's unrealistic. Unrealistic? Like nine-foot wolfmen populate the real world? When this happens, it's time to lock the book away for awhile. Go to a movie. Read a book. Take a walk. Do whatever it is you do for fun and remember that this is a game. It's supposed to be an amusement! While some people might find rules lawyering stimulating, most people find it a distinct turn off. That's why we want you to remember the most important rule and the only one we really insist you follow:

Have fun!

If you aren't having fun, something needs fixing. Feel free to tinker with things until it feels right. After all, we haven't been ordained to hand down gospel. We've found certain things that work for us that we can pass along, but in the end it's your game. Do with it what you will. So long as you're having fun, we promise we won't come by your house looking for Wyrm taint. Enjoy!

How to Use This Book

This is a book primarily for Storytellers, who have the job of creating worlds, engineering stories and reconciling the rules and the characters with what he's created. Here we offer our advice gleaned from our own experiences and clarify a few things that may provide better insight into the world of the Garou. There may be a few secrets or surprises lurking within these pages; there are certainly ideas for crafting a better story. Use what you like. The intention is to provide you with the tools, then turn you loose to carve your own work of art.

Chapter One: The World of the Garou takes a look at the structural bones of the Garou and their culture: the becoming, Garou senses, Renown, spirituality, the Litany, rites and several other important aspects of Gaia's defenders. It contains information designed to help you convey the experience of life as a werewolf to your players, from the Garou's internal passions to the nuances of their society.

Chapter Two: The Battlefield deals with more setting-related issues, the things to consider when bringing the world around the Garou to greater life. Topics include detailing the city and the wilderness, using human cultures and myths to greater effect, and roleplaying animals and spirits.

Chapter Three: The Chronicle, naturally enough, contains advice on building a chronicle, from the moment you sit around the table to generate characters to the final dramatic climax that leaves everyone talking for years.

Chapter Four: The Adversaries dissects the enemy, explaining how to use antagonistic forces including the Triat, Pentex, Black Spiral Dancers and other dangerous opponents to best effect.

Chapter Five: Breaking the Mold is a guideline to deviating from the usual **Werewolf** game in various ways, whether exploring historical settings, post-

Apocalyptic chronicles, alternate takes on werewolves, alternate timelines and crossovers.

Finally, **Chapter Six: Odds and Ends** contains a few miscellaneous elements to highlight a **Werewolf** game, from a look at the Kami — the incarnate "fomori" of Gaia — to an expanded listing of potential sources of inspiration for the game.

How the Game is Played

Now that we've reiterated the idea that the game is what you make of it, we do need to say a few words concerning the main themes to be found in **Werewolf** and how you can learn to handle an ongoing chronicle. We've identified certain themes that occur again and again and these may help you by pinpointing things you need to consider in your own games.

Beyond finding common themes, however, the most important thing you can learn about running any game is to find out what your players want. Even if you follow every suggestion we make, use every possible enhancement presented here and plan your game meticulously, unless the players are having fun, the game will fail. Naturally, trying to devise a game that doesn't also interest you is futile. If your heart's not in it, you can't run a good game, especially over the long haul. So how do you please yourself and keep the rest of the troupe interested? Ask your players what they'd like to see in the games you run. What do they enjoy? What frustrates them and makes the game less enjoyable? What would they like for their characters to accomplish? If you're thinking "roving troubleshooters" and they're picturing "becoming leaders of the sept," someone's not going to be happy. These two aren't necessarily exclusive, but you'd have to make it clear that their work as troubleshooters will pay off with gaining the status that will lead to becoming movers and shakers in the sept. You might also talk to them about what you want to do as a Storyteller. Let them know what it is you expect from them and the kinds of stories you'd like to tell. Knowing what each side wants will help you structure your stories to please everyone. Letting them help you create the stories you all want will make your job that much easier. Of course, themes aren't the only measurement of what players want. If you have a couple of hell-or-high-water combat commandos, some who prefer deep personal discussions or the sneaky approach and a couple who like to explore their Gifts and rites, you need to provide opportunities for all of them to experience the kind of game they prefer. If you open your game to embrace all these elements, you can always let the ones who aren't interested in certain parts go "offstage" to do something else while you run things for the others. Of course, players who actively participate in all of it would naturally get more experience…. Then again, if you can make it all appealing through creative descriptions and interactions and throw in a few twists to the usual way such things go, you just might train the reluctant participants to like the parts they thought they wouldn't.

As long as you give them what they want, they'll even forgive you for setbacks and disappointments and use it to become stronger characters rather than complaining when everything doesn't initially go their way. In fact, this may be one of the few games you'll ever run in which the characters already know they are, in all likelihood, doomed from the start. After all, no one can really expect the game of savage horror to serve up lightweight fluff. The enemies aren't at the gate; they're already inside and ravaging as they go. The defenders are too few and expect to go down fighting. Will their sacrifice be enough to save the world? That's part of the horror — and the appeal — they won't ever know for sure.

Major Themes

Certain themes come with the territory when you decide to run a **Werewolf** game. Noted below are two of the most obvious and two that may not be so apparent initially. All of them do interweave with various elements in defining what the game is all about. If you've been playing **Werewolf** for a while, you've undoubtedly touched on one or more of these, but they bear repeating, if only to remind you of the roots you can return to for inspiration again and again. Of course, you don't have to use a hammer to drive the point home. Subtly inserting just a hint of these is usually most effective and ties your chronicle together even when stories seem independent of one another. You will find many other themes within your stories as well, so don't take these as the final say of what to include or exclude in a chronicle.

• Warriors Doomed to Eternal Struggle

The most obvious theme surrounds what the Garou are and what they consider themselves to be. Whether they call themselves warriors or defenders, the Garou embody Gaia's need to fight for survival. Forever at war with the forces tearing Gaia's creation apart, the Garou can never win their fight. And they know it. Eminently suited for battle, even the Garou's supernatural Rage cannot fully defeat their enemies. For those enemies are so numerous it's almost pointless to oppose them. Time and again, the Garou throw themselves into the fray, expending their best and brightest in stopgap measures that cannot coalesce into a resounding victory. The Wyrm slithers onward, gaining ever more allies and followers, causing such corruption and destruction that ten Garou lifetimes would not be enough to repair the damage. Like the hydra of legend, wherever one of the Wyrm's tentacles is severed, two more spring forth to continue the fight. The Garou, however, possess limited numbers and few resources. Every Garou lost in battle sounds the death knell for their kind, for each is irreplaceable. All Garou know that they are a dying breed. All know that their enemies are legion. They feel the jaws of the trap closing around them and know that slowly, inevitably, the Wyrm is winning. Little wonder they fall into Harano!

The sense of futility and defeat underlies every story to *some* extent, no matter how glorious it may be short term. How can beings that were born to fight accept the fact that their battle is over before it begins? This is where much of the horror comes in. Created to be great warriors, the Garou cannot simply give up. They must strive for victory, expending their last ounce of strength to strike a blow for Gaia, fighting until their last breath emerges in a death rattle curse against the foe.

This doesn't mean that the struggle should be presented as completely hopeless; after all, you want to give your players ample reason to return to your chronicle on a regular basis. Somewhere within themselves, the characters need to come to an understanding that despite everything, despite the pain and loss of death, somehow it may all make a difference. If nothing else, they may be worthy of a song.

• Savages Within the Civilized

No Garou can escape either the savage or the civilized aspect of her being. Just as those Garou born human must embrace their wolf heritage, even the most fanatic lupus Garou have a human side, whether they'll admit it or not. The metis may be the most aware of the drawbacks and blessings of their dual nature, as they experience the earliest years of their lives trapped in Crinos form, which blends the two sides most fully. In order to act as Gaia's defenders, the Garou call forth the most savage portions of themselves, loosing their Rage to wreak vengeance on those who harm their Mother. Yet to remain dedicated to their goals, Garou look to community, ceremony and alliance with spirits — all requiring a high degree of civilization — to keep them focused and spiritually renewed.

As a Storyteller, you need to give the players the chance for their characters to explore both sides. Lead city-focused characters into the countryside and encourage them to explore the wolf within. Let them feel the hot, savage joy of the hunt. Find reasons for country Garou to enter the city and discover their human sides. Let them see that there are things worth saving in an urban environment. Play with the idea of using rites to bring out both sides at once. Graphic descriptions of what happens during combat go a long way toward spotlighting the savagery of the Garou. On the other hand, when helping the players visualize rites and moots you don't have to focus on boring elements, but should bring out the passion that underlies the Garou's existence. Have fun devising barbarous or animal-like por-

tions that must be enacted to correctly perform rites. Dig for ways to bring more civilized elements into the more savage of the pack's doings.

• The Individual Versus the Pack

One of the main features of **Werewolf** is the concept that characters bond together in a pack or are members of the same sept. A few chronicles may be exceptions to this rule, but for the most part, Garou normally function best in groups. Pack mentality demands certain behavior — accepting that one person is the overall leader and finding your place within the social structure of the pack and sept. Those of higher rank expect those of lesser rank to respect and obey them while lower-ranked Garou demand that those of higher rank be just and true leaders.

While this unity makes the Garou strong, it also causes some friction as individuals strive for recognition of their efforts. It often seems that individual players resent not being the most important, the strongest or the most admired within the group. Such players go for Renown at all costs, sometimes ignoring all other aspects of the game to gain power — higher rank, more Gifts, cooler rites and above all, some sort of title within the sept. While there's nothing inherently wrong with wanting to gain recognition and increase the character's abilities, it shouldn't be done at the cost of meaningful group interaction. Rather than confronting such a player directly, however, you as the Storyteller can use the idea of the individual in conflict with his group as a theme to play up in your stories. If approached in this way, you can stress the idea that characters should strive for individual success within the structure of the pack. To true Garou, the sept and the pack are far more important than the individuals within them. Survival of the group takes precedence over that of a single werewolf. A quick look at awarding Renown makes this very clear. Nonetheless, its an underlying theme of the game that singular characters have the desire to excel and prove their prowess, which is sometimes in conflict with their assigned roles within the group. Bringing the two into accord can be the basis for either stories or chronicles.

To some degree, this dichotomy carries over into and spotlights the idea of tribal conflict. Despite their best intentions, Garou tribes don't always understand, appreciate or get along with other tribes. In this case, the idea of the individual is expanded to include individual tribes in conflict with other tribes, keeping the whole of Garou from uniting to destroy their enemies. Highlighting the distrust or antagonism between tribes can reinforce the individual versus pack theme and vice versa. In an age when every Garou is desperately needed to fight Gaia's enemies, this becomes a powerful theme to weave into any chronicle.

• Corruption and Cleansing

This is such an ongoing theme it might seem almost silly to bother mentioning it. Many **Werewolf** games focus on finding and neutralizing the works of Pentex, Black Spiral Dancers and other Wyrm minions. While this does indeed speak to the idea of corruption, there exists a great potential within the game to explore this theme more fully and on a more personal level. When young Garou first take up their responsibilities, their heads may be filled with glorious tales and pure desire to rid the world of the Wyrm's decaying touch. They throw themselves into the fray with the gusto of those innocent enough not to have really tasted defeat or corruption themselves. Yet as they continue the fight, they experience things that inevitably erode their innocence, replacing it with knowledge and wisdom the characters may wish they'd never had to acquire. The first bloom of conviction shrivels into the knowledge that this is a lifelong battle, and one that may indeed be futile. They see friends die and enemies prosper.

How do the characters confront such enemies, continue fighting against overwhelming odds and touch on the Wyrm's most tainted places without becoming corrupt themselves? Can they do it at all or is it inevitable that as time goes on, they'll give in to internal corruption of one kind or another? How do the characters react when innocents are caught in the crossfire between them and those they hunt? Or do they even believe there are any innocents left? After a time, the characters may become tarnished soldiers, struggling within themselves to maintain any joy or sense that they are doing something worthy. Veterans can become jaded, believing they deserve special consideration for what they go through or they may lose the ability to feel compassion for others or to see beyond the needs of the immediate moment. Warriors can become addicted to battle, to the blood and stench of combat and be unable to walk away from it even when other solutions present themselves. Excessive pride or feelings of superiority over most others may corrupt some Garou. Many feel that this underlies the Silver Fangs' insanity — corruption from within.

Naturally, there also exist outside forces that can taint Garou who aren't wary enough. What appears to be a good cause and a way to serve Gaia may emerge as a front for Leeches trying to gain influence over an eco-group. A fetish may appear genuine but prove to cause dissention among those who look at it, causing each person to covet it.

Since Garou do not generally mate among their own, they look to others for that bond. Too few Kinfolk in existence means that Garou must sometimes look outside their usual group, and such

lovers may corrupt the Garou either directly or indirectly. What if a character's lover demands time he would usually spend with his pack? The pack bond is strong, but so is a love commitment. Thus, merely spending time with a lover can lead a Garou to neglect his duties. What if the lover has been carefully groomed to seduce the Garou? By the time he learns that his apparently loving partner is a trap laid for him by Pentex, it may be too late for the Garou to extricate himself. Any of these can prove fodder for a story or two while emphasizing that corruption isn't something limited to the Wyrm.

And what about cleansing? Garou who have let themselves be seduced or corrupted may not be salvageable through a simple rite or two. First, the Garou must recognize that she has become corrupt and take steps to rid herself of it. This may involve journeys or trials she must endure, but the main focus is on her internal struggle. Does she really want to cleanse herself or does she secretly revel in her corruption? And what if it's only a little taint? Can she reach beyond her internal darkness and still remain dedicated to Gaia and the struggle? Who judges what constitutes taint and what is simply a fault? These themes can be brought out alongside your more mundane "clean up the Wyrm spawn" sessions. Playing one off against the other will actually strengthen and deepen both stories.

Enhancing the Game

Storytellers are faced with a difficult task: making the story come alive for their players in an age of television and video games. People are used to having the visual aspects handed to them on a platter, but in a game, you must help your troupe create their own picture of what is happening through description and whatever other enhancement you can find to do so. Below are a few of the ways you can enhance the game for your troupe so they come out of a session feeling as though they've helped create a great story.

Appropriate Setting In and Out of Game

To really make your scenes come alive, you need an appropriate setting. Outside of the game world, this means you need a comfortable place to play where possible distractions remain in the background. Having a space where there is seating that allows everyone to see one another and places for paper, books, pencils and dice (if you use them) makes it far easier on you to keep the players' attention directed toward the troupe. Lighting plays an interesting role as well.

Keeping the lights low or playing by candlelight creates a wholly different mood than sitting beneath blazing overhead lights. Dimmer switches, while no longer in the vogue they once enjoyed, can be very helpful in getting the troupe to react to different settings (such as dim light in a cave or heavy forest, brighter light for a daylight scene in the city). This is part of enlivening the scene by disguising what you lack.

Few troupes have the luxury of playing in a forest setting, but playing a soundtrack of trees swaying in the wind or birdcalls or rain can evoke an outdoors feeling. Don't forget the sense of smell either. Spraying lightly with a pine scent can call forth visions of the forest too. Pictures of the setting or special items help others visualize what it is they're seeing or experiencing, and music can help set the mood.

Though it may never actually happen, it's a good idea to ban food during the game unless you're recreating a feast of some kind. Rattling potato chip bags or hunting for the crunchy candy during a poignant scene or someone else's big speech kills the mood and wrecks the game. Set aside a few minutes break time for consumables or find some way to work them into the story.

One overlooked aspect of preparing for the game is to gather any items needed for the characters to perform rites they know. Even having a painted stick that symbolizes a fetish can help players establish such things in their minds. You might even want to mark out an area in which the rite is to take place and have the players gather within it. Don't be afraid to experiment with aids like these. We really aren't enacting any real rituals, just using props to enhance your fun.

Big Versus Little Picture

Obviously, you want to focus on the characters as the main movers and shakers of the game, but occasionally, you can expand the game by looking at the big picture rather than the personal one. Whether at a moot, on the battlefield or even during a challenge, it can help your game to describe things happening outside the characters' immediate range of influence. Consider the following: Fangs of Venom thrashes in a life-and-death struggle against a Nexus Crawler. Naturally, you'll want to get into the low-down and dirty depiction of this epic battle. But it means more if she can see the rest of her pack cut off from her, under siege and dying unless she can get by her immediate foe and come to their rescue.

Likewise, if the pack is part of a sept-wide raid on a Black Spiral Dancer hive, you'll take up most of the time describing and running their individual battles. Still, by pulling back from their central position and briefly describing things happening elsewhere, you not only make their battle mean more, but give them a sense of being part of something larger and more important. It's in such scenes that brave and noble sacrifices most often occur. That presenting their personal actions within the context of the larger picture also encourages players to go beyond individual goals and work for the sept or pack is all to the good.

Playing to the Max

Since you have to use supporting cast (the players' characters can't exist in a vacuum), you may as well maximize their potential and effectiveness. Making them sidekicks for the players' characters or allowing them to just take care of things the players can't be bothered with robs you of roleplaying opportunities and shortchanges the troupe. Use your Storyteller characters to point the way, when necessary or to force the characters into making hard choices. Give a supporting cast member the same traits as a difficult player character and highlight how much of a pain she is to give the player a hint about his character. It's been said often that you need to make each one unique in some way. Even more important than being absolutely unique, however, is to make them come alive. If the characters don't hate your villains and want them to die a slow, painful death, they aren't being utilized as well as they might. And if a Storyteller character gets close to the pack, they should feel something for that person. They aren't cardboard cutouts or pushovers. They aren't in the game to provide the characters with easy solutions. Sometimes, they should even seem like more trouble than they're worth. Still, if you manage to depress the players (and their characters) when a favorite cast member dies, you're doing it right.

Branch Out

Even playing Gaia's chosen can pall given time. Go beyond Gaia, the environment, Pentex and other mainstays of the game. Throw your troupe into a story that ostensibly has nothing to do with Garou. Take them on a spiritual journey. Find ways to make the lupus embrace the homid and vice versa. Take the Bone Gnawers out of the city and lure rural Garou into the sinful city. Provide the characters with moral quandaries. Use your imagination and challenge your players. Just remember, the best way to enhance your game is to have fun and provide fun for everyone else.

FAQ
Or, Things You Always Wanted to Know About Werewolves
Werewolf Physiology

• **Is there such a thing as a "Garou gene?" Can it be detected with DNA analysis? Can werewolves be cloned?**

Not really, no. The factor of being Garou is largely spiritual; it's something that some Gifts and spirits can pick up on, but not scientific blood tests or anything like that. A Garou bloodline reads much like any other; Pure Breed is nothing more than a stronger penchant to carry the genetic traits of your ancestors, scientifically speaking. Thus, werewolves can't really be cloned through science; you'd get a clone of the breed form person, but no werewolf traits. Metis can't be cloned at all, nor can a metis embryo be successfully transplanted to a surrogate mother; it takes a womb with spirit power and Rage to successfully bring a metis to term.

• **Can werewolves regenerate severed limbs?**

If the injury that severed a limb or digit didn't cause a Battle Scar, then yes. However, a severed head doesn't grow back; decapitation kills a werewolf pretty readily.

• **If you sever a werewolf's arm or head, does it revert to breed form or remain in the form it was previously in?**

It reverts to breed form, just like the old legend about a hunter chopping the paw off a wolf that attacked him, wrapping it up and taking it home only to find he was carrying a human hand. Werewolves don't make good trophies unless they're metis, and the Garou go to *great* lengths to make sure that all metis bodies and severed parts are reclaimed. It's that Veil thing, you know.

• **Are werewolves considered Kinfolk before the First Change?**

No, they are not. They're werewolves from the moment of birth. For instance, if they have kids with another Garou before undergoing the First Change, the progeny will be metis.

• **Can werewolves breed and produce offspring with dogs?**

Short answer: No. Long answer: Not if the pregnancy could result in human or homid babies (i.e., a female Garou mating with a male dog), and in no case will any of the puppies be shapeshifters. For a viable mating that might produce a Garou, the animal partner must be a wolf-dog hybrid at least 75% wolf, and even then the chances of a werewolf offspring are low. Even though wolves (and Garou) can produce viable offspring by breeding with dogs, the difference between wolf-spirits and dog-spirits is so vast that dogs — in fact, *any* domesticated animal — cannot produce shapeshifter offspring.

• **Do matings between Garou and Fera produce metis?**

Nope. Metis are the result of two shapeshifters with too-compatible spirit halves mating; it's kind of like incest, only on a spiritual rather than genetic level. If a Garou mates with a member of another Changing Breed, their spirit halves are incompatible — hence, no metis. The child is the breed of the mother; this may mean that the child can't be of the father's shapeshifter race at all (for example, a lupus mother's pups can't be Bastet even if their father is Bastet). The chances for "breeding true" are drastically reduced in such a mating, anyway; there's only a 5% chance that a child will breed true to the mother's race and only a 5% chance of breeding true to the father's race. If being of the father's race is impossible, there's still only a 5% chance of breeding true to the mother's race — hence such pairing are far from honorable in the sense of "taking a good mate and trying to breed true."

Character Creation and Traits

• **Other core rulebooks have Merits & Flaws/ Natures & Demeanors; but not Werewolf. Why not?**

Merits and Flaws are optional rules. There wasn't room for anything but the not-so-optional, "you need these to play" rules in the main rulebook (like rules for the Umbra), so Merits and Flaws were left out. Until we do a revised version of the list, feel free to keep using the ones listed in the **Werewolf Players Guide**; they generally work just fine with Revised rules. The same holds true for Natures and Demeanors; these are particularly optional because werewolves regain Willpower according to their auspice, not their nature.

• **If a werewolf is born under a lunar eclipse, what auspice is he?**

Despite what you may think, the lunar eclipse isn't the mysterious "sixth auspice." Lunar eclipses occur only during the full moon; hence, werewolves born under an eclipse are going to be Ahroun.

• **Older supplements talk about a Background called Past Life. What is that?**

The Background: Ancestors, which was more accurately named. The name was changed to "Ancestors" to reflect what the Background actually did; it wasn't about remembering past lives, it was about contacting ancestor-spirits, hence the change for clarity.

• **I have a supplement that gives first-edition Renown awards. How do I convert these to second or Revised edition Renown?**

There's no hard and fast rule, much as some would like. An old-form Glory Renown of 500 doesn't neatly convert to one temporary dot of second-edition Glory. You have to compare the relative scale of the Renown award and adjust accordingly. The **Werewolf Storytellers Companion** has a set of guidelines for this.

• **The Uktena tribal description says that their totem grants a talent for disguise to its followers, but the totem description doesn't match up. Was there an omission?**

No, the tribal description should read that Uktena encourages his followers to learn the skill of disguise (read: Performance, Subterfuge & Stealth), not grants them the power. Sorry.

• **The core rulebook says the Stargazers' initial Willpower is 5, but the Storytellers Companion says 4. Which is right?**

It should be 4.

• **If a werewolf joins a pack, but doesn't pay any points into the Totem Background, does he get the full benefits — traits and ban, pack tactics, the "opener of the way" rule — of being a member of the pack?**

Said character can learn to use pack tactics as usual, and he can be "led" into the Umbra by an opener of the way. He cannot be nominated as the opener of the way, however, and he doesn't share in the totem's traits or ban until he's made a commitment to the totem (via spending experience).

• **Does a dot of Totem cost two or three experience points?**

Two.

• **When rolling Rage, Gnosis or Willpower, do you roll temporary or permanent ratings?**

Usually permanent, although some Storytellers prefer temporary. Either way is fine. The exception is Rage; you always roll temporary or permanent, whichever is *higher*.

Gifts and Rites

• **What happened to the Gifts of previous editions that didn't make it into Revised, such as Scent of Sweet Honey?**

The nice thing about Gifts is that they're bought individually; not all Rank Two or higher Bone Gnawers would have to have Scent of Sweet Honey, for instance. Simply assume that said Gifts aren't quite as popular these days; characters who had them before can still use them, of course, and the Storyteller can still allow players to purchase them, they're just not as common any more.

• **Do Garou that renounce their auspice lose their Gifts, or keep them? The book's inconsistent.**

They keep them. A Gift is a trick you learn, kind of like tying your shoe, and the power to perform that trick resides within the Garou. You can't "unlearn" a Gift, although you can lose the ability to use it if you lose all your Gnosis or Rage.

• **If the Rite of the Opened Bridge or Rite of Caern Building fail, the ritemaster (and possibly others) take damage, but what sort of damage?**

Lethal damage.

• **When the Rite of Accomplishment is performed, is it only to convert temporary Renown in one category, or can it convert in two or three all at once? For instance, if a werewolf has 10 temporary Glory and 10 temporary Wisdom, can he have both converted to permanent at the same moot?**

The youngster has to challenge for each Renown type separately, but generally speaking, the Rite can be extended to cover each Renown type as needed. In such a case, though, the ritemaster must roll for each Renown type separately; hence, a Rite of Accomplishment converting both Wisdom and Honor would require a separate roll for each. If either roll fails, the entire rite fails; hence, some prefer to undergo each rite separately.

• Also under the Rite of Accomplishment, it says "three moons," which is translated into "the next month and a half." Shouldn't this be more like "three months?"

Ah, why, yes, yes it should.

Umbra

• Spirit combat seems pretty rough. A Scrag with a Rage of 10 is difficulty 10 to injure and still rolls 6 dice to soak damage! How are you supposed to kill one of these guys?

Yeah, that is harsh. We recommend that for lower-ranking spirits you adopt the rule that a spirit has a soak pool of Willpower -2 (no minimum; a spirit with Willpower 2 had better have Armor if it wants to soak damage), and that the difficulty to injure one is Rage -2 (minimum of 3). And go ahead and drop the Scrag's Rage to 6. The footsoldiers of the Wyrm shouldn't be *that* tough.

• Does the soak pool granted by Armor replace the Willpower soak pool (if any) or add to it?

Adds to it. Earth elementals are still pretty hard to take down if they use their Charm.

• In the previous edition, werewolves rolled Gnosis to soak damage in the Umbra. Is this no longer the case?

It is no longer the case; they use Stamina as usual. Storytellers who prefer giving high-Gnosis characters more of an edge in the Umbra often continue to use the old rule, though; we don't mind.

Combat

• Do klaives and grand klaives really do the same damage?

Whoops! No, they don't. The weapons chart (pg. 210) has the correct rules for a grand klaive.

• The rules for soaking damage, regeneration and silver by form are confusing. How exactly does it work by breed?

All werewolves soak bashing damage as normal in all forms. Homids can soak lethal and aggravated damage in any form except Homid; in Homid, a homid can soak bashing damage as normal, but not lethal or aggravated damage. Lupus cannot soak lethal or aggravated damage in Lupus form, but they can soak them in all other forms. Metis soak all forms of damage as normal in all forms.

Regeneration follows the same rules. A homid cannot regenerate in Homid and a lupus cannot regen-

erate in Lupus; in these forms they simply heal as mortals do. However, they can handle silver without Gnosis loss in their breed forms, and silver does not cause aggravated damage to a homid or lupus in breed form. A metis regenerates in all forms, but also loses Gnosis from carrying silver and takes aggravated wounds from silver in all forms.

Those who feel that this is a bit complicated can simply allow werewolves to soak all damage equally well in all forms, but we don't recommend letting them regenerate in all forms unless they're metis (who can't handle silver in their breed form to make this advantage a little more even).

• Some questions on frenzy: If a Garou whose Gnosis exceeds her permanent Rage spends a Willpower point during a berserk frenzy, can she distinguish between allies other than her packmates and enemies?

Yes.

• If a Garou whose Rage exceeds her permanent Gnosis spends a Willpower point during a berserk frenzy, can she distinguish between her packmates and others?

Yes, although she cannot accurately identify them; the Storyteller will tell them they are attacking an enemy, but not which enemy. She will only be able to distinguish between "packmate" and "not packmate."

• If a Garou's Rage is equal to her permanent Gnosis, can she distinguish between her packmates and enemies?

Yes. The frenzy section should read "a Garou whose permanent Gnosis *equals or* exceeds her permanent Rage will not attack her packmates (unless she is in the Thrall of the Wyrm)."

• You can only spend half your permanent Rage in a turn for the purpose of gaining extra actions. Is the fraction rounded up or down?

Up.

• In the description of the Fur Gnarl maneuver, it's stated that someone attacking the exposed area has their difficulty raised by two. But the example states it as a +1 difficulty penalty. Which is right?

The maneuver is right, not the example.

Setting

• Can't I play a White Howler/male homid or lupus Black Fury/homid Red Talon by having an accident of birth or genetic quirk?

No, because that's not the way tribes work. Tribe is a matter of adoption more than genetics; a male homid Garou who's born to a Black Fury mother doesn't count as a Black Fury from birth. He's simply

Garou, in effect tribeless, until he undergoes his Rite of Passage and is accepted into a tribe. Thing is, Pegasus won't accept him, so any Rite of Passage meant to bring him into the Furies automatically fails. Same with homid Red Talons; Griffin won't allow it. As for White Howlers, they just aren't a tribe any more; there is no more tribal totem, so a White Howler Rite of Passage would automatically fail. You have to be initiated into a tribe to be a member; birth alone isn't enough.

• **How many werewolves are there in the World of Darkness?**

The answer, alas, is up to you. The stock answer is "not enough," but generally speaking it's assumed that each tribe numbers between about 500 members at the low end (such as the Stargazers) up to maybe 2000 at the high end (Bone Gnawers, for instance) — and notably more in the case of Black Spiral Dancers. Although **Vampire** has a neat ratio of vampires to humans that lets you see how many vampires are in a given city, **Werewolf** doesn't work like that; the biggest concentrations of Garou population are often well away from cities, in the middle of wolf country. When determining the population of a local sept, a good rule of thumb is to work out the ideal number of werewolves to cover all the sept roles, rotate guard shifts, and have a couple of packs who are more or less full-time in the field — then halve that number. It's the best way to get across the very bad situation the Garou are in.

• **One of my players has an old Stargazer character. Should I still let her play that character, now that the Stargazers have left the Garou Nation?**

Of course! Not all Stargazers have packed up and headed for Tibet. Let her roleplay out the difficult choice she faces between tribe and sept, and let her experiences the consequences of whatever she chooses. Will the other Garou trust her, or assume that she's just going to leave sooner or later? If they don't trust her to stay, will that affect her decision if she gets treated like a second-class citizen? This can make for a fantastic story.

• **In the Setting chapter, it says that werewolves undergo their First Change at around 10-16 years old (if homid) or 1-2 years old (if lupus). However, on page 104 it says you begin play at 14-18 years old (if homid) or 2-3 years old (if lupus). Is this a contradiction?**

Not necessarily. Characters may well have undergone their Rite of Passage and some training between their First Change and the time they begin play, if they were too young to be risked in the field at the time of their Change. This depends on the chronicle, of course.

• **On page 32 of the main rules, it says metis can undergo First Change early in life, around the same time a human child begins to walk; but on page 96, it says metis don't shapeshift until eight years of age. Which is right?**

Page 96 should read "it *typically* cannot shapeshift until eight years of age." Some metis prodigies learn to shapeshift while toddlers, but most must wait until they're eight or so.

Miscellany

• **Here's an art question: Why don't female werewolves have breasts in Crinos?**

The Crinos is not a form designed for giving birth or nursing. Breasts would get in the way. The Crinos *does* have breasts and nipples, of course, but they don't become evident unless the werewolf is lactating in Crinos, which happens only if the mother is nursing a metis cub. If there isn't a direct need for milk, the breasts aren't noticeable through the Crinos coat.

And by the way, a Crinos has only two breasts. The number of mammary glands depends on how many offspring a mother is likely to have; since metis are typically born in ones or (rarely) twos, as with humans, a Crinos has only two mammary glands, as with humans.

• **Where can I find official stats for the White Howlers?**

There aren't any. This is the tribe that's been dead for the longest time; there's really no chance of running into one of these folks, even in the time frame of Werewolf: The Dark Ages. If you really need one for a Roman-era game, fake it with a mix of Fianna and Ahroun Gifts.

• **What about the Bunyip?**

Some general Gifts and totems of the Bunyip are presented in **Rage Across Australia** (reprinted in **Rage Across the World, Volume 2**).

• **And the Croatan?**

See **Croatan Song** for details on what the tribe was like in the time they were still around. Modern-day stats for them don't exist, for all the obvious reasons.

• **Wasn't there supposed to be a Werewolf video game?**

Twice. Both were devoured and vanished into the void of time, never to be heard from again. Ask us no more.

• **Is Gaia really Lilith?**

Not everything has to be shackled to the **Vampire** mythology, you know.

Chapter One: The World of the Garou

A tremor ran through the body of the terrifying creature, followed by another and another, until it was shuddering violently. After a minute a young female wolf was standing among the people in the clearing.

"That's Lena from Tambov," someone said in Sasha's ear, "she's really talented."

— Victor Pelevin, "A Werewolf Problem in Central Russia"

Becoming Garou

The First Change is seen by many as the defining moment in a werewolf's life — it is the moment when he realizes that he isn't a human or wolf, but something other. Certainly, it forms a marker post in the werewolf's life as the moment he discovers his true nature. However, actually becoming Garou takes longer than the few seconds that a form shift requires. It's a slow process of adapting to dramatic physical changes as well and a cataclysmic shift in the character's lifestyle.

A young Garou needs to adapt to bodies that can do things he never expected. He needs to learn to walk, run and rest in bodies that are entirely unlike the one in which he has spent his life to date. He has to adapt to leaving his old life behind. Then the young cub is taught to fight. He's indoctrinated into a whole new society, with its own myths and legends. He learns about a whole new aspect of reality that he can enter and explore. His teachers are far from kind and understanding; instead, they're often brutal and ruthless. Then, just as the

character is beginning to find acceptance amongst these strange, and none-too-friendly people, he's pushed away from the safety of his new home on a mission that is dangerous at best, and deadly at worst, with a group of cubs just as inexperienced as he is.

The introduction to Garou life is never easy. It's a tale, worth telling though, especially if you are running a chronicle for players that are new to **Werewolf** and its concepts. They get the chance to learn as their characters do, which is usually far more effective than absorbing knowledge from assigned reading. Even if your players know **Werewolf** pretty well, it gives you the opportunity to reinforce some of the key ideas of the game in their minds right at the outset. So, how do you go about it?

Well, as you, the Storyteller, sit down to work out how to tell the tale of a newly-changed werewolf, there are several things you should bear in mind. A new werewolf doesn't so much become Garou as become aware of his true nature. The First Change is not a matter of becoming something you weren't before, it's a process of accepting a heritage that has always been part of you. The character was never really human or wolf, even if he lived amongst them. The initial emphasis should be on making the player feel how much their character has changed, and how the world around him senses those differences. As he comes to terms with those changes, then you can work on making the character feel at home in his new existence. Over a period of time, the world of the Garou should become the norm, and increasingly the world of the humans, and to a lesser extent the wolves, should become alien and hard to understand.

A New Body

While a newly changed werewolf doesn't literally gain a new body, it feels like it. The First Change is at once exhilarating and terrifying. The sensation of bones shifting, growing, changing, and your whole body moving with them is initially terrifying. It's as if your body has left your control and gained a mind of its own (in a way, it has, but we'll discuss Rage later). The ability to shift your form is like having teenage growing pains multiplied by a million. Like those teenage growth spurts, it doesn't so much hurt as feel odd. This is something to communicate to the players in the early sessions. As the chronicle progresses form shifting will become a fairly mundane event. In these early sessions, though, it's a big deal as are the physical sensations that the characters endure with each change are a new experience. Be careful not to overdo it, though. If you repeat those descriptions too often, they'll become as tired and irritating as repeated stock SFX shots in a TV series.

As well as the change itself, the new werewolf has to learn to use four new body shapes. Consider for a moment a human child, and the length of time it takes to get used to its body — well over a year. Even a wolf cub needs months. The new werewolf has to adapt to four new forms, some of which are very unlike its original body. Learning to walk on four legs when you've spent the majority of your life on two is no easy task. The only thing that keeps it from being impossible is that fact that the Garou have a degree of innate ability with each of the forms and the fact that the difference between, say, Lupus and Hispo is mostly a matter of bulk rather than actual physical movement.

Even once the werewolf adapts to the physical aspects of the change, there's a whole new set of sensations for the character to deal with. No two forms receive exactly the same sensory input: hearing or smell becomes more or less acute depending on the form one adopts. The lupus has to learn to deal with forms where its principal sense — smell — is significantly less acute.

Probably the best way to convey this sense of adjustment to your players is by increasing the difficulty of rolls for physical or sensory actions made in a form other than their birth form (at least while you run through the portion of the story that deals with them becoming used to their new abilities). A modifier of +1 for Crinos and +2 for the two forms that aren't related to its birth form (Homid and Glabro for lupus, Lupus and Hispo for homid) is likely reasonable. Metis, of course, would suffer no penalty in Crinos, +1 for Hispo and Glabro and +2 for the two other forms.

You can also help simulate it by actually omitting certain pieces of information in your descriptions of what characters sense when they're in forms other than their own. However, this sort of manipulation should be agreed with the players before the game gets underway.

A New Mind

The lupus Garou undergoes the most profound mental changes when she becomes aware of her nature. The change marks her transition from instinct-based thought patterns to full, reasoning intelligence. It's a dramatic change in her whole perception of reality. Human beings take years to develop reasoning abilities as they grow from babies to children. A lupus werewolf has to go through this process in a matter of days, or weeks at the most. Even though it's more a matter of accessing previously unused capabilities than gaining new ones, it's still a challenging shift in consciousness.

However, even a homid werewolf has some major adjustments to her way of thinking to deal with. A werewolf isn't simply a mass of human thought processes wrapped in a powerful and mutable frame — it's a whole new way of thinking. It's a mindset that accepts the reality of the spirit world implicitly (more on this later) and which commits the werewolf to a life of battle. Make no mistake: all werewolves are warriors, even the Ragabash, Theurges and Galliards, and their mindset is designed to help them pay their part in Gaia's defense.

There are few cultures left on the planet where the warrior ethos is central to the society in question — and the odds are that the characters in your chronicle don't come from them. Even wolves themselves aren't inherently warriors — hunters, yes but actual committed warriors? No. Coupled with this is the sudden knowledge of a new language, the inherent tongue of the Garou, which they have to develop and deepen their understanding of in those initial weeks.

Perhaps the most fundamental element of the First Change with which a character must learn to cope is the birth of her Rage. A werewolf's Rage is one of the most fundamental and defining parts of the game, and it is something that requires some close storytelling attention in the early sessions, until such a time as you're sure that your players have a handle on it. This can be problematic, though, as Rage can be looked upon as an intense, controlling emotion the werewolf feels and telling a player what her character feels is tricky business at the best of times. However, in the early stages of the game it may be worth risking it, to help the player translate those Rage dots on her character sheet into what her character actually feels. Keep track of the levels of Rage each character has, and quietly emphasize to the player the growing anger and lack of control.

It's important to establish Rage as a feeling, not just as a source of supernatural power, and the sooner you can do so in a chronicle the better.

Kin Rearing

Many years ago, the transition from human or wolf to werewolf would have been somewhat easier. Kin families, relatively knowledgeable about the ways of their Garou family members would train those children that seemed likely to change in the ways of the tribe to prepare them for the experiences they undergo. This practice is still in use here and there, although some tribes forbid such "coddling" of young cubs, and many Kin bloodlines have lost all knowledge of what they once were.

Thus, many of the difficulties outlined in this chapter will be eased by a life spent preparing to be Garou. The culture shock won't be so great, the character is already prepared for some of the changes to his thought processes and way of life and he has been exposed to the idea, if not the reality, of the Umbra.

However, no amount of coaching can prepare the cub for the physical and sensory learning curve he goes through once he starts changing forms. Neither can talk of the Umbra and spirits really prepare him for actual travel into the Penumbra and those first encounters with spirits.

Such characters are increasingly rare as the Apocalypse approaches and unless you have a player who is already well-versed in the game's setting who chooses a character from such a background, most of the characters in your game are likely to fit the broad outline given here. Since the change is more dramatic (and therefore often more satisfying) for a cub that's ignorant of his true nature, most players will be happy to sacrifice potential "bonus knowledge" for a more gripping personal story.

A New Life

For a homid, the period before the change is teenage angst writ large. Most teenagers go through a stage of believing themselves to be different — special, even. They feel alienated from their peers. For most, this is just a phase they go through. This is not the case for a young werewolf. Both before and after the change, people sense that there is something different about the child. Some shy away from her, instinctively shunning the predator in their midst. Others become more confrontational, seeking to cow the perceived threat. Of course, these reactions are not reasoned ones; they occur on an instinctual level, much as exposure to a werewolf in one of the obviously supernatural forms causes the Delirium. These social handicaps don't disappear the moment the cub changes, either. As the werewolf starts to come to terms with what she has become, the predator will probably be closer to the surface and less under control than it will be later in her life. As the Storyteller, it falls to you to make the reactions of the human Storyteller characters in your game fit this mould.

For a lupus character, the reaction of her packmates is much more clear-cut. Wolves operate under a social hierarchy system that is more rigidly defined than that of humanity. As the cub approaches her First Change, the other wolves usually start to perceive her as a threat, even if they are Kin. In the end, the werewolf-to-be is likely to end up in a position where she must challenge for dominance and the alpha position, or be driven out as a lone wolf. The former option is likely to trigger the change in and of itself: the fierce combat for prime position may well drive the Rage of the cub high enough that the change overtakes her, and she recovers surrounded by the entrails of her packmates.

The lone wolf has a curious double position within wolf society: she is either pitiable, or the hope for the future. The young and strong that aren't capable of challenging the alpha, but that desire a pack of their own often leave the fold, and hope to pair up with a mate who has also left a pack. However, the "alien" nature of the werewolf-to-be usually prevents the young Garou finding a mate, leaving her to wander until some danger presents itself that triggers the change.

In either case, the character feel like an outcast already by the time she changes. Others are able to sense the inherent difference of the character from their apparent peer group before she can, and both humans and wolves, being social creatures, shun the threat. The apparent advantage of all this pre-change suffering is that, once the character has accepted what she has become, she should find it easier to leave her old life behind. After all, if her old life had become a misery, why stay with it?

This is certainly an angle to play up in your story, as it will give the character greater motivation to accept and spend time with the experienced werewolves that find her — however bizarre they initially seem.

Garou Society

Even after the cubs have accepted their new nature, dealing with werewolf society is going to be a significant culture shock for them, unless they are born metis. One of the few advantages the mules have is that they are aware of the workings of Garou society their whole lives. Those werewolves born amongst the humans and the wolves have no such advantage.

To a lupus, some of the ways that Garou society work are going to seem more familiar. You can use words like "dominance" and "submission" when describing the actions of other werewolves to players of lupus characters. These are social interactions that lupus characters understand explicitly. After all, it has been part of their day-to-day existence for their whole life.

The same can't be said of the homid. Instead of seeing one werewolf submitting to another, he is going to see bizarre social interactions that are not going to make much sense to him until he becomes adept at reading body language. You can even omit the descriptions of key physical signals if you don't think the character has the knowledge to understand or even recognize them yet. Only once they've come to understand some of the aspects of society, or had it explained to them, can you start to introduce these cues into your narrative. Even once they come to understand it, they might find it hard to accept. Modern society, in particular Western culture, teaches equality as one of its guiding principals. The werewolves have little truck with this idea, existing as they do in a hierarchical society with defined roles. Many characters, almost always homids, will have a hard time adapting to this. The other Garou in the caern will always be willing to "educate" them when they step out of line. Lupus characters, used to a simpler structure in a pack, may have more problems accepting this than homids who have the school and work experiences to teach them to survive in hierarchies.

For the metis, of course, all this comes naturally. He's always been Garou, so he understands how the relationships work. What is harder for him, though, is that fact that people from outside the community he was raised in are suddenly accorded more respect than the metis himself. The poor creature might know more about the werewolf culture and the set-up of the particular caern than all the other new cubs put together. In most caerns, that won't matter a jot, and the metis remains stigmatized and his ignorant cousins gain all the attention. Play this up in the reaction of the Storyteller characters to the different cubs. It's possible that the other characters might start turning to the metis for advice. By all means let them, but be prepared to let a Storyteller character upbraid them for paying so much attention to an affront to Gaia.

Spirituality

For all but metis and homid Garou raised in Kin families, one of the most profound mental shifts they have to make is accepting the spirituality of the werewolves, in two senses of the word. Not only do they have a belief system that is both fundamental to their culture and often directly opposed to many of the religions of the mundane world, they also meet the spirits that form a core part of that system in person.

Hearing elder werewolves talking about the spirits is probably the first way the characters encounter the idea. Most Garou use a mixture of reverence and acceptance that will come across as little different from the way truly religious humans talk. The real shock comes when venturing into the Umbra for the first time. Here the characters face direct evidence of the reality of the spirit world and the Garou belief system. You should take the time to describe those first voyages into the Umbra in vivid detail, taking care to emphasize the differences between the velvet shadow and the physical world.

Homids, at least, may be intellectually prepared for the idea of a different world. That doesn't mean actually going there has any less impact on them. This is a profound spiritual experience, one that should promote both a feeling of awe and of homecoming — or a great crisis of faith, if the homid was previously very religious. Lupus face a slightly greater challenge. They're only just coming to grips with whole new thought processes, and now they have to come to terms with a reality that is markedly different from the physical world that their previous existence was centered in. That said, they have a greater affinity for the Umbra, and when they have come to terms with the idea, they should adapt more quickly. After all, for all werewolves, regardless of breed, the Umbra is as much their home as mundane reality. While it may have been dormant all their lives, they possess a spiritual side that is more at home in the earth's shadow that it is in the reality of their birth.

The characters can't avoid it, either: Meetings with spirits are crucial to learning their first few Gifts (and indeed most Gifts thereafter). While there will no doubt be elder werewolves on hand to help them deal with the spirits, it is still the character that must do the work. While few first rank Garou are going to meet a spirit directly representing any of the great powers, their first meeting with a spirit, even if it is one they will later come to regard as low-powered and somewhat inconsequential, should be a profound experience. As the Storyteller, you have two major things to bear in mind during this sort of scene. First, remember that the spirits are not merely animal or plant-shaped humans, they are creatures with their own identity distinct from humanity. (For more details on portraying spirits effectively, see Chapter Two.)

Second, the characters are much like clumsy, brash tourists in a land whose customs they have little clue about, certainly no more that they would glean from a basic guidebook, and whose language they have only a loose grip on. And here they are, trying to beg favors from you with no real sense of the vast structure you are part of and represent. With this mindset in place, you should be well set to deal with the characters as a spirit might.

Settling In

As the first months of life as one of the Garou pass, the penalties, both roleplaying and mechanical, should pass. Certainly by the time the pack is deemed worthy of a Rite of Passage, each member should be comfortable with their forms and senses, have a working understanding of Garou society and be able to approach spirits with offending them utterly.

The tone of your storytelling should shift from the strangeness of Garou society to the weirdness and horror of the enemies that the werewolves now face. As they return from the Rite of Passage, the pack should feel in some way that they are coming home. Mentors who were once terrifying and alien now seem more familiar. A return to human or wolf life would seem strange, now, for they are seeing those worlds through different eyes and minds than they were scant months before. You job is now to emphasize the taint of both Weaver and Wyrm in human society as the young cubs grow to a greater understanding of the world around them. For more details on that, read on….

Senses

Garou are not wolves or humans, but rather the children of both, creatures of savagery and civilization. They live in the material and the spirit world, at home in either, yet strangely disconnected from each one. Most spend their lives searching for meaning through the endless battles that their very nature drives them to fight. In many respects, perception is reality, so in order to understand werewolves, we must know their senses. By focusing on the different ways werewolves remain aware of the world around them, the Storyteller can add depth to the description of a scene and give a greater sense of reality to her chronicle and stories.

Everything that we perceive comes from our senses. Most people focus on sight and have a visual form of thinking. During roleplaying, they can "see" the events unfolding in their mind's eye. More rarely, an individual may rely on hearing, remembering the words and listening to the experience, able to quote parts of the session, while the visually oriented person may describe things that weren't ever described by the Storyteller. A very small percentage of people focus on one of the other senses for their primary perception. For this reason, many Storytellers forget to use other senses in their settings. The sense of smell has a stronger memory trigger than any of our other senses. Touch can change our body chemistry immediately. Perception does become reality.

Wolves rely not on sight, but on smell as their primary sense. Wolves are not wild dogs; they have abilities that their domesticated cousins lost millennia ago. A wolf has a sense of smell many times more powerful than that of a bloodhound. If a wolf catches a scent, he knows not only that he smells a human being, but also what that person last ate. He can also remember it and track the scent for hours. In some ways, a wolf's sense of smell almost works like postcognition. With a whiff, the wolf learns enough to know events that have taken place many hours before.

Werewolves have powerful senses. They constantly check their environment, aware of possible trouble. Instincts, buried deep in their subconscious, help them notice dangers. In an urban setting, the constant blare of noises and sensations can cause some, especially lupus, to go mad from the noise, the sights, and the smells. The opposite is sometimes true. Many a Glass Walker finds the quiet and strange smells of the wilds disturbing. Some Garou deaden their senses, choosing to ignore the world around them. Often, these are lost children, many of whom have difficulty stepping sideways into the spirit world.

Even when werewolves are in Homid form, their senses are stronger than those of normal humans. Garou pay more attention to their sensations than humans do. A werewolf doesn't hear any better, but she listens more attentively. Her predatory instincts guide her eyes to notice things out of the ordinary. She tastes her food carefully, savoring and giving attention to the flavors, instead of inhaling the meal unconsciously. The smells of the world hold meaning for her, and she may unconsciously interpret them instead of ignoring the aromas of the modern world. A Garou craves touch, feeling the breeze on her flesh, detecting subtle changes in temperature, and remaining aware of the clothes on her back.

Senses change as forms change. Glabro form heightens smell to some degree. Instincts come to the fore far more readily, usually as pricklings on the neck or uneasy

But There Are No Rules for This!

Some Storytellers may rankle at our blatant tendency to describe Garou senses as strong in all forms when *really*, there's no rules assisting Perception checks for any forms but Lupus. It's okay, really. Even if your players are reading this book (and we know certain cheatericious people are eyeballing this very sidebar for "secret information" even as we speak), you don't have to cave in to any demands to lower difficulties or grant extra dice on Perception checks. The idea here is to use description to show the players how even as their characters shift shape, the texture of sights, sounds and smells seems to rearrange itself, not to grant the characters limited omniscience thanks to their uncanny senses. Use the material here for descriptive flavor, to catch their attention; don't feel forced to make it easier to find crucial clues. If the players really want to take better advantage of their werewolf senses, encourage them to raise their Perception, Alertness or Primal-Urge Traits. It's as good a mechanic as any to rationalize how a werewolf learns to perceive her environment.

That said, if you want to give players a circumstantial -1 difficulty modifier for Perception checks involving a sense that the form is stronger in (such as sight in Homid or smell in Crinos), you're welcome to. It might make your players more interested in experimenting with all their forms, as actual werewolves likely would be.

feelings in the gut. Sometimes these instinctive feelings are positive, conveying trust. Some werewolves believe that they can tell Kinfolk apart from the rest of humanity by a glance or with a scent. In Glabro form, the sense of taste improves. Meat becomes immediately fresh or stale. Liquids may do the same. Night vision also improves, although some werewolves believe that they have trouble seeing certain colors in Glabro.

The Crinos may have the most acute mix of senses found in any form, but a werewolf's ability to interpret those senses becomes a big problem. Rage always burns in the heart of a Garou in Crinos form. The instincts that help a werewolf stay in tune with her surroundings, suddenly all demand the hunt, craving the taste of hot blood, and the sound of snapping bones. Maddening violent desires to test the strength of her sinews and bones against her prey quickly overwhelm most senses. Any unusual movement instantly attracts the attention of a Crinos. The dark holds little difficulty, yet a Crinos still enjoys the bright colors of her human heritage. Eyes see things at distances beyond the range of humans or wolves. A Crinos' ears perk up and determine the direction of the faintest sounds. High sounds beyond the normal human range, such as the hum of electrical appliances, dog whistles, even distant bells reach the werewolf's ears. A Garou becomes aware of deeper vibrations as well, even feeling the deep rumbles below the world. Like many animals, a werewolf can sense impending natural disasters like earthquakes before they happen. Smell is as powerful as sight for a werewolf in Crinos. An enemy doesn't need to be seen or heard for a Crinos to be aware of him. Touch heightens, although feelings of pain diminish. A werewolf feels every brush of air against her fur. How many claws and blades are dodged because the Crinos feels them before they make contact?

Still, the constant rush of adrenaline, the roar of blood in the ears, and the pounding rage within the heart of Crinos make perceptions blur. Sometimes, everything becomes a threat and control is a constant battle. An angry tone of voice becomes a direct threat. Sudden movements are unexpected attacks. A Garou can taste the flesh of her opponent before the first bite. While rage varies with individuals, every werewolf in Crinos carries a threatening edge.

Hispo form brings a werewolf much closer to her lupine heritage. The dire wolf can see much farther than humans and retains the ability to distinguish colors. A Hispo has excellent night vision making her capable of detecting even slight movement in near dark conditions. Yet, Garou comfortable in Hispo form don't rely so much on sight, as much as hearing and smell.

A werewolf in Hispo form can detect even small noises over great distances. She can filter even small sounds and quickly determine their sources and direction. Certain sounds reach the dire wolf from miles away. Howls will wake a Hispo from sleep even after they are inaudible to human ears.

Very little gets past a Hispo's ears, but even less gets past her nose. In dire wolf form, a werewolf may seem to possess almost spatial awareness. Her sense of smell allows her to remain aware of everything going on around her. Shifts in the wind have some effect on this sense, but surprising a werewolf remains fairly difficult. Furthermore, she can recognize scents and find trails that may be days old. A Garou doesn't need to ever see the human who trespassed near her caern to identify him weeks later. The scent works just as well as actually having seen the individual. Many werewolves are especially aware of the scent of blood and the sounds of violence.

In Lupus form, the sense of smell rules. Although it's stated above, a werewolf can piece together pictures of past events with her sense of smell. For example, at a caern, she could recognize which members of her sept had been present and when. Now, the wolf's ability to smell is not infallible. Natural events, like storms and snowfall can wash away or bury scents. Strong odors, anything from toxic chemicals to animal musk, can mask other smells. Hunters often have sprays to disguise their scents. On the natural front, a skunk can be a problem, though Ragabash have been known to introduce new homid cubs to them just for a good laugh. This form has excellent hearing. They can see well at night, but Garou in Lupus often have trouble telling the differences between colors. Unlike actual wolves, most Garou can see in color in all their forms, although Storytellers may wish to change this for their chronicles if they think it will make play more fun.

Werewolves have other senses as well. The Umbra affects werewolves in a number of ways. Even without "peeking," Garou can feel changes in the spirit world. Members of a pack can tell when they enter an antiseptic lab, before they've even caught the scent of the dead air. When a spirit on the other side passes through a werewolf, she feels something, either a sense of warmth or strength if it's friendly or chill and dread if it's a potential enemy. These senses are real and powerful. Werewolves with strong Gnosis may experience the spirit world with even more intensity.

Garou have powerful racial memories as well. Some werewolves directly experience the memories of their ancestors, but even those that don't often have strong feelings of déjà vu. Many times, a Garou has fled through a wilderness that she's never visited, and yet, somehow managed to elude pursuers and avoid obstacles instinctively. Other times, werewolves have recognized and instinctively known details about items or events in the past. These experiences usually occur in Lupus, Hispo, and Crinos forms, but they aren't limited to those forms.

Strong packs may develop a bond, a link with each other. Members of some long-standing packs can almost read each other's thoughts. Packmates have difficulty hiding emotions from their fellow members. If something is wrong, all the members of a pack will know. They may not share the details, but they will know that something is wrong. Some packs even have a sense of when other members are in danger. There are many stories of a single pack member being attacked and other members feeling pain or a sense of urgency. Sometimes, other members may even feel compelled to go to a certain place, even if they've never been there before, to help out a packmate. Theurges debate whether this "pack-sense" is a true sense belonging to all werewolves, or if instead, it is a function of the pack totem spirit.

Regardless, packs that stay together seem to develop this strong bond, even between members who dislike one another. A Storyteller can use this pack awareness to help keep characters together, making them realize that their pack bond is more than just a verbal commitment.

Many spirits teach Gifts that use the senses. For example, Sense Wyrm works differently for individual werewolves. A lupus may detect a foul stench of corruption and decay coming from fomori. A homid may see a dark glow surround a Wyrm-tainted creature. Other possibilities include having a feeling of dread and unease when a Garou thinks about the target. Sensations may change as forms change, adding variety to the use of sensory Gifts and giving players an even greater feeling of the differences between forms.

Heightened Senses deserves some special mention. Storytellers may want to incorporate this Gift into sensing packmates or knowing when their caern may be in danger. While "average" Garou may have sharper perceptions than humans or wolves, a werewolf with this Gift should have the possibility of performing some extraordinary feats (although remember that it's still only a Level One Gift, and shouldn't outstrip more powerful Gifts).

Although a werewolf's senses are her allies, they can also be turned against her. Experienced hunters use powerful high-frequency sirens against a Garou in Hispo or Lupus. Sudden bright flashes can blind a werewolf and even cause her to lose control. Pepper sprays aren't as effective on Garou as they are on humans (thanks to a werewolf's healing abilities), but they still cause problems. Indirectly, the distraction of realizing a packmate is in pain or feeling a cold presence in the Umbra, can spell doom in a fight. Just the cacophony of smells and sounds in an industrial plant can make it difficult for a werewolf to focus.

Using a werewolf's senses gives the Storyteller an arsenal of description to help liven up any scene. Many of these acute senses can provide material for scenes and stories and allow a Storyteller to take control of a scene that's gotten out of hand. Has a pack member gone off by herself and done something stupid that's going to ruin your story for the evening? Have the rest of her pack show up because they felt that they "just had to be there." Are the players and their characters stumped about a mystery that's gone from intriguing to frustrating? Use a wolf's scent to give them more clues. Maybe a chance encounter causes a werewolf to recognize a strange smell. Don't be afraid to let the hunters take advantage of senses. If your pack laughs at band of humans that they rip apart before the hunters can breathe twice, slow them down with flashes or sonics. Above all, just remember that werewolves have powerful senses and that as Storyteller, these all provide opportunities for you to enliven your games and flesh out your scenes.

Demographics

"How many werewolves are there in the World of Darkness?" It's an interesting question, and one that's been left unanswered fairly deliberately. There is no "official count," at least not as far as White Wolf is concerned. But it's worth exploring how many there *could* be.

Werewolf has a tradition of avoiding hard-and-fast numbers about werewolf populations, and for good reason; one person's figures can be completely antithetical to another person's idea of how many should be left in the End Times. True to that idea of "one Storyteller's meat is another's poison," this section discusses principles and possibilities, rather than laying out definitive answers.

Who Knows?

This isn't a rhetorical question. There's a crucial difference between the facts you know as Storyteller and what anyone in the game world, player character or otherwise, knows. Ask yourself how an individual finds something out. There is no Census Bureau in the Garou Nation, no central authority to compile definitive records. There are plenty of good reasons for various groups to exaggerate their numbers and also to conceal some of their strength. Individuals make mistakes, and tradition can enshrine those mistakes just as readily as it can preserve the truth.

So nobody in the World of Darkness can confidently say anything like "there are 6,423 members of the Twelve Tribes as of noon last Monday." Characters who set out to investigate the numbers of their kind will end up learning things that surprise them, and which conflict with the prevailing assumptions around them. An accurate tally, even a good approximation, of Garou numbers must involve travel throughout the world and careful diplomacy with a great many powerful Garou who won't easily part with the facts of their respective communities. The would-be students of Garou demographics must show themselves deserving of many people's trust, and deal with the schemes of those who'd like to deceive others.

True knowledge of anything important in the World of Darkness comes at a cost, and the quest for understanding is a great hook on which to hang many adventures, both during the search itself and afterward, looking at the implications of what the characters now know.

The Basic Numbers

Worldwide, the yearly birth rate among humanity is a bit more than 20 live births per thousand people — slightly more than 10 per thousand in some parts of the developed West, up to nearly 40 per thousand in the poorest parts of the Third World. Garou are not hugely more fertile than the human beings around them, and only about one Garou offspring in ten is itself Garou. That means that it takes about 500 Garou of a particular tribe to reliably produce one new member of that tribe each year.

The Garou are not, of course, evenly distributed among the twelve tribes of the Garou Nation, Stargazers and Hakken, but it simplifies matters to consider them so for now. We'll add complications as we go. It takes about 7,500 Garou worldwide to let each tribe have one cub *somewhere* in the world each year, or the equivalent of one to two new packs each decade… if all the cubs could be gathered together, but that's another complication to consider later.

The Garou depend on two distinct Kinfolk populations, human and wolf. In general, where there are a lot of people there are few wolves, and vice versa. It's not quite an inverse correlation, but it's close enough to average out. North America, Europe and Asia each host about one-third of the world's Garou, with the remaining ten percent spread through South America, Africa and Australia. At the level of one cub per tribe per year, about fifty cubs are

born each year on the three major continents, and ten to twenty throughout the rest of the world.

Not all those cubs survive. Some are lost to the routine problems of infant mortality among both humans and wolves, and to the distinctive causes of death among each species, including violent crime, disease and hunting. Some cubs simply go undiscovered. All told, about half the cubs born in any given year become functioning members of Garou society. Since some cubs go into new packs and some into existing ones, anywhere from one to five packs form each year in North America and about the same number in Europe. The werewolves of Asia under the Beast Courts mingle with other Changers, contributing to anywhere from five to 25 new sentai.

Overall, there is about one Garou per 500,000 people in areas relatively hospitable to werewolves. That's presumably one-fifth the number of vampires and maybe twice the number of mages, for those looking for quick comparisons, but keep in mind that the different sorts of supernatural beings favor different environments. Vampires flourish in the midst of places that are painful and dangerous for werewolves, and vice versa. Mages cluster in their own communities, pursuing aims that seldom make sense to werewolves and in general staying out of werewolves' way, just as sensible werewolves usually avoid hassling magicians unnecessarily. Unless you're running the World of Darkness as farce, the supernatural communities don't all share a block in some residential suburb, and indeed are likely not aware of each other at all except in the vaguest terms: "It's good not to go stirring up trouble there, because you get trouble back."

The Implications

Above all, new cubs are precious. The Garou Nation is not thriving. The escalating violence in this era preceding Apocalypse takes an ever-greater toll on the Garou. There aren't even enough new werewolves to make up for the losses in most years, let alone any for expansion.

The Garou have often been guilty of overwhelming pride and foolhardiness, but they're not altogether stupid. Cubs are not expendable cannon fodder. They get thrust into battle before they're ready in many cases, because there's no alternative: if they don't join the fight, there's no one else to call on. But only a profoundly foolish elder pushes a cub to death, despair or flight. Of course, once cubs start to figure this out, natural human (and lupine) tendency toward rebellion can and does conflict with the duties of the Litany. It's hard to maintain a really strict hierarchy when both superiors and subordinates know that there are limits on what the superiors feel at liberty to dish out in punishment and correction.

A Living World

Keep in mind that arithmetic cannot tell the whole story when it comes to the Garou. They are not entirely creatures of the mechanistic universe. They live surrounded by the spirits, and indeed must spend part of their time beyond material reality to be fully themselves. Gaia and powerful spirits can and do override statistical averages when it suits their purposes.

The extent to which you emphasize this aspect of Garou existence as it applies to population can greatly color your whole chronicle. PCs who are aware of themselves as chosen, watched players in the game of the world's survival develop very different outlooks from PCs who are aware of themselves as drops in the great ocean of humanity, whose ability to participate in the life of the Garou Nation depends on the luck of encounter with others of their kind. Both styles fit within **Werewolf**'s overall themes, so it depends on how you want to balance out the competing influences of fate and chance. You can, of course, let some PCs start off emphasizing fate and others emphasizing chance in their preludes.

Complications and Variations

The basic numbers are a starting point, not the last word. Population dynamics are a tool for making your game feel the way you want to.

Metis

Almost ironically, werewolves are at their most fertile when creating the exact sort of cubs that will do nothing to further their lineages — Garou/Garou matings tend to "take" a lot more often. Furthermore, the metis population of a tribe won't contribute a damn thing to the breeding efforts. If you want to go the simplest route, simply assume that the rate of Litany violations that result in metis cubs is more or less proportionate to the smaller birth rate that a tribe would suffer from having a portion of their number being infertile. However, the number of metis in a tribe can fluctuate wildly between generations. If there are a large number of metis within a tribe, you can expect that there's added pressure on the homids and lupus to breed more homids and lupus, and therefore fewer metis being born in the next generation. Similarly, if there are few metis in a tribe, that may mean that the current generation might feel a touch less pressure to avoid "wasting" their reproductive years — or perhaps even *more* pressure. This can go all sorts of ways, but it's something to consider.

The Black Spiral Dancers

Are the Dancers part of the totals given above? The answer will significantly affect how close the Garou Nation is to the brink of complete collapse in your chronicle. The Dancers exist on the fringes of Garou society. They recruit out of the Garou Nation and the Beast Courts, and of course they kill members of both communities. But they also have their own Kinfolk and therefore their own sources of new cubs.

If you cut a slice out of the above numbers for the Dancers, everyone else's share shrinks, of course. The smaller tribes end up with less than one new cub a year (see below), and even the numerous, well-established ones in an area suffer. Instead of 3-5 new packs in a year, there may be no more than 1-2, and in the parts of the world where Garou are scarce, a new pack of any kind may be a rare occasion to celebrate and venerate.

If the Dancers exist in addition to the above numbers rather than as part of them, then you have the freedom to keep their true strength both mysterious and ominous. At this point in the saga of the world's twilight, they're as numerous as any tribe, indeed, more numerous than most. This generalization gives you a lot of room to maneuver in when preparing surprises… but keep in mind that Dancers don't come in inexhaustible quantities either. If every victory your players win is followed only by more huge hordes, after a while your players as well as their characters will feel discouraged.

Size and Distribution

There just aren't as many Red Talons or Uktena as there are Bone Gnawers and Children of Gaia. There are two broad categories of Garou tribes.

• **Large:** Bone Gnawers, Children of Gaia, Fianna, Get of Fenris, Glass Walkers, Shadow Lords, Silver Fangs, Uktena, Wendigo; Hakken

• **Small:** Black Furies (limited by gender), Red Talons (limited by breed), Silent Striders; Stargazers

The tribes in each category aren't all the same size, but the variations don't matter much for this purpose. The large tribes all get their cub or so a year, and three or four of the tribes most numerous on a given continent get another one or two each. The small tribes often have years without new cubs.

Note that the tribes aren't spread evenly around the world like so many smooth layers of varnish. Red Talons cluster in wilderness, Bone Gnawers and Glass Walkers in cities. Uktena and Wendigo are far less common in Europe or India, Hakken unknown outside Asia, and so on. The typical sept does not include members of every tribe, only of those relatively common in that particular area and a more or less random smattering of the others. The fact that a cub enters a tribe this year doesn't mean it does so anywhere the characters or anyone they deal with ever goes or even knows about.

Varying the Numbers

• **Fewer Garou:** If you want each cub to be even more precious than it already is, and each death among the Garou that much more tragic, simply adjust the total down.

At least two very different kinds of atmosphere can emerge from a shrunken Garou Nation. The Garou may be largely isolated, so that the handful of werewolves in a region feels very much alone in the face of a large and hostile world. Or the Garou may be very closely bound together, making heavy use of spiritual communication and travel to preserve their unity even though spread thinly around the world. Shrinking the Garou Nation by a factor of two would make it as small as the total population of mages, but very different in feel: more unified in some ways, given the shared reality of Gaia and the spirits in Garou lives, but more intimately connected to place and environment than most mages are.

In either case, in practical terms the Garou would have to cluster for mutual survival as a people, so that there'd be enclaves of werewolves and large areas, even whole countries, where now nobody performs the Garou functions of guarding and avenging. This won't make the spirits happy, and of course it means that there are holes in the world's armor. The guilt and frustration that follow should play a major role in any chronicle of very scarce Garou.

If the total world population of a tribe falls below a few hundred, then the tribe simply cannot be a global presence. Its members must cluster near their Kinfolk to have any chance of survival at all. A chronicle in which

The Shape of Things to Come

This kind of greatly diminished Garou Nation is one way to play a chronicle set in the near future, against the backdrop of a world that combines the pervasive decay of the modern day with the edgy futurity of cyberpunk and post-cyberpunk visions. See Charles De Lint's novel *Svaha* and John Shirley's short story "Shaman" for examples of how to fuse cyberpunk and shamanism. The desperation engendered by vanishing tribes and isolated septs fits the mood of approaching darkness quite well.

there are, say, only 2,000 Garou worldwide is one in which the tribes very likely interact only occasionally in passages between the greatest caerns. It's a situation more like the Garou in prehistory, gathered in their places of origin and scarcely aware of each other, except in the modern day there'd be a constant pervasive sense of lost community. If the total Garou population falls below a thousand, either some tribes exist only as single extended family lineages or they cease to exist altogether.

• **More Garou:** Alternatively, if you want a somewhat mightier Garou Nation, increase the numbers. Double the population of werewolves and you'll ensure that no nation or region need be altogether free of werewolves, even though some may have a single sept or even a single pack to cover broad territories. There are still not nearly enough Garou to waste casually, but there are enough to assemble war bands for special needs, drawing on the relatively unattached individuals around large caerns, young Garou looking to prove their merit and earn a place in the world and other available warriors.

If the Garou become as numerous as their foes, then the chronicle turns thematically into something quite a bit different than **Werewolf** as written. The perils (and opportunities) that come from confronting superior odds with courage, cunning and grim resolute faith frame Garou life. Trying to preserve that when the Garou can assemble whole armies and lay waste to great cities is likely to lead to a berserk spiral of escalating force. This can be a lot of fun, but it ceases to be a game of brave spirits standing in the breach against the world's doom in favor of being a game about furry superheroes or out-of-control agents of brutal carnage. Think ahead before committing yourself to this sort of setup.

Other Changing Breeds

The way **Werewolf** works, it's presumed that the Fera population is in considerably worse shape than that of the Garou. If each Changing Breed had comparable numbers to the Garou, not only would the Apocalypse's outcome be less in doubt, but the Garou would become a minority — something that would be very wrong for a game called "**Werewolf**." Storytellers with a fondness for one particular Breed or a distaste for another may wish to adjust these figures further, but the assumption is that few Fera have been able to prosper since the Wars of Rage.

The Ananasi and Ratkin (including Nezumi) are the most populous Fera; each Breed might rival the Garou in numbers, and (depending on the Storyteller's tastes) even exceed them. Of all the Fera, these are the most fertile.

The Bastet, Corax (including Tengu), Mokolé, Rokea, Nagah, Kitsune and Kumo all fall into the "moderately populous" numbers; each Breed is probably about the size of a healthy Garou tribe. The Rokea were once more populous, but the disaster at Turna'a (see Rokea) has reduced their numbers considerably.

Finally, in the "painfully few" category come the Nuwisha, Gurahl, Same-Bito and Ajaba. Individual Bastet tribes and Mokolé streams fall into this category as well. There's unlikely to be more than 500 of any of these groups, and 100 is probably a more accurate estimate.

Religion and Spirituality

"All Garou are spiritual; not all of us are religious."
— Jonn Lao, Stargazer Theurge

The inherent spirituality of the Changing Breeds can never be stressed too much. A werewolf's connection with the spirit world is as crucial as the air she breathes; she is intrinsically tied to all things spiritual and would quickly perish if that link were to be severed. Perhaps more than any other denizen of the World of Darkness, a werewolf depends on her spirituality to give her strength, purpose, and hope for a better tomorrow. Spirituality is more than belief for a werewolf, it's a way of life; in fact spirituality is life itself.

But there's a huge difference between "believing" and "knowing." Werewolves do not have faith, as most people define it. Their absolute, unshakable knowledge that Gaia does exist is a fact. From a werewolf's First Change, she can literally *feel* Gaia. While Garou debate many topics relating to spirituality, one that would never be overheard is an argument about whether Gaia is or isn't real. While some Garou are more in tune with their Goddess than others, even the Black Spiral Dancers would acknowledge that Gaia is very much alive.

What *is* open for debate is exactly what and who Gaia is, and more importantly what She represents. Even an actual avatar of Gaia Herself doesn't answer these questions such that there's no room for doubt. Because no mortal can ever really understand Gaia completely, religious factions do exist within the Chang-

ing Breeds, even if they aren't as wildly diverse as those of humanity. While most of the shapeshifting races credit Gaia for being the grand creator, others give Her a more minor role in their creation mythology. This is particularly evident in the various Fera societies.

What does this have to do with Storytelling? Simply put, some careful attention paid to the religious side of Garou life can open up new levels of roleplaying for your characters. If you're able to properly represent the faith of the Garou, players will ask themselves just how their characters relate to their colleagues' beliefs. Obviously, you'll need to use some discretion when dealing with religion and spirituality, as personal and important issues as they are to anyone (player and character alike). And certainly, there are no hard and fast rules for what werewolves do and don't believe — describing a character's faith as integrating Gaianism with Catholicism isn't "inappropriate" unless you feel that way.

Places of Devotion

A good example of the personal level of Gaian faith is the tendency to worship or meditate in a place of one's own choosing rather than a formal temple area. While it would be somewhat unusual to find a "traditional" worship house for those who celebrate Gaia, places abound where a werewolf can find a bit of peace and quiet to reflect and hear the whispering of her Goddess to her soul. The most obvious is a caern. In fact, the majority of werewolf sacraments take place in a caern. The function of a caern in a werewolf's spiritual life is manifold. Performance of any ceremony in a caern not only invigorates the Garou present, but also enhances the sanctity of the caern itself. Since the energy of a caern is vital to the meditation and worship habits of werewolves, they take great care in insuring the general health and overall good condition of their most sacred places.

A werewolf may also choose to pay homage to her Goddess in various places throughout the Umbra. If a Garou opts to worship in a place other than her caern, there is generally a reason behind her actions. Perhaps she seeks answers that would not be readily available to her in the physical realm, or maybe she does not have access to a caern. Nevertheless, she can seek places in the Umbra specifically built for devotion to Gaia. Shrines dedicated to Gaia and other celestial beings dot the spirit world. Such locales are visited less often, and as a result may not be as well kept as a caern. Occasionally a werewolf will visit a particular shrine only to find that it has been pillaged or destroyed. While the Garou used to actively build sanctuaries in the Umbra, modern concerns have left little time for such activities.

In the Final Days, the Umbra is filled with places that reflect the death throes of the end of an age. While many locations in the Umbra are frightening to even the bravest Ahroun, locales still exist that represent a gentler time in Garou history. After the rise of the Gauntlet, werewolves desperate to keep their spiritual roots strong built many temples to honor Gaia and other Celestines. For a period of time, the number of Umbral shrines was roughly equal to the number of caerns developed on the physical plane. As time rolled forward, and the War of the Apocalypse began in earnest, many of the shrines were destroyed, or even abandoned as the primary focus was given to protecting caerns. A few well-known shrines still exist, and while they are considered important, a Garou would, without hesitation, leave an Umbral temple to fall in favor of protecting a caern in danger.

A favorite tactic of Black Spiral Dancers involves a two-fronted attack. A nearby caern receives the initial onslaught, and as the few Garou who act as caretakers to a shrine leave to defend the caern, a second troupe of Spirals desecrates the recently abandoned temple. In this fashion the enemies of Gaia have demolished the majority of sacred places in the Umbra. Despite the losses, a few temples still exist and are used as places of refuge, meditation, and worship.

Allytis

The Black Furies constructed Allytis not only in reverence to Gaia, but also in homage to their totem Pegasus. The temple is located in a Penumbral Glen near to the corresponding physical homeland of the Furies. The area has a very Hellenistic feel and the surrounding area is ripe with olive trees, vineyards and other trappings of ancient Greece. The shrine itself is small, but radiates a sense of peace and prosperity. Fantastically carved pillars of white marble support an impressive tympanum, which spans the front of the structure. Within that pediment visitors can see a carving depicting the creation of the Garou

according to Fury mythology. The interior of the temple is airy and welcoming. On the main alter a statue representing Mother Gaia gazes over the sanctuary. Allytis is a serene haven to a weary traveler. While there was a time when only Black Furies were allowed to visit, now any Garou who wishes to pray or give offerings to Gaia may do so.

The Glade

If a fatigued werewolf were simply looking for a place of introspection and renewal, the Glade would be a perfect destination. Rumored to have been developed by the Children of Gaia, the Glade is little more than a small clearing amongst mighty ancient pines that seem to touch the sky. Those visiting can hear the murmurs of many different spirits that have made their home near the shrine. The Glade is actually considered to be one of the many sub-realms of Pangaea, although the shrine is free of predators and a Garou does not lose her sense of identity. The challenge for the werewolf that seeks to spend time at the Glade is in finding it. Because of the numerous pocket realms that split off from the primordial realm, the Glade, which is particularly small, is easy to overlook.

Serenity

As the name denotes, Serenity is a place of place of utter relaxation and peace. These qualities make Serenity a popular destination for a Garou that has begun to burn out from the constant warring that dominates her life. While no one is sure who crafted this shrine, none could deny its calming influence. Serenity appears as a picture perfect shoreline along the bluest of oceans. High cliffs overlook majestic waves, and the smell of sea spray perfumes the air. Even the most ardent warrior will relax as the shrine works its magic. Garou from all tribes have traveled to Serenity in order to pay homage and find a sense of balance. While Serenity has been attacked in the past, the land seems to heal itself over time, or perhaps its unknown creators quietly return to repair any damage done.

Daily Devotions

So many cultures and customs exist within the Garou Nation, it would be impossible to say with any accuracy, "The Gaian religion is practiced *this* way." There is no wrong way for a werewolf to worship his Goddess, so long as he offers the proper reverence and respect. Some Garou follow a very rigorous creed, while others are more casual with respect to the amount of time they actually spend paying homage to Gaia. De-

spite the variety of attitudes concerning religious habits, some common ground exists between all Garou.

Since spirituality is so innate to Garou culture (and even their nature), many gatherings of the werewolves involve some sort of expression of sanctity. The most pointed example of werewolves expressing reverence is during moots. While moots are primarily social functions, designed to foster the communal feeling that is necessary in werewolf society, they also serve as a religious observance. During moots, werewolves give thanks and praise to Gaia and other spirits that are important to those in attendance. Certain traditions have become an integral part of moots, and are the closest thing that the werewolves have to a formal sermon. One such act of piety is performing a rite.

Rites essentially reaffirm werewolves' connection to their spirit nature, Gaia, and each other. Rites come in every flavor, from celebratory to punitive and are an intrinsic part of the Garou belief system. Theurges theorize that without the performance of rites, a werewolf would quickly lose her ties to Gaia. Although the specifics of a particular rite vary from tribe to tribe, there are enough similarities to give werewolves of different cultures some common ground. Because of rites, werewolves who would otherwise be at ideological odds with each other can find a sense of brotherhood.

Another way that Garou give praise to Gaia is through many celebrations that are held at various times of the lunar calendar. The solstices of the seasons are observed by all of the tribes. While the particulars of the festivities vary from tribe to tribe, every Garou does their best to find their way to a caern to find fellowship during these feast days. The summer solstice is a popular time for rites of accomplishment, marriage, renewal, birth announcements and so forth. The winter solstice by contrast is a time of reflection, remembrance, and contemplation of the end of the season. While the solstices are the two major Garou holidays, a host of minor holidays fill the calendar. Most of the smaller commemorative days are specific to certain tribes. During major celebrations, the population of a sept swells as packs find their way home from their rangings. Such occasions also mark the rare times that Kin are welcomed at a caern (usually as guards for their reveling cousins.)

So how many Garou holidays are observed? Hundreds, although most werewolves show up only for the two major holidays, and perhaps one or two minor ones throughout the year. After all, it's hard to find time to party when you're trying to save the world.

Introducing Religion

Too many avenues exist to adequately cover the introduction of religion into a storyline. The key is to use spirituality as a device for adding drama, flare, and depth to a story, rather than making oblique comparisons that come off as cliché and cheesy. It's a Storyteller's responsibility to understand, and help her players understand the beliefs that drive a particular character. Also impor-

tant to note are the reasons behind a character's beliefs. Was the character raised in a particular environment that encouraged or discouraged spirituality? How does a character's culture dictate his beliefs? How does a character mesh her old beliefs with a new reality? If a player and Storyteller hammer out all of the details on a character's spirituality, her strengths and her hang-ups, a truly epic personal tale can be woven into the fabric of the main plot. Using Spirituality in a game can add insight and wisdom that might otherwise be lacking. Generally speaking, a character's prelude, or her background, is going to dictate how she reacts to a sudden intimate awareness of a greater power.

How does a newly changed werewolf react to the revelation of the existence of Gaia and a previously unseen spiritual world? Typically a young shapeshifter reacts with awe, and perhaps even some initial disbelief. Hopefully the character in question will seek out a mentor to help him sort out his thoughts and emotions, although an intriguing story might involve a character or two trying to come to terms with their newfound knowledge on their own. However a Storyteller chooses to introduce the topic of religion and faith into her game, the main rule is to make sure that her players are aware of, and more importantly, comfortable with what the Storyteller has in mind.

Holy War

The signs are clear for even the youngest pups in the Garou Nation, the final days are nigh. Battles and skirmishes between the Garou and the enemies of Gaia have become more frequent, fiercer, and more deadly. Never can there be a treaty, or conciliation. The only option the Garou Nation has in order to survive is the total annihilation of their foes. Because the whole of werewolf society has made such a huge, unrelenting commitment, it begs that question, why?

While some in the Nation would claim that the Last Great War is only reflective of the out of control Triat, others feel that the War of Apocalypse is no less

Missionary Work

If a werewolf has grown up in a particular faith, the sudden knowledge of a creator other than the one(s) she has worshipped in the past can create quite a conundrum as the faithful Garou tries to make sense of what place her original beliefs should play in her newfound life. Wise Garou throughout the nation are quick to help a new pup define her beliefs before she succumbs to feelings of depression or anxiety over any perceived betrayal of trust on the part of those who taught her original faith to her. Minister James Mesecher, Fianna Galliard, explains how he views his faith following his change.

"Gaia is the sum of all life here. While this may seem to be at odds with the dogma of Christianity, it merely provides us with a supreme Mother in addition to our already supreme Father. So, the goal is to make sure that we separate their domains so that we might give praise to both in a way that is reverential and true to what our Heavenly creators require. One's proper attitude towards God and Gaia should be humble and pious. We should celebrate their goodness and mercy every day as they touch our lives. My personal belief is that the word of God has been twisted through the ages to fill political ambitions of those who would have claimed to follow his will. For instance, our very existence is considered a sin on Earth. This cannot be true, for if it were, we would not be here. God created the Universe, and in his grand vision he provided us with our Earth Mother. I believe that we, as Garou, are special. We are soldiers of righteousness and goodness. We represent the light amongst the darkness of evil. We are crusaders against the forces of Satan and protectors of God's other children here. Gaia provides us with our unique talents to fulfill God's will. Our purpose for being is to experience and act upon the struggle of good versus evil. Gaia is God's gift to us, and we are instruments of their will."

Other werewolves do not make such a smooth transition in their religious beliefs. Some Garou become bitter, or cynical after being "lied to" in regards to their faith. Other werewolves will drop their former beliefs after experiencing the epiphany that Gaia exists. As with any topic relating to personal morality, there is no set outcome for a newly changed Garou.

than a battle versus genocide. It's a conflict of preserving the beliefs, religion, and lifestyle of the werewolves and their Kin. Those opposing the Garou directly threaten everything that the werewolves hold dear.

Fear of loss drives the Garou, perhaps even more so than any potential reward possibly could. Every day a werewolf can hear Gaia's cries become a little more distant as the stranglehold of calcification and corruption erode Her energy. Werewolves are the ultimate holy warriors, fanatical in their pursuit of ferreting out any potential threat to their Goddess. Even those that are not outwardly religious would give their lives in order to preserve Gaia and the Garou belief system.

This is a very tricky theme to handle, but it can't be avoided completely. Shapeshifters do what they must because they *believe* that creatures other than humanity deserve to prosper — because they *believe* that it's necessary to kill certain individuals in order to make a better world. The question is: How much do you want the Garou's war to reflect the holy wars of the real world? Holy wars never have pretty outcomes. They are brutal, cruel, and unforgiving. If you focus on this aspect of shapeshifter religion, your game will be considerably darker. While most Garou would not acknowledge that on the whole they can be as underhanded as their fallen brothers, there is no tactic too low, no strategy too savage when it comes to defeating their enemies. Gaia must survive, no matter the cost, even if it's at the expense of the very souls of Her servitors. However, bear in mind that it's entirely possible that someone you know lost someone close to them as a result of the religious conflicts that plague our own world. Be sure to handle this approach with caution.

Finally, though, remember that one of the most appealing aspects about **Werewolf** to some players is that it *is* the good fight. Many players enjoy the drama of doing things they'd never do in real life (such as tearing out a poacher's throat), but having some confidence that ultimately, they're on the "right side." While this may seem a little too black-and-white for the World of Darkness, it's not an approach to be automatically scorned. There are already thousands of shades of gray in **Werewolf** — intertribal politicking, the ethical and moral dilemmas most werewolves are faced with, the constant necessity of sacrifice. If your players really want to believe, at the end of it all, that Gaia is indeed worth saving and that their enemies are worth fighting, don't dismiss the thought out of hand. **Werewolf** is about horror, but also about heroism; it's a poor chronicle that doesn't address both.

Intrigue

The Garou Nation has always been hierarchy-driven. From a werewolf's first rites, the importance of status, honor, respect, and unquestioning loyalty are continually impressed upon a young pup until those beliefs are firmly ingrained in her behavior and belief system. The pack mentality is stressed for obvious reasons; without a pack, a werewolf is little more than a sitting duck for the enemies of Gaia. However, in a society that lives and breathes status, there are sure to be individuals who twist the letter of the law to their advantage.

By their very nature, werewolves are aggressive creatures. This is not only evident in their fierce combat abilities, but in the way that they handle themselves in social situations. Werewolves are predatory. As a result, their natural cunning in the wild carries over to their dealings within their tribes, septs, and packs. Signs of weakness in a particular Garou can be met with disdain, mockery, and outright humiliation. Since a strong reputation is such a highly valued commodity amongst the werewolves, some go to great lengths to insure that situations reflect their prowess as a servitor of Gaia. Whether their appellations of greatness are deserved or not, the appearance of power and prestige is all that matters to some.

Don't make the mistake of thinking that such individuals are heavy-handed or obvious in their methods, however. Those who engage in the game of subterfuge within the Garou Nation understand that one misstep could land a devastating blow to their honor. As a result, they skillfully manipulate their way to the top.

Why Can't We All Get Along?

"Have a care when selecting your most trusted advisors. Don't fall victim to the sweet words of a sycophant. These parasites will fill your mind with delusions of grandeur only to mock your subsequent quivering demise at the hands of your own imagined self-importance."

— Sergey Dimitrinov, Seneschal to heir apparent Balaksa Vasil'ev Kriukova, Silver Fang Nation, circa 1642.

There was once a time when all of the tribes were one. They acted with one mind, heart and spirit. Any act was possible for the children of Gaia as they committed themselves to the task of sheltering their Goddess from any threat, be it perceived or real.

Those days are long gone.

With the formation of the tribes came differing customs, traditions, laws, and political structures. As time would roll forward, the tribes became more divergent from each other until their differences often outweighed their similarities. This created friction as each tribe sought to carve out a niche for themselves. As a result, werewolves that had once shared the same lands became territorial, loyalty to one's bloodline became paramount, and tensions arose. While the reorganization of Garou society never led to an outright civil war within the Nation, the threats of violence and strongarm tactics that came from those in positions of strength formed the geographical boundaries between the tribes that for the most part have remained the same.

With the migrations of the individual tribes came new ideas about the way werewolf society should be. While all of the tribes would place courage, strength of purpose, valor, honor and wisdom in their collective credos, the pragmatic approach to most challenges and disagreements between the tribes would be met with some degree of ruthlessness and cunning. Over time, the bickering of the tribes as a whole lessened as the werewolves found themselves distracted by a collective enemy. Nonetheless, some of the old prejudices have carried forward to the present day.

Cultural, racial, and breed bias can create an atmosphere of antagonism that hampers the overall effectiveness of the Garou as an army for Gaia. Why don't the werewolves put aside their squabbles and focus on demolishing the forces of the Wyrm? While some say that pride is the poison killing the Nation, the answer is really far more complex.

Because the werewolves are so status conscious and prestige is given so much importance in their way of life, none of the tribes wishes to weaken their own position by giving control to another. It's a case of too many cooks in the kitchen. While there are many great leaders amongst the werewolves, their philosophies, tactics, and ideologies can vary to the point of contradiction.

While on occasion, the werewolves can put aside their preconceived notions and work well with those not of their tribe, more often than not the door of opportunity is slammed shut from both sides. Sometimes such actions aren't intentional. After all, *everyone* knows that Bone Gnawers don't work with Silver Fangs, and who would dream of the Get pairing up with the Children of Gaia? While such stereotypes might seem ridiculous, and extremely counter productive, they do occur every now and then.

However, stereotypes aren't the main cause for the tribes working separately from one another. Rather, individuals of high rank and esteem refuse to bow before, or work beneath leaders from another tribe. To do so would be to show weakness, and of course, weak Garou have no right to lead. Those who play such games understand how petty their reasons for not pursuing alliances with other tribes would sound to their own followers. As a result, they elaborately dance around the real issues, weaving a tapestry of half-truths to secure their own place of dominance within their tribe. So well are these fabrications displayed, that even those who construct them sometimes forget what is real, and what is fantasy.

The Sept

If a werewolf can ever truly have a place to call home, it would be within her sept. Septs serve many purposes in Garou society; the most apparent is the protection of the caerns that they are built around. A

In a militant society such as the Garou Nation, one could assume that decision making is a straightforward, efficient process. Nothing could be further from the truth.

While there is a very clear-cut chain of command, many variables exist that create a bureaucracy that can turn into an absolute headache for those individuals in command. Since elders hold a great deal of decision-making power over their followers, it's critical that an elder not overstep her bounds too seriously lest she end up with a mutiny on her hands. What those lines in the sand are going to be will vary depending on the attitudes, customs, and dispositions of those she leads. A great alpha balances what is best for the group against the individual concerns and needs of her people. When those two elements are in conflict with each other, an alpha had better be prepared to explain her actions concisely and without hesitation. Any confusion or contradiction in an alpha's actions and decrees can lead to disgruntled followers.

Only a foolish leader would dig in her heels and proclaim that things will be her way or the highway on every issue, but it's inevitable that an alpha's decisions will be met with criticism at some point.

The individual that protests a decision may work her way up the chain of command in an attempt to receive satisfaction. In a pack, she would directly question her alpha. In a sept environment, she would approach her alpha first. If she were not able to get the desired outcome, she might next approach another well-respected elder within the sept. If still she were not able to get the answer she seeks, she would go to a member from the Council of Elders. If the Council member were not able to settle the situation, she would go directly to the leader who stirred her anger. This is generally when challenges arise.

While logically, the resolution to a challenge should solve any issue, sometimes there are sore losers, particularly if reputations were tarnished during the course of events. Since there is no appeals process after a challenge has been completed, it's critical for those in command to make sure that backstabbing and undermining does not occur. Some werewolves take a very hard-line approach on post-challenge behavior, while others use a softer touch. If a sept has no established post challenge process to deal with those who have lost a contest of wills, trouble is sure to follow. In a society that places so much importance on maintaining face, the garnering of prestige and honor can outweigh the important issues of the day.

sept can be rather large, encompassing several packs. Politically, septs are very diverse from one another, even if they happen to be located in the same geographical region. The bureaucracy of each sept has its own distinct flavor, and a young pack that has grown accustomed to the rules of their sept might find themselves with a case of culture shock upon visiting a neighboring sept.

Despite their surface differences, the hierarchy of septs follows the basic rules of dominance. Those that have earned the most prestige are regarded as leaders, and fealty is expected. While such a system may seem crystal clear, some werewolves despise the trappings of renown that their leaders cloak themselves in. While an alpha may be challenged, those who desire to move up the rungs of leadership may not have the abilities required to defeat their elders. A werewolf that has become bitter and cynical may discreetly undermine her alpha amongst her septmates. Innocent-sounding comments that make others question the morale, status, and general operation of the sept can start a snowball effect that may be devastating to an alpha's reputation. While such rumormongering can generally be brought to a screeching halt by an astute alpha, occasionally the insidious whisperings can turn into a full-blown situation. An alpha can find herself scrutinized by her sept, every word and action dissected as her suspicious vassals try to find fault or weakness.

While such acts may seem childish, on the eve of Apocalypse, it's easy for sept leaders to fall into a storm of harsh criticism. Every Garou either has lost, or knows someone who has lost a close friend, family member, or packmate. Anger and grief can easily cloud reason. Naturally, the werewolves look to point a finger, and the easiest scapegoats are those in positions of power.

Sept leaders decide more than the military actions of their lessers. Everything from promotion in status to arranged marriages are decided upon by a sept's Council of Elders. Younger Garou may begin to feel as though those in command are little more than puppet masters who strangle with their strings of control. Modern day alphas find themselves playing politics more often than they'd like. While the Garou Nation certainly hasn't turned soft, present day attitudes concerning individuality, freedom of expression, and antiestablishment force werewolves in command to adjust their governing styles. After all, a ruler with no followers is as worthless as a car without wheels.

The easiest way for an alpha to maintain an even keel in their sept is to be well liked and respected. While this may seem an easy solution to the headaches of running a well-oiled sept, it's far more challenging than most would-be leaders believe. If a werewolf is too straightforward and by the book, they're seen as petty

dictators; too friendly, and they're pandering. Getting to a place of high esteem is a tricky dance, and remaining there can be daunting.

It's important to note, not all schemers go straight for the top commander in a sept; in fact, *most* do not. More often than not, a werewolf will choose to discredit someone of similar rank and position, slowly climbing her way to the top. By eliminating potential rivals early, some werewolves hope to secure their place later on. Carefully laid plans of an ambitious werewolf might take years to fully come to fruition. For the Storyteller, this is a perfect device to feed bits and pieces of political struggle into a campaign. Long term plots of a particular Garou can touch the characters at the most unexpected moments. While an event or two may seem out of place, perceptive characters may be able to connect the dots after a period of time. Of course, when the time comes for any character to expose another werewolf's dubious behavior, she better have more than theory to back up her statements, lest her own reputation become marred for making 'unfounded accusations.'

The Pack

"The strength of the pack is the wolf. The strength of the wolf is the pack."

A werewolf's pack is probably the most important facet of her social life. Few things hold more importance or require more devotion than a werewolf's relationships with her packmates. Without a pack, a werewolf is little more than a target for the enemies of the Garou nation. From a logistical point of view, it would be foolish at best for a werewolf to go through life without a pack. Packs provide protection and security. More importantly, the pack plays a crucial role in a werewolf's emotional and spiritual well-being. The pack surrounds a Garou with camaraderie, a sense of purpose, and a spirit of belonging. As a result, most werewolves are extraordinarily loyal to their pack, to the point of fanaticism. Stories circulate throughout the Garou nation of pack versus pack rivalries that are similar to folk tales of the Hatfield and McCoy feuds. When two packs tangle on ideology, territory, or any number of issues, the grudge can be carried on for years.

Most disagreements stem from different packs trying to decide if they are getting the respect, the recognition, and the space that they deserve from neighboring packs. While those kinds of attitudes might seem juvenile, acknowledgement of success and prestige is serious business for most werewolves. In a culture built on the concept of renown, a pack's reputation for influence in any given region is paramount if that pack wishes to be known as serious players in the War of the Apocalypse.

Packs are sometimes the only family that a werewolf has. As such, relationships between packmates tend to evolve into something more than friendship. Many werewolves consider their fellows to be more like brothers and sisters rather than comrades in arms. Just as there is contention in most families, jealousy, frustration, and ambition can cause friction within packs. In extreme cases these feelings can cause antagonism that leads to scheming. While most quarrels are dealt with before any serious repercussions arise, it is possible for unchecked conflicts to evolve into inter-pack rivalries. The end result of an adversarial relationship within a pack can be dangerous to the entire group as the focus is drawn away from the good of the pack onto the drama of the individuals. Wise alphas put a stop to backstabbing within their packs. Being a member of a dysfunctional pack can be more dangerous than not being a member of a pack at all.

The Individual

"Don't you almost despise yourself when the only thing you think about is your needs, your wants, your desires? Ours has always been a life of servitude. Service to our Mother, service to our Kin, service to our people. When you find things aren't going the way you desire, it's because you started thinking about what was best for you. None of our great heroes were created that way. Not one. They always remembered why we are here. To give, to defend, to protect those who can't do it themselves. Live your life that way, and I promise that you'll create a legacy that none will forget."

— William Cray, Fianna historian

While most Garou have heard similar sentiments from other werewolves, sometimes the allure of stature or personal gratification is too much to resist. Personal intrigue in **Werewolf** can vary widely depending on the goals and ambitions of a particular character. Sometimes greed or lust can be the motive behind a werewolf's behavior. Some werewolves are not content to lead a modest life and want all of the riches that modern living can provide them. Others crave notoriety, power, and control. Pride, vengeance, or any other type of emotion drives werewolves. The key element in creating an effective story of personal intrigue is in understanding the motives behind a character's actions, and knowing that despite the risks, the character is willing to move forward to accomplish her goal, consequences be damned. It is very plausible for a character to start out with good intentions and later find herself on the slippery road of deceit.

Once a character has reached the point of no return, it becomes imperative for her to reach her destination so that she can justify her actions later. Garou are masters of rationalization. In the final days, the end always seems to justify the means.

The Food Chain

What does an aspiring Garou have to look forward to? If a werewolf is looking to claw his way to the top (figuratively or literally), what steps must he take?

The first step along the way is surely that of pack alpha. Within the pack the hierarchy is pretty cut and dried. The alpha is the top leader, and the rest of the pack is expected to defer to his judgment, particularly if imminent peril exists. While the alpha may be challenged, and certain situations require flexibility in who is chosen to lead, an alpha that is seen as fair and just by his pack can expect to keep his position for some time. As the leader of a progressive and effective pack, an alpha receives commendations from his sept as well as having some limited name recognition with other local packs. Occasionally an alpha selects a trusted advisor to help him make difficult decisions. The beta acts as a seneschal, and if the situation warrants, she can speak on behalf of the alpha. This position can also bring emotional rewards and prestige, and some Garou actually prefer the role of beta to alpha — less responsibility, but if you can manipulate your alpha, there's no loss of power.

From there, the next logical step is that of a sept office. Most of these offices are filled according to merit — a Talesinger should optimally be the best Galliard in the tribe, while the Master of the Rite should have the most mystic knowledge — but that's where intrigue comes in. After all, there are more ways than one to win office. Of the various offices, the most influential and coveted are Warder, Master of the Rite or Master of the Challenge. Each one allows a clever Garou to reward his allies and discredit his rivals as need be.

As a member of the upper echelons of a sept, unless a gross mistake of honor, or death occurs, a Garou can expect to move onto the Council of Elders at some point. To be on the Council is not only the culmination of a successful career, but also a place of high honor due to distinguished service. As a member of a Council, a werewolf is fairly well known in his region. Very few would openly question his judgment, and fewer still would bring a challenge against him. The top spot is reserved for those with the ambition, tenacity, and wit to win the title.

The Grand Elder of a sept is known not only regionally, but also throughout the Garou Nation. A Grand Elder has an established reputation. He receives respect not only for his accomplishments, but also for his ability to negotiate through the sometimes-hazardous waters of the Garou caste system. Once a werewolf has attained this esteemed rank, there's little room to go further — but those who've attained this station via intrigues usually spend most of their time trying to keep it.

Intrigue is a natural element of **Werewolf** games. Pack members vie for the position of leader, a position not always won in battle. The various offices of a sept hold great prestige, and an added ability to pursue one's agenda. Tribes duel one another at moots for important rights such as caerns, territory and the right to lead. And why is that? Because, at heart, werewolves are not that unlike ordinary people. They have the same wants and desires, but writ large; a Garou's emotions run hotter than that of any human. Plots and intrigues are bound to follow.

All too many Garou crave rank for a simple reason — they either consciously or unconsciously want to be loved, respected and appreciated a thousand times more than they want prestige itself. The affirmation of other Garou becomes remarkably more important when you take into account that werewolves live in a society that is hidden from the world at large, with no outside recognition, no outside thanks, and certainly no monetary compensation at the end of the day. For many Garou, the feeling of acceptance and accomplishment is addictive in a life filled with negatives.

For some Garou, though, the weight of responsibility can lead them to do things that would otherwise be unthinkable. Few werewolves look forward to their dying day; even the Get of Fenris care more about dying well than dying soon. The werewolf who sacrifices his own life for the good of the pack does so because his conscience or sense of duty will allow no less. Likewise, some Garou are willing to sacrifice their personal honor by doing dirty work that nobody else is willing (or able) to accomplish, all for the good of the Nation. The Shadow Lords are a good example — popularly held to be the tribe most likely to dabble in skullduggery anyway, they have little preventing them from using underhanded tactics to achieve their goals. Even if the goals are noble.

Conversely, some werewolves might delve into intrigue to preserve the façade of their honor; this is particularly important when you consider the emphasis many tribes put on ancestral ties. A Silver Fang who falls into dishonor is not the only one affected by his shame; his entire bloodline, his ancestors, his House, even his tribemates share his disgrace. Small wonder that some Garou will avoid bringing such a stain on the family honor at all costs.

Not all intrigues are as closely related to the values of Garou society, of course. A desire for vengeance can send a werewolf down the path of double-dealing and plotting just as surely as a desire for added prestige might. And we'd be completely remiss not to mention love as a motivator. There's already a terrible pressure in Garou society not to mate with other Garou — two werewolves in love with one another must resort to secret assignations merely to be together. The plot is further complicated if one werewolf is in love with another, and means to win the heart of his intended, all while keeping his passion secret. But who said all romantic intrigues have to be between werewolves? Kin aren't as physically or spiritually powerful, but they have no less ability to manipulate the emotions of those who have fallen for them. In some cases, that's all the power a given Kinfolk has — little wonder they'd be inclined to use it.

And, of course, the motive of power lust can't be ignored. Although theoretically all Garou are expected to set aside their personal ambitions for the good of tribe, sept and Nation, in practice it doesn't always work out that way. Garou hold power that most people in a civilized country don't — immediate power over life and death, the ability to kill almost without fear of punishment. After all, if you want to kill a human that few would miss, who's to stop you? Combined with the spiritual and political might available to an aspiring elder, it's little wonder that this power can grow addictive.

Movers and Shakers

Wherever there are leaders of importance, there's speculation about what those leaders do behind closed doors. In the war against genocide of the Garou, many heroes have been created overnight as tales of their exploits traverse territory after territory. Other werewolves of note inherit their reputations because of their lineage. While many great leaders exist amongst the ranks of the Garou, only an elite few who could rightfully be called legends in their own time. These werewolves hold a vast amount of responsibility for and decision-making power over their respective tribes.

Each tribe has at least one larger-than-life, living hero. These elders, and their direct followers, tend to be on the front lines. Their combat tactics are scrutinized by up and coming alphas, tales of their victories spread through the nation like wildfire, and their defeats are mourned.

Rumors circulate through the Garou Nation of discreet meetings between the top alphas that determine the actions of the werewolves as a whole. While many Garou dismiss such talk as nonsense, a few have begun to wonder how much truth there might be behind the tales. The political stance of certain alphas is no secret. And while messages of werewolves working together in harmony despite tribal differences might make for a great speech in front of a large moot, the reality of werewolf leadership structure makes implementation of such philosophies tricky at best.

Although the likelihood of every elder of note sitting down around a campfire and agreeing on strategies to improve the overall effectiveness of the werewolf army is not great, it certainly is possible for a few leaders to maintain contact with each other. Whether quiet pacts or treaties are actually formed between the key leaders that would, in turn, affect many members of their respective tribes is purely speculation. Such "meddling" would likely manifest itself as an increase in arranged marriages, subtle shifts in territories, and more tolerance between certain groups. While some Garou would see those kinds of activities as a step in the right direction, most would view change with suspicion. Any act that could conceivably weaken a tribe's position, thus threatening their collective reputation, is to be avoided.

Storytellers wishing to dabble in intrigue of this sort are well advised to remember that unless the players have some way of getting involved, or some ability to alter the paths of these agreements in some way, there's no point to building a story around it. Your players' characters are the stars of the show, and they have better things to do than find out about secret meetings between elders that they cannot possibly influence in any way.

All in the Family

Politics and bureaucracy extend beyond the werewolf tribes, septs and packs into their Kin. Many Kinfolk organizations and fellowships dot the globe. The philosophical and political agendas of such groups are as diverse as those of their Garou cousins. Werewolf social laws are difficult enough to navigate, but when the Kin are thrown into the mix, situations can get down right hairy.

All too often, an individual Kinfolk's lot in life is determined from a young age. This isn't universal, of course; a Shadow Lord probably has the motive and ability to manage his family affairs rather more closely than a Silent Strider of equal rank, and European septs tend to be more strict in such affairs than American septs do. But lineage, age, and aptitudes can easily determine whom Kin will marry, where they will live,

the type of career they will pursue and so forth. While some Kin are humble (or, sadly, browbeaten) enough to accept this lot in life, others look to build their own prestige in a society that values personal reputation. If a werewolf really wanted to take an unbiased look at how effective their own tribal systems are, she would need only look as far as her Kin and how they act. As with all people, Kinfolk act based on what they have seen, heard, and learned throughout their lives. While this can be a good thing, werewolves have also perpetuated a number of bad social habits. Kin frequently mirror their Garou cousins on everything from biases to political views.

Kinfolk also serve as the backbone for werewolf social structure. They are not only companions but also caretakers, guardians, and of course, that all too important connection to the mundane world. Werewolves largely dictate the actions of their Kin. While Kin are still children of Gaia, they are viewed as subordinates in the eyes of their werewolf relatives. The opportunities for stories of intrigue involving Kin are endless. A Storyteller could create a large plot involving a number of Kin that are trying to achieve a goal that might not necessarily jive with the werewolf party line, or a story might be more personal, relating to a single family. In any caste society, there will be individuals who go with the flow because, "That's the way it's always been." On the flip side, there are those who will use the system to their own advantage.

Creating Intrigue

There is enough political strife, family secrets, and hidden motives inside of the Garou Nation to create a tale of subterfuge without ever having to use any influences outside of werewolf society. The key to a successful plotline involving innuendo, hidden truths and shocking revelations is in involving a player's character personally with the scandalous goings on. Characters might accidentally stumble into a situation where they quickly find themselves in over their heads. A simple omission of information when reporting to an elder could start a snowball effect of white lies that if uncovered could mean a serious loss of respect for a young Garou. Not all scheming may be premeditated. A particular werewolf might hide the truth in an effort to avoid punishment. Another Garou may accept responsibility for an action that she didn't perform in order to help a respected elder save face.

Whatever plot device a Storyteller chooses to implement, she should understand inside and out the motives, feelings, and intentions of those who are perpetuating the cover up. A werewolf very well may have honorable goals, but perhaps her methods of bringing these goals to fruition are questionable.

The following are some questions a Storyteller may wish to ask herself when creating a plot chock full of intrigue:

• **What am I looking to accomplish with this story?**

What is the underlying moral or lesson you are trying to convey, if any? Is there a particular mood you're trying to create? Are you simply trying to get your players to think along terms of politics and alliances, rather than simple military objectives? A plot involving subterfuge need not be serious, in fact a pack trying to accomplish a particular objective by indirect means can have elements of comedy, particularly if that pack is accustomed to acting in a more forthright manner. On the other hand, you might want to create an atmosphere of paranoia. Is a particular individual actually an ally to the pack, or are they being used as a convenient stepping-stone?

• **How are the characters involved?**

Is the secrecy of the characters' own creation, or have they stepped into something inadvertently? How deeply involved is the pack? Are they the center of a particular plot, or more on the periphery? How large is the scale of the scheming? Does it encompass a pack, a sept, or even go straight to the top alphas of a particular tribe? How do the pack fit into the big picture of the plot? Can the characters change the course of events significantly? If not, why not, and what do you expect them to do?

• **Who plays a minor role in the plot?**

Are other packs associated with the course of events? have any kinfolk been touched by the dubious goings-on? How many lives will be touched by a particular conspiracy? Is it wise for the characters to try to glean information from a specific group or individual? Who might be watching the characters from afar?

• **What are the consequences?**

Can the characters bring the truth to light? If so, what kinds of enemies will they make? What is the effect on their reputations? What are the intentions of a conspirator; honorable, selfish, or something else? What would happen if the truth were never discovered? How serious are the consequences of hiding the facts? Who might lose prestige if those in authority were to uncover the truth? How serious is the transgression occurring?

• **What's in it for the characters?**

Is it in a character's best interest to concoct a way to hide the truth, or to expose it? Will there be a great gain or loss for the characters involved? How high are the stakes if the characters fail in their course of action?

You needn't answer all of these questions in order to formulate every plot; some intrigues aren't as remark-able as others, and can be dealt with in the space of a night. What's more, after a few plots of this sort, you may find your players are the ones concocting their own intrigues, trying to play the game of politics to achieve their own goals, whether noble or selfish. Don't panic when that happens — take delight in their enthusiasm. They've taken their first steps into a larger world.

Using the Litany

The Litany serves a fairly basic role in most **Werewolf** games; it's the code of rules for Garou to follow. Most packs follow the Litany most of the time, and gain Renown for doing so under difficult circumstances, and they also break the Litany now and again, either from necessity or as a show of independence.

However, after a while it becomes obvious that some groups don't hold all the tenets of the Litany in equal regard. They may live rigorously by the law of "Combat the Wyrm Wherever it Dwells and Whenever it Breeds," as that tends to provide plenty of action, but disdain "Garou Shall Not Mate With Garou" as a silly law that's not worth obeying. Some players even divide the tenets between "real laws" and "laws that are meant to be broken."

Obviously, that wasn't the intent of the Garou that agreed upon the Litany so long ago. All the laws *do* have a purpose, and were enacted for good reason. Similarly, any Ragabash worth his auspice should be able to challenge hidebound obedience to any tenet of the Litany — which's what the Questioner of the Ways is meant to do, after all. The idea is that most Garou will obey the Litany if at all possible, and have very good reasons if they are forced to do otherwise.

The following section is meant to give the Storyteller a little more ammunition when it comes to matters of law. The two perspectives on the Litany listed are those that will probably be most useful in a chronicle. The first is the perspective of the Philodox who sees the reasons behind the laws, and champions the tenets as good and worthy overall (if sometimes abused). The second is that of the Ragabash who, like any good Questioner of the Ways, looks at things a different way, challenging Garou to analyze their own assumptions and actually *think* about their decisions

Garou Shall Not Mate with Garou

The Philodox: This law was not created to make frustrated adolescents miserable. This law was not created to give our people license to torment their metis. This law exists to protect our relations with our Kinfolk. Gaia deliberately made us reliant on humans and wolves to pass on our heritage. However, if we were permitted to take other Garou as our mates, then our Kinfolk would no longer be our mates — they would be our chattel, our wretched breeding-slaves kept only for the purpose of producing fine offspring, and discarded when no longer useful. Because we are not allowed to love one another as mates, we seek solace in the arms of our Kin — and we love *them*. We love them, and we remain tied to their world, and we remember what it is to be, in our own way, both human and wolf. If we did not, we would become more and more insular, more distanced from the world as Gaia meant us to live in it. One tribe has already fallen down that path — or should I say, that Spiral.

The Ragabash: Meanwhile, resentment grows up in Claws-the-Silver-Path over there, who's truly in love with Cassandra but forced into a loveless marriage with Maria. You know who cops the brunt of that resentment when it turns to anger, don't you? Changing Kinfolk from mere breeding object to mere sex object doesn't assist them in any great way.

Viability of the species, now there's something that was previously valid. Yes, if we'd happily humped each other silly a few centuries ago, we'd end up with a bunch of inbred, sterile Garou, no Kinfolk, and no damn future within fifty years. Newsflash: We now do not have any damn future within fifty years as it is anyway. The Apocalypse is upon us. The math here is not hard. Change our tactics, and within fifteen years, we can have nine times our number of useful soldiers. Tell me that's not appealing.

Combat the Wyrm Wherever It Dwells and Whenever It Breeds

The Philodox: Any Garou who cannot see why this tenet was written is unworthy of the Mother's gifts. Had the Wyrm not become the Corrupter, there would be no need for us. The wording of this law is absolute, yes — for a reason. Too many warriors forget that the Wyrm dwells in the hearts of humans. It breeds in domestic violence, in hate crimes, in things that cannot be solved with claws. You cannot ignore the Wyrm's subtleties because you prefer to fight the more obvious threats. You cannot cure the disease by treating a few symptoms.

The Ragabash: Take the lesson from Tennyson's "Charge of the Light Brigade": If you're heinously outnumbered, outgunned and outflanked, then you do not fight. Do not attack Wyrm caerns unless you have a damned good reason to do so, damned good reasons including such rationales as "We can win" or "We're going to die anyway if we don't." Otherwise, you accomplish nothing except killing large numbers of us for no good reason.

There's some real wisdom to working out where the Wyrm is getting stronger and culling it before it can become massive trouble for us later. But making vague statements of "Wherever it dwells" is asking for War of

Rage kind of trouble. Because as we all know, the Wyrm bred in the hearts of the Bastet and it made them betray us by not sharing their secret stuff. We all know the Wyrm corrupts humans, because their kids pull the wings off flies. Our response to both situations? We rip their heads off. We "combat" the problem. This is counter-productive.

Respect the Territory of Another

The Philodox: Some like to say that it is "unnatural" for people — Garou and human alike — to kill one another over such things as boundaries. These pundits know little of the "natural" world. Countless animals fight, and kill if need be, over territory. Territory is food, and water, and the chance to pass those things on to your children. These things are important to all living creatures. This rule was not written to justify the slaughter of trespassers — this rule was written with the traveler in mind, a call for him to respect the boundaries that are important to others. When this rule is violated, the result is a situation like that of the conflict between the "Europeans" and the "Pure Ones," or the extermination of the Bunyip. When it is honored, greater cooperation between septs and packs is the result.

The Ragabash: This is one of those tenets that worked better in years past. We don't have territory any more. Multi-tribal septs are one of the great proofs of this. We don't lope around marking our borders with urine and feces. I mean, come on.

Let me spin you a story. Some pack, desperately seeking to evade powerful pursuers, runs to the nearest caern they can think of. They are being hunted. They cannot howl for every obvious damn reason. If they are stupid enough to howl, they attract the notice of those pursuing them, leading them directly into the caern. That would be a high level threat to which we likely lose many warriors. Or worse, their pursuers listen to the howl, learn the location of the caern, and then go and get help. That's an unstoppable threat. We lose the caern. So for their prudence, these young ones are dishonored for disobeying the Litany, or in the worst-case scenario, turned away at the bawn for their disrespect and then murdered.

Accept an Honorable Surrender

The Philodox: If you refuse to accept an honorable surrender, you have just killed an honorable person, and proven yourself dishonorable in the process. Gaia needs honorable people. It is a stain on the honor of our race that such a law is even necessary. My only clarification is that a wise Garou must be able to tell the difference between an honorable surrender and a dishonorable one; surrendering to the Wyrm is unacceptable, and mercy is sometimes a mistake, given the enemies we so often face.

The Ragabash: There are a lot of positives to this tenet, I'll grant you. I'm all for anything that that is in place to protect Garou's lives from useless deaths, and this tenet does that. But it doesn't go far enough. Right now, it encourages politics and responses that weaken us all. I've seen would-be politicos use it to pamper the young warriors they see as "the future," (What future? We've fifty damn years left and probably not even that,) by pulling them out of fights in which they damn well deserved to be throated. Not killed, but smacked upside the head a bit for sure.

Why would eradicating the tenet help? For one, it would immediately dislocate the word "honor" from "surrender." Much as we talk and preach about there being no dishonor in surrender, the talk which flies about speaks otherwise. It's humiliating to be beaten. And rather than try and fight this, this tenet immediately reminds us of that.

Submission to Those of Higher Station

The Philodox: To be sure, this law does stem in part from our wolf nature. However, for a society of warriors, a chain of command is frankly necessary. A democratic army cannot fight a war effectively, particularly if they opposition has a chain of command they lack. Lines of communication must be clear and direct, even in peacetime. I think we all know (or used to be) some cocky adolescent absolutely convinced that they knew everything there is to know about the world until they were actually forced to *live* in the world, at which point they started to realize just how ignorant they were. Although this tenet can be — and is — abused, there's a very good reason that werewolves should show their elders respect.

The Ragabash: When this tenet is misused, it is damaging beyond all else. It is a carte blanche to tell those below you whatever the hell you want them to do. Worse, it favors those who are adept at ensuring they get credit for positive actions — they receive Renown, retain their high rank, and can continue to order their subordinates to do their dirty work.

I am not for a moment advocating disobedience in battle. That's a fool's game and a good way to get us all killed. It's not "submission" I'm arguing, it's "higher station." Whatever good this tenet may do is destroyed by our highly subjective system of station.

The First Share of the Kill for the Greatest in Station

The Philodox: Despite the grumbling of some cubs, this is not a law crafted by elders to enable them to have whatever they like. This, like the previous law, is a formal recognition of our wolf nature. We are not lions, where the beast that does the least work on the hunt receives the largest portion. We are wolves at heart, and our station is earned. And, if I may be blunt, this law will never encourage a Garou to be more or less selfish — but at least it will only benefit those selfish Garou who have proved that they are worthy of the benefits they claim.

The Ragabash: This tenet not only gives the most powerful weapons, the most impressive tricks and the most useful gadgets to those who least need them, but it acts to ensure that those who are "in station" stay "in station." This is where, supposedly, challenges come into play, but suddenly we have a problem. This is the first share of the kill. Underline kill. It is not unfair to argue that the moment a kill is made, we can be said to be at war. Cross-reference this to "The Leader May Not Be Challenged during Wartime."

And right now, all the ferals out there are screaming how this all proves we need to just get rid of the monkey politics, and its all their fault. To them I say, shut up. I've seen wolves pull this excrement, too.

Ye Shall Not Eat the Flesh of Humans

The Philodox: Theoretically, this tenet should add "or Wolves", but the fact is that, historically speaking, there have been far more Garou who eat the flesh of humans than those who eat wolf meat. For one, humans are simply more plentiful, and it's easier to rationalize a human "deserving" a fate as food. However, devouring human flesh is an activity that conveys Wyrm-taint; therefore, it is clearly wrong. It is also a health issue in modern times; humans do things to their bodies that make them frankly unfit. Nonetheless, as poorly as humans may have treated the planet, they're one-third of our own nature, so they shouldn't be treated like prey animals. Enemies — as needed, yes. But never prey.

The Ragabash: Yep. No problems. Frankly, the idea of my sister being a snack for some Red Talon frightens me and any rule that stops it happening is good in my books. What, you expect me to fight against all of them?

Well, I will anyway. Fact is, we're predators. Humans are, for the most part, prey animals. They have flat teeth, designed for grinding plants, and vegetables tax their digestive systems a lot less than meat does. Eventually, these things are going to happen for a whole bunch of reasons. Plain primal instinct. Revenge against the monsters who slew your family because they thought their fur would look better as a hat.

There are some real dangers in the human eating thing. Discussions of chemical imbalances and nutrition aside, a lot of the stuff stinks of hatred and there's an element of torture in it, that old "eaten alive" cliché. I think we've all seen that man-eaters tend to become very cruel very quickly, and Banes start flocking around them. But making it punishable by law is asking for trouble. I shudder to say this, but a few less humans won't hurt Gaia and it won't hurt us. If they end up in some wolf's stomach, so be it. Make sure our elders lecture cubs on the dangers, but don't give us excuses to get caught up in debates of punishment for something that's nigh inevitable.

Respect Those Beneath Ye — All Are of Gaia

The Philodox: Garou should know their place in the scheme of things. They should know to defer to those above them, and they should know to be generous to those below them. Everything *is* of Gaia; that's why you thank a deer's spirit after slaying its body, and why you ask permission to enter sacred Glades. To take this to the extreme, it is a good thing to mourn for the fomori and Black Spiral Dancers you slay, mourning the death of what they might have become if not for the Wyrm's taint. This tenet is very important for keeping our people focused: We must remember that we are warriors, and we are not allowed to relent in our battles against the Wyrm, but we must also realize that we have to see the difference between what we're fighting and what we're protecting.

The Ragabash: I'd be really inclined to respect this rule if I ever saw it followed. It makes some sense, it's well worded, and it doesn't get too much in our way. The only time it would get in our way is if frankly, we don't have the time for social niceties with, say, some small animal-spirit who wants to properly chat when we're on the hunt for something *dangerous*. At that point, you ignore the rule, obviously.

That said, I'd also point out that there *is* a practical problem with this tenet existing alongside "Submission to those of Higher Station." I'll call it the "Bone Gnawer" problem. It ain't exclusive to 'em, they just typify it. They argue that they can't follow the Submission one, or they'd spend their whole life submitting, but they don't have to respect anyone cause no one's lower. Now that's BS, but it highlights the problem in the rules being there together — they don't directly contradict but they still confuse each other. Now for us smart folk, it's fair enough to play it by ear, but, hey, if we all know when to give ground and when to hardline, we wouldn't need the Litany, would we?

The Veil Shall Not Be Lifted

The Philodox: If you cannot appreciate the potential danger of humans (and more the fool you if that is so), then think of the Wyrm. Set aside the possibility that, if humans knew we existed, they would begin exterminating all the wolves they could find, bulldozing the forests and developing new silver weapons. Instead, remember that the Wyrm lives where humans do. What a human discovers, the Wyrm's creatures can discover. Secrecy is one of our greatest weapons; we must hold on to it for as long as we can.

The Ragabash: I've always been really puzzled by this one. How, exactly do you lift the Veil? We've all seen what happens when we get in there and start going nuts — People scream their head off, run like damn hell and forget we ever existed. Those who don't do so become marginalized and do not pose a threat to us. There are exceptions. I completely understand this. When these happen, they need to be dealt with like any other threat, and preventing them is good.

But come on! If, God forbid, someone actually got their hands on a video of werewolves doing their thing, do you think it'd get played? No. It'd get laughed out the door. No one would believe it. Between the options of avoiding people seeing us and missing our chance to eradicate an enemy, we should always choose to eradicate the enemy. This goes all the way back to my basic premise: we are not in a position to hamstring ourselves with pointless rules.

While we're on the subject, do we really know humanity would act aggressively toward us if we opened our doors a little? A lot of humans are really desperate for some new spiritual truths, and we've got one hell of a better product than some New Age neo-pagan. I'm not advocating a widespread "Hey guys! Guess what you didn't know!" campaign, but couldn't we, like, experiment a little?

Do Not Suffer Thy People to Tend Thy Sickness

The Philodox: Why does this tenet exist? Partly because we are *proud*. Few of us want to descend into senility or a bed-ridden state. But more importantly, it is a question of a race at war not wasting resources on someone who can't contribute. Death is *not* the end for us. You can still serve, in a new role, after a noble and honorable death. An elder who wants to hang on to life as a Garou at all costs, no matter the shape he's in, is being selfish.

This rule is at the very least pragmatic and appropriate for a culture at constant war. And the greatest abuses of this tenet are easily avoided if one realizes that the wording is not in fact "Do Not Suffer an Elder to Live." This law asks us not to be a burden on our people. The burden of obedience falls on the ailing Garou in question, not on the tribe or sept, nor even on the aging werewolf who is of sound mind and can fill a role on the Council of Elders. If your "sickness" is something you can bear, then it is not an issue.

The Ragabash: As with many of these, there are some very valid reasons for it. The key words "Suffer thy people" are a great qualifier, it provides for allow-

ing those whose talents are no longer on the front line of battle to keep helping in other ways. Better yet, it ensures that we're not looking over our shoulder to make sure our comrades haven't suffered a heart attack or something. When you're in battle, you want to know you can rely on someone.

But it's still a rule. It's still something just dying to be turned inside out, used, abused, and manipulated for the gain of the unscrupulous. I mean, let's not forget the gravity of this rule. We are talking about killing our own.

Now, you can talk about how the ailing wolf gets to choose what happens as much as you like. But you know something? I know a lot of my tribe out there, and they all know how to put a little pressure on someone, either spiritually, or, if need be, physically. It ain't hard. Meanwhile, talk to a few Pattern Spiders here and there, and I'll show you how to create a situation that will put a Garou in a state of "sickness." None of this is hard, especially if they're not looking for the move.

Fine, tell me I'm citing the extremes. Tell me it doesn't happen.

The Leader May Be Challenged at Any Time during Peace

The Philodox: Lead, follow, or get out of the way. This is a vital tenet because it is meant to keep unfit leaders from hoarding power beyond their worthiness to do so. The nature of Garou existence demands that the leaders be the most competent ones available, and this rule exists so that the most qualified Garou can rise to his proper role in the right circumstances.

The Ragabash: Hold on a second. I want to talk about this one and its twin sister at the same time.

The Leader May Not Be Challenged during Wartime

The Philodox: The battlefield is no place for a power struggle. You must be unified in mind and deed when you're up against the enemy, because it's a rare day that they do no outnumber and outgun you. This rule is vital to ensuring that the aforementioned chain of command is healthy and effective when the Garou need it most.

The Ragabash: Right. These two go right next to each other, since they're basically covering the same territory — If you're at war, you're not allowed to challenge, if you're not, then be our guest. Front up to the leader — the guy who, quite possibly, is the meanest, nastiest brute we have capable of wrecking mass damage on the Wyrm, and injure him. Or yourself. (Okay, so it's not that black and white. But people getting challenged play to their strengths.)

Apart from general complaints at the way we handle challenges in the first place, these two tenets assume a basic comprehension of the definitions of "wartime" and "peace" and that's not as easy as it sounds. When are you at war? If random street gangs attack three of our Kinfolk, then are we then at war with those street gangs? OK, what about if fomori attack those same Kinfolk? There are absolute limits here, obviously. If a caern is invaded, then we're pretty much at war. But there are groups out there who would argue that we are now always, twenty-four hours a day, seven days a week, at war. Hell, I'm one of them. Do we never challenge, then?

We can't operate that way. I appreciate, once you're in the field, or if the enemy could strike at any time (and there is a difference between "always at war" and "always vulnerable"), then please, shut the hell up and listen to orders. I cannot stress this enough. The last thing we need is to fall into squabbling at that point. But if we're at war, the plan is being laid out and it sucks, then for goodness sakes say so. Challenge, please. It is much better to earn some ire before a battle by showing up an incompetent strategist then lose lives by leaving the poor plan unquestioned.

Ye Shall Take No Action That Causes a Caern to Be Violated

The Philodox: A portion of Gaia falls ill or dies whenever one of Her caerns is polluted by the Wyrm, sapped dry by thirsty sorcerers, or razed entirely. If enough caerns die, the world dies with them. This is not a *game*!

The wording states "No Action," and I agree with that severity. You are forbidden from bringing outsiders such as magi or fae into the caern, because if you have made a mistake in judgement, and they return later with friends, you aren't the only one to suffer for your error. Gaia Herself suffers for your indiscretion. There is no more inviolate rule, and there should not be.

The Ragabash: This again leads us to a tactical question.

The enemy is huge, capable of destroying any one sept we have. However, they might not be able to beat out three or four combined. Do you stick your ground, get ready to lose all three or four, or do you abandon three of 'em to save the fourth, and finally beat the menace that could logically keeping going and taking caerns?

It's not pleasant. It's an unfortunate choice that we have to make and we will have to make very damn soon. It's coming to this. And I have to say; I think the choice to abandon caerns is probably the more efficient choice. It is better for us to abandon our holy ground and preserve our lives, and in thus doing, save other ground.

But look at what I've just said. Yes, I've praised efficiency the whole way through my challenges, or tried to at any rate. But some times I've noted that yes, some of the Litany has a lot of good in it, and we'd be

worse for not having it. I've even, damn me, called for more tenets at least once. Yet more fodder for manipulative scum to play us with.

And then, I go ahead and say yes; let's let the enemy kill Gaia a little more. Yes, that makes sense.

I can wrap my head around that, but I can't wrap my heart around it. Yes, we can't let our war be lost by trying to adhere to pointless rules, and in ten years or even less, I may change my mind about this, but for now — no. Don't question this tenet. Guard the caerns. Because ultimately, they're Gaia. And Gaia is what we're all about. It's what we can't let the Litany get in the way of, but we also can't let our debating over what should be in the Litany get in the way of it, either.

Rank and Renown

Garou society consists of a carefully observed hierarchy, a pecking order in which every member has a place. Garou honor those of greater Rank and receive homage and respect from those of lesser Rank. Some Storytellers and players prefer to downplay the social aspects of their chronicle in favor of greater emphasis on combating the Wyrm or Weaver or discovering the secrets of the Umbra. Ignoring the complex protocols and privileges of Rank, however, deprives all concerned with many occasions for intense and satisfying roleplaying.

Beginning characters start as Rank One — lowly warriors in service to Gaia and subject to the commands of any werewolf of greater status. Achieving higher Rank and the rights that pertain to that Rank can take many game sessions. Even progressing from Rank One to Rank Two involves accumulating the proper levels of Renown, not to mention the successful enactment of the Rite of Accomplishment. Storytellers can whet their players' appetite for exploring the social side of Garou life by running a chronicle where the characters begin as veterans of higher Ranks.

Veteran chronicles assume that the characters have already gone through their First Change and their Rite of Passage. In addition, veteran Garou possess Attributes, Abilities and Gifts at greater levels than characters that start out as pups at Rank One. How does a Storyteller determine a fair way to create advanced characters?

The following suggestions may give Storytellers some ideas. As usual, if you don't like these guidelines, tweak to your tastes. Just make sure that you take into account that most elusive of qualities — game balance. You want to allow your players to start out as powerful and experienced warriors, not super-Garou. Remember, even elders can advance and gain experience, so make sure that you leave them something to aim for.

Filling in the Blanks

As with creating beginning Garou characters, the character sheet marks the beginning of the process for designing a complex individual. Elder characters have even more back history than starting characters.

Storytellers should advise players to spend some time thinking about how their elder characters achieved their previous Ranks, what events shaped their personalities and what deeds gave them the necessary Renown for their current status.

Consider asking your players the following questions. The information gleaned may also provide you with ideas for sub-plots within your chronicle. By the time a Garou has achieved any status at all, she has probably made a number of friends as well as enemies within her sept, her tribe and the Garou nation in general.

- **What was your First Change like? Your Rite of Passage? How did you fit in to your tribe when you first discovered you were one of the Garou?**

These questions pertain to any Garou character, whether beginning at Rank One or Rank Five. The answers to these questions set the tone for all future character development.

- **How did you achieve your earlier Ranks? What deeds did you accomplish to gain the Renown necessary for you to instigate a Rank Challenge? Who performed the Rite of Accomplishment for each Rank and how successful was each instance?**

Answering these questions helps a player anchor her character firmly in her history and carves out a place for her within her pack, sept and tribe. Ask for detail, or offer suggestions — work with your players. If their Garou received Glory Renown for defeating Wyrm-spirits in the Umbra, it'll be that much more real for the player if she knows what specific sorts of spirits her character overcame. If she protected a caern from an invasion by Black Spiral Dancers, help her figure out the numbers and personalities involved. Certainly help your players determine what their previous Rites of Accomplishment were like; all of this gives your players added "bragging rights," and lets them refer to their past deeds with the same certainty they'd use if they actually roleplayed them out.

- **Who are your friends? Your enemies? Do the younger Garou in your sept respect you or do they just pay lip service to you because of your Rank? Does anyone in your pack or sept covet your position? Who will stand beside you when you face censure or criticism? Who will come to your defense? Who will accuse you of wrongdoing at the slightest provocation?**

Fleshing out a character's relations with the members of his pack and sept provides more than just background information or stage setting. These questions are a great blessing, as they encourage players to help you with the work of fleshing out your supporting cast. The more detail you get into, the more comfortable your players will be in roleplaying their relationships with these Storyteller characters.

• What have your greatest failures been? Have you ever lost Renown or even Rank, and if so, why? What are your regrets? Have you lost anyone important to you as a casualty of your war?

Werewolf is, at heart, a game about horror and tragedy as much as it is a game about heroism. Even great heroes of the Garou Nation have their failings and imperfections; some have even made horrible mistakes before regaining their honor in the eyes of their people. If the players are asked to think about the losses their characters have suffered, they're more likely to produce characters with believable backgrounds and motivations. Not only does this bring the darker aspects of the setting home, but it also gives players a chance to provide you with wonderful plot hooks, everything from quests to redeem themselves in the eyes of those they personally failed to old rivalries and enemies. A character might even begin the game with a metis cub — talk about roleplaying opportunities!

Making Renown Count

Werewolf: the Apocalypse gives some general examples of ways to gain and lose Renown in various categories. When you allow players to create advanced starting characters, suggest (strongly) to them that they come up with specific examples for each Renown category. Your players need not detail every point gained or lost, but they should have a few "Renown tales" to tell around the fire or at moots. Knowing that Rank Three Theurge Severine Claw-of-Starlight gained Glory (and a battle scar on her right hand) from defeating a Black Spiral Theurge and its pet Bane at the gates of her caern provides an insight into the mindset of the character and provides the Storyteller with a potential story seed. What happens when the deceased Black Spiral Theurge's packmates seek revenge?

If Nobody Sees It, Does It Count?

One of the time-old questions about Renown in **Werewolf** is whether or not a deed has to be witnessed and related to other werewolves in order for a Garou to gain or lose Renown. Do two werewolves instantly lose Honor and Wisdom for having sex, even if nobody but the two lovers is the wiser? If a young cub sacrifices himself to save a caern, but nobody is there to witness his final deeds and write his death-song, will anyone ever credit his spirit with the Renown it deserves?

The default assumption is that no Garou witnesses are necessary for a Renown loss or gain to take effect. Perhaps the spirit world as a whole counts as a witness to each of a Garou's deeds; perhaps honorable or dishonorable conduct slightly changes a werewolf's appearance to the spirits that empower the Rite of Accomplishment. Whatever the formal rationale, the character's Renown is always matched with his deeds — fairness wins out over "realism." This is also probably the best system for teaching new players the sort of actions that their characters would be encouraged to take — nothing encourages a new player to behave more honorably than an on-the-spot Renown bonus (or penalty).

As an interesting outgrowth of this system, if you're willing to make extra work for yourself, you can also keep the characters' Renown totals secret from the players — adding to the sense of realism, but also to your workload. Under such a system, characters tend to gain Rank a little more slowly, as the players tend not to ask for the Rite of Accomplishment until they're sure they're worthy. This might be a good or a bad thing, depending on how you like to pace your chronicle. This can lead to some interesting situations, of course, as the characters stand a good chance of finding out during their Rites of Accomplishment that they're considerably more worthy than they'd thought (if they're humble), or that they've been fucking up a lot more than they'd assumed.

Of course, you can always go the other road, and assume that only Renown that's formally acknowledged by a Galliard at a moot counts. This is certainly a valid choice, particularly if you're looking for Renown to work more realistically and less supernaturally. One advantage of this approach is that the pack's Galliard rises in importance, and becomes as valuable as the bards of old. The Garou gain a much stronger interest in having their deeds related, which certainly suits the motif of the tribal society.

However, be aware that some groups will really abuse such a setup. If the Galliard is willing to look the other way when the characters violate Litany tenets that the players don't themselves believe in, you can quickly wind up with a pack full of charach who never demand discipline, break the Veil without a thought, and invite potential enemies back to the caern. If you're not careful, you'll find yourself telling stories about a band of laid-back, oversexed teenagers that just happen to have superpowers — not Garou. Make sure your group's a good one before you try this method out.

The Greatest Honor: Achieving Rank Six

Most Garou characters aim at advancing in rank and gaining the privileges and responsibilities associated with each new step upward. Only the most respected Garou (Rank Five) may learn the powerful and often deadly Level Five Gifts. But what comes next after your character has achieved Rank Five? Where do you go from there?

Exceptional Garou may receive a special reward for their courage and service to Gaia. A very few Rank Six Garou do exist in the World of Darkness. These are more than legendary individuals. They are the superstars of the Garou nation. The most respected Rank Five Elder gives way in the presence of a Rank Six Garou, regardless of her tribe.

How does a Garou elder join this august company?

The Best of the Best

Only Rank Five Garou can advance to Rank Six, but such advancement does not depend solely on achieving more Renown. Rank Six Garou form an exclusive club. In order to qualify, an elder Garou must distinguish herself in an extraordinary fashion on more than one occasion. Rank Six is more than the acknowledgement of a lifetime of achievement and service — that's Rank Five. Rank Six is nothing less than legendary status — such a worthy's name is spoken by her people in the same tones that we reserve for legends such as Hercules, Miyamoto Musashi and Joan of Arc. It's *that* important.

As such, the attainment of Rank Six has nothing whatsoever to do with rules — it's not about accumulating enough Glory, passing a certain kind of challenge or anything like that. It's a matter of personal judgement on the Storyteller's part. The existing guideline is quite simple: If you have to ask yourself if a character is worthy, he's not. If there's any doubt in your mind whether or not he has surpassed the mighty deeds of even the greatest Garou elders, he hasn't. Only when there's absolutely no question of the character's legendary status should you consider letting him strive for the ultimate Rank.

The story of a character (or a *pack*!) attaining Rank Six is, to be honest, quite possibly the most epic story you could possibly tell. Very little compares in terms of scale; even the esteemed Silver Pack is outranked by an elder of this magnitude. You may want to forgo the actual challenge to rise in Rank for such a story; after all, considering the nature of the deeds a character must have undergone to be worthy of consid-

eration, any challenge might well be anticlimactic. If you do choose to make a challenge part of the process, make it truly memorable; a raid into the heart of Malfeas, the task of learning one's own genealogy back to the days of the Impergium, or other such nigh-impossible tasks. Break out your book of old fairy tales — this is where the mountains of glass, redirecting of rivers, and similar astonishing feats come into play.

Still itching for an example? Okay, here's one:

When a Rank Five Garou's reputation spreads so far throughout the Garou Nation that it reaches the ears of existing Rank Six Garou, one member of this group may take it upon herself to travel to the caern of the individual in question and investigate her worthiness. The Rank Six Garou usually adopts a pretext for making the visit and may voice her true purpose only to the sept leader (unless the leader is the target of the investigation) or to the eldest Garou not in the running for a rise in Rank. Once she has satisfied herself as to the candidate's worthiness (or unworthiness), she returns to her home and contacts three other Rank Six Garou to present her case — if that many are alive at the time. (There's certainly no guarantee of it. We reiterate: Rank Six Garou are *rare*!) If she succeeds in convincing them that the Garou candidate is truly worthy, all four Rank Six Garou descend on the caern of the candidate and call a challenge on their subject. If the candidate succeeds in the challenge, she undergoes a special version of the Rite of Accomplishment performed in tandem by the Rank Six Garou along with the Master of the Rite of the candidate's caern (as a courtesy). A successful enactment of the rite creates a new Rank Six Garou. The Storyteller should determine what perks accompany the new Rank.

Marks of Achievement: The Writing on the Wall

The Rite of Accomplishment honors a Garou's deeds, acknowledges his advances in Renown and provides him with the accolades and status of a new Rank. Within Garou society, the Rite of Accomplishment serves as a way to "promote" a Garou, making him able to learn new Gifts, take on new responsibilities and serve as an example to other, younger Garou.

Not only does the Rite of Accomplishment proclaim a Garou's advance in status to his packmates, septmates and other Garou, the rite also has a spiritual side that announces the Garou's new Rank to the Umbral spirits that serve as teachers of Gaia's many Gifts. Spirits do not part with their knowledge lightly and they hesitate to teach what they know to Garou that are unready for the knowledge.

How does a spirit recognize that a Garou has achieved the proper Rank for learning a Gift? What sort of indication does the Rite of Accomplishment give a spirit that the Garou petitioning for a Level Two Gift truly deserves to learn that Gift?

Although no hard and fast rules exist for determining how a spirit recognizes a Garou's Rank, Storytellers may wish to consider the following optional system for making the Rite of Accomplishment more than just a formality.

The Mark of Achievement

The successful completion of the Rite of Accomplishment bestows upon the Garou a mystical symbol that denotes the Garou's new Rank. This symbol differs from tribe to tribe and sometimes from auspice to auspice. The Storyteller may decide what form the symbol takes — whether glowing runes, an aura of a particular color or the presence of a spirit badge when in the Umbra. This mark is perceptible primarily to spirits, although the Storyteller may choose to allow werewolves to see the mark while in the Umbra. Thus marked, a Garou proclaims her true Rank to any spirit she encounters in the Umbra or elsewhere.

The nature of the mark reflects the character of the tribe. A Mark of Achievement for a Red Talon may appear as a bloody glowing scar on the Garou's flank, while a Glass Walker's Mark of Achievement may consist of a luminescent band around her neck or biceps. The mark should always appear as some sort of badge of respect; it's no laughing matter.

If someone succeeds in disputing the Rite of Accomplishment or if the rite fails for any other reason, the Mark of Achievement does not appear on the Garou until a subsequent performance of the Rite of Accomplishment is successful.

Breaking the Rules of Rank

According to Garou tradition and the will of Gaia, Garou may not learn higher level Gifts until they attain the proper Rank. This is, plain and simple, a game balance issue, and one meant to reward players for making the sacrifices and dedicated roleplaying required (we hope) to rise in Rank. However, some Storytellers may feel that some spirits, realistically, might not always flawlessly follow the rules. Can a clever werewolf pass himself off as being of higher rank to a spirit? Can a fickle spirit choose to mess with the order of things? From a pure balance standpoint, no — but for those Storytellers interested in bending the rules in the interest of spicing things up, here are some guidelines. Use with caution.

Roll 'Em and Weep: Taking a Chance on the Dice

When a Garou attempts to convince, cajole, coerce or otherwise bamboozle a spirit into teaching her a Gift above her current Rank, the Storyteller *can* require a simple dice roll (although some hefty roleplaying on the player's part is in no way an unreasonable request). The nature of the roll depends on the method the Garou uses.

• **Convincing the Spirit:** The Garou uses a reasoned argument in order to convince the spirit that she deserves to learn the Gift in question. The Garou rolls Charisma + Expression (difficulty equals the level of the Gift +4). For example, Miara Rainwalker, a Rank Two Uktena Theurge, wishes to convince a spirit to teach her the Level Three Gift: Exorcism by arguing that her pack has immediate need of someone to enact this Gift and currently lacks a qualified person. Miara's player rolls her Charisma plus Expression (four dice) against a difficulty of 7 (Level Three Gift + 4) and achieves a single success. The Storyteller decides that spirit reluctantly agrees to teach her the Gift, but may attach some restrictions on its use. More successes would have had a more positive effect on the spirit, while a failure would mean that the spirit refused the request. A botch would incur the anger of that particular spirit.

• **Cajoling the Spirit:** A Garou tries to engage the spirit's sympathy or make an impassioned plea calculated to win the spirit's approval in order to learn a Gift belonging to a Rank he does not have. Gregor Wyrmsbane, a Rank Three Get of Fenris Galliard, tries to enlist the approval of an avatar of Fenris to teach him the Level Five Gift: Horde of Valhalla. Gregor performs a stirring rendition of an ancient skald-saga illustrating the use of this Gift by a tribal hero. Gregor's player states that he is using a point of Willpower as insurance before he rolls Charisma + Performance (seven dice) against a difficulty of 9 (Level Five Gift + 4). He achieves three successes with the addition of the success from Willpower. The spirit grudgingly approves of the Galliard's nerve (as well as his performance) and teaches him the Gift without requiring additional considerations.

• **Coercing the Spirit:** The Garou attempts to browbeat or badger the spirit into teaching her a Gift for which she does not yet possess the appropriate Rank. Growls-At-the-Wyrm, a Rank Three Red Talon Ahroun has failed to achieve Rank Four due, he feels, to a bias against lupus Garou within his mixed-tribe sept. He attempts to learn the Level Four Lupus Gift: Gnaw from a wolf spirit by threatening the spirit with imprisonment in a fetish. Growls' player rolls Wits plus Intimidation (six dice) against a difficulty of 8 (Level Four Gift +4). He achieves three successes and sufficiently cows the spirit.

• **Conning the Spirit:** The Garou attempts to run a scam on a spirit and convince it that she truly possesses the correct Rank. In order to do this, the Garou must somehow either conceal her current Mark of Achievement or else must fool the spirit into believ-

ing that she possesses the correct Mark. If the Garou attempts to disguise or hide her Mark from the spirit, she must first roll Wits + Subterfuge against a difficulty of 7. (The Storyteller may wish to make this roll for the player in order to maintain some suspense, since the Garou does not necessarily know if her disguise will work until she comes face to face with the spirit.) Danna Spoonbender, a Rank Two Child of Gaia Ragabash, decides to learn a Level Three Gift in response to a challenge from a Glass Walker packmate. She determines that she needs to fool a Gremlin into believing she is a Rank Three Garou. She works to disguise her Mark; the Storyteller rolls in secret (getting four successes!). Once she has cornered the Gremlin, she tries to fast-talk the spirit into accepting her as a worthy candidate. She rolls Manipulation + Subterfuge (a dice pool of 5) against a difficulty of 7 (Level Three Gift +4). She receives five successes — a phenomenal success. Augmented by her Storyteller's concealed roll to determine how well Danna disguised her Mark, this stellar achievement completely fools the Gremlin. Danna walks away with a Level Three Gift and the possibility of receiving Glory for her bold Umbral prank in keeping with her auspice.

While this method allows for a hard and fast approach to tailoring the rules, players and Storytellers who use it must respect their rolls and accept the results, whether good or not so good. Since **Werewolf: The Apocalypse** is a game that emphasizes creativity and imagination, players may wish to opt for a more intense and interactive method of bending the rules.

Talk Fast, Think Faster: Roleplaying Up the Ladder

In the above examples, both Storyteller and player elected to use the dice as the only determining factor in whether or not the Garou succeeded in learning a Gift beyond her Rank. A Storyteller and her players may prefer to place more emphasis on good roleplaying rather than on random dice rolls. We can illustrate this using the same examples as in the previous section.

• **Convincing the Spirit:** Miara Rainwalker's player engages the Storyteller, who acts the part of a spirit minion of Uktena, in a polite and reasoned discussion in which she explains why she needs to learn the Level Three Gift even though she is only a Rank Two Theurge. The Storyteller feels that Miara's player has made a good enough case to convince the spirit. At this point, the Storyteller can do one of two things: he can inform Miara's player that the spirit agrees to teach her the Gift, or he can decide that Miara must still make a roll at a reduced difficulty of 4 or 5 due to good roleplaying.

• **Cajoling the Spirit:** Gregor Wyrmsbane's player decides to roleplay his character's impassioned plea. He launches into an extemporaneous poem in free verse that describes a grand battle that revolves on the knowledge of the Gift Gregor desires to learn. The Storyteller is so impressed with her player's performance that she does not even require a dice roll. She simply awards the Gift to the Garou character (and perhaps gives the player an extra Experience Point at the end of the session for good roleplaying.

• **Coercing the Spirit:** Growls at the Wyrm's player tries to roleplay his character's attempt to badger the wolf-spirit into granting him the Gift he wants. Unfortunately, the player does not do a very good job at acting belligerent. The Storyteller decides to allow Growls' player to roll the dice but assigns a higher difficulty to the roll, determining that the spirit did not believe that Growls would carry out his threat. Growls fails his roll and the spirit sends him back to his pack in disgrace.

• **Conning the Spirit:** Danna Spoonbender's player decides to roleplay her encounter with the Gremlin spirit she wants to fool into teaching her a Rank Three Gift. She describes her character's attempts at disguising her Mark of Achievement — something that involves an elaborate display of paint and glitter and strategically placed piercings in the general area of the Mark. When Danna confronts the Gremlin, her player launches into a comic routine that entertains and amuses not only the Storyteller but the rest of the players as well. The Storyteller asks Danna's player to make a Wits + Subterfuge roll at a lowered difficulty. Even though Danna's roll is not very good (she only rolls two successes), the Storyteller decides that the spirit, while not fooled by Danna's scam, admires the Ragabash's daring and delivery enough to teach her the Gift — provided she return once a month to entertain the spirit with a new comic routine.

This system may seem a little bit *too* easy — but remember that it's completely optional. No player can ever demand that you use these rules. Also, bear in mind that by violating the laws of Rank by claiming an unearned privilege, a werewolf is disrespecting some of the basic principles of Garou society. Storytellers should feel free to slap painful Honor losses on cubs that try to exceed their station for any but the most compelling of reasons.

If the Story Fits: Letting the Story Come First

The final method presented here for determining the outcome of an attempt at learning a Gift without possessing the necessary Rank consists of simply acknowledging that certain results are necessary to a successful story. If a pack needs a particular Gift for an upcoming critical confrontation and no player possesses the appropriate Rank, you wish to ignore botched rolls or bad roleplaying in favor of advancing your chronicle. Of course, this shouldn't happen often, or else players may believe that their actions have no effect on a game in which events are predetermined. Judicious Storyteller license, however, can often save a game from falling apart because the characters lack access to a particular Gift. Likewise, Storytellers may capitalize on a failure by integrating into the story the enmity of a spirit angered by one of the characters.

This is also useful if a player is trying to learn a powerful Gift from a spirit that you decide might not really *care* about the rules of Rank — Coyote springs to mind, as do other tricksters or Wyld-spirits. In such a case, you may simply choose to grant the audacious player the Gift without the necessity of die rolls or heavy roleplaying. However, the sort of spirit that is likely to ignore the precepts of Rank is also the sort of spirit that gives Gifts with… eccentricities. The Gift might never work entirely properly; If Coyote teaches a Rank Four Ragabash the Gift: Thousand Forms, perhaps the Ragabash retains the paws of a wolf in every form she takes. There are plenty of good reasons for such flawed instruction; it may amuse the spirit to see the youngster struggling with a power that's rightly beyond them, or the spirit might not care at all that the Gift they've taught doesn't work right for lower-ranked Garou. This sort of mixed blessing goes very well with one of the cardinal themes of bargaining with spirits — you never get something for nothing.

Allowing a Storyteller the freedom to use this sort of creative plotting requires a great deal of trust from the players. They need to feel that you aren't simply twisting events to suit your own purposes or to make fun of or defeat the players, but that you're trying to create a challenging and entertaining story for everyone.

Moving Upward: Rank and Its Challenges

Most players and Storytellers familiar with the game know what steps a Garou must take to rise in Rank. After a Garou has acquired the requisite points of Renown in the appropriate categories for her new Rank, she seeks out a Garou of equal or higher rank and issues a challenge. The challenged Garou (usually played by the Storyteller) must then come up with a suitable challenge.

Creating a challenge that sufficiently tests a character's mettle without proving impossible to overcome often tests the Storyteller as well. What kinds of challenges are suitable for your ambitious Garou characters? Simple combats don't always work, particularly when the challenger belongs to an auspice not touted for its straight-ahead warrior prowess. Challenges can also vary by tribe.

A Red Talon Galliard may expect a different challenge for a new Rank than a Child of Gaia Theurge.

The following examples of Rank challenges may give you some ideas for creating your own unique and entertaining tests for your Garou characters (as well as for their players).

Rank Two Challenges

Attaining the status of Fostern or Rank Two means that a Garou has passed from the position of raw recruit in the war against the Wyrm to seasoned veteran. Rank Two Garou have some familiarity with Garou society and know the nature of the war they have been born to fight. Challenges for these Garou should provide a moderate level of combat, stress or creative thinking. Since most Garou that survive for any length of time eventually attain Rank Two, these challenges should test the challenger but should not prove unbeatable.

Sample Rank Two Challenges

• "Acquire" a specific item hidden by a Rank Three Ragabash. Though a challenge of this nature comes almost naturally to Bone Gnawers, Glass Walkers or Shadow Lords may find this a good test of their New Moons.

• Gain a boon from a minor spirit. This challenge tests the ability of a Theurge to communicate with Umbral spirits. Uktena, Wendigo and Silent Striders frequently employ this type of challenge for their Crescent Moon members.

• Use reasoned speech to convince the Garou you challenge to admit you to Rank Three. Silver Fangs, Children of Gaia and Black Furies place great emphasis on the power of words, so this type of challenge appeals to them. This is also suitable for Philodox of any tribe.

• Compose a song or story honoring the Garou you challenge. A challenge of this type tests the ability of a Galliard to respect his adversary and is particularly appropriate for Fianna or Get of Fenris, though Red Talons sometimes appreciate a new song honoring one of their own.

• Defeat an Ahroun of your sept in a formal duel. Stand vigil at the caern's borders for three days and three nights without falling asleep.

Rank Three Challenges

Garou who reach Rank Three (Adren) take on major responsibilities within their sept. These Garou hold most of the positions of consequence in a sept, fulfilling the duties of Warder, Master of the Rite, Gatekeeper and other positions. Challenges for this Rank should weed out individuals who cannot act quickly or think on their feet. The future leaders of the sept and of the tribe come from Rank Three Garou.

Not all Garou should pass their Rank Three Challenge on the first attempt.

Sample Rank Three Challenges

• Borrow a fetish from an elder without using words to ask for it (or without irritating them — charades just won't do!). Ragabash recognize the importance of body language, gestures and non-verbal cues. Hence, this challenge tests the abilities of New Moons. Complete a difficult scavenger hunt in a specific time limit.

• Create an original and useful fetish in a specified amount of time. In order to accomplish this, a Garou needs to succeed in locating and binding a spirit, creating a fetish vessel and ensuring that it serves some useful purpose.

• Make peace with a long-time enemy or bring about a truce between two feuding werewolves. While best used to test the negotiating skills of a Philodox, this type of challenge can also gauge the abilities of future leaders of any tribe.

• Find a little-known past hero of the Garou and create a tribute to that individual and perform your composition at an inter-tribal moot. This challenge not only tests the skills of the Galliard, it also creates a sense of solidarity and pride among all Garou.

• Endure a solid beating or taunting from your septmates without going into frenzy. Warriors need to show not only strength, but also discipline; frenzy at the wrong time is a Garou's worst enemy. This challenge is particularly suitable for Ahroun, who need to learn that violence is not always the answer.

Rank Four Challenges

Rank Four Garou (Athro) have risen nearly to the top of the hierarchy. Mighty warriors, renowned lorekeepers, wise sept leaders, notorious tricksters and famous judges come from this Rank. Garou who desire a place in this elite group need to demonstrate exceptional skill and intelligence. Though some Garou may attain Rank Four the first time, those who do should inspire awe in their peers. Rank Four challenges should be just that — challenges.

Sample Rank Four Challenges

• Find out every aspect of the business plan of an organization of potential interest to the Garou, without getting caught. Beat a Lupus-form elder in a footrace (likely through a forest or other obstacles) without shifting out of Homid.

• Unearth a lost treasure of the tribe. Convince a spirit to act in a fashion completely opposite to its nature (such as encouraging a fire elemental to go for a swim) without harming the spirit.

• Take the place of the sept's Truthcatcher or Master of the Rite for a month. Convince a local street gang (or other belligerent group of humans) to participate in community service for a month.

• Create a praise song for a rival and end your differences with that person by honoring her.

• Rescue a Garou captured by enemies of some sort, whether Black Spiral Dancers, Pentex teams, Leeches or sorcerers. Beat every other Ahroun in the sept at wrestling with only five minutes to rest in between each match.

Rank Five Challenges

The most difficult challenge, however, faces the Rank Four Garou who wishes to rise to the powerful position of Elder. Elder Garou occupy a place at the heart of a sept or a tribe. These individuals hold the fate of the Garou Nation in their hands. Their decisions guide the Garou; their deeds stand as examples for younger werewolves; their mistakes can cause irreparable hurt to Gaia and the to the Garou. Challenges for this Rank should test every possible quality the challenger possesses — regardless of auspice.

Sample Rank Five Challenges

• Visit a caern of each of the twelve tribes of the Garou Nation without being noticed, recognized or challenged, and bring back proof of each visit. This is a test of all a Ragabash's best skills. It also serves as a way for Garou of any tribe to practice stealth and cunning.

• Locate a lost caern and convince a totem spirit to adopt it. Redeem, cleanse and rename a powerful Bane without using Gifts other than Spirit Speech. Visit the courts of each Planetary Incarna, and bring back a token of each one's favor.

• Find a Garou lost in Harano and reclaim her for Gaia. Destroy a powerful Wyrm-artifact by hurling it into the Abyss.

• Accompany an Elder on her final quest and record her deathsong for the tribe. While this may seem simple and unworthy of a Rank Five Challenge, in reality this test places the Garou who accompanies the Elder in a great deal of danger. Not only must she witness the Elder's final glorious battle, she must also survive it herself and remember what transpired — all without detracting from the heroism of her subject.

• Lead a group of Garou against a major Wyrm-creature or other enemy. Defeat the creature without losing any of your comrades, even if it means sacrificing yourself. Those who would lead in battle must know how to win without uselessly sacrificing others. Occasionally, this challenge leads to a posthumous attainment of Rank Five. Suited for Ahroun, this kind of challenge also tests potential leaders of any tribe.

Rites: Ceremonies from the Heart

In a game in which the characters often let their Rage dictate their actions, where savagery rules the day, the less bestial aspects of characters need to play a vital role. Characters who are nothing but combat machines quickly become boring caricatures, both to other characters and to themselves. After awhile, mature players want something more than posturing, experience points and kick-ass battles. Obviously, roleplaying hooks (an odd speech pattern, a tendency to fall for redheads) help players figure out the personality of their characters. The Gifts and rites a character chooses to learn also speak volumes about the character's personality, outlook and goals and can help define her role in the pack, sept and chronicle. Many players (and not a few Storytellers) tend to look on these as "kewl powers" they have access to rather than essential pieces of the characters' existence, however. It's up to the Storyteller to coax her troupe into seeing their powers in a different light. This is especially true for rites, which usually require time invested in them and have few combat applications.

So how does the Storyteller encourage making rites important to the players? By making them a central focus of the Chronicle. All too often rites are ignored or take place offstage and aside from the main action. In the midst of a game, many Storytellers and players don't want to take time out to do the "housekeeping," so someone who has a rite simply announces he's doing it and the troupe moves on to more interesting pursuits. And by doing so, they miss some of the most significant, compelling roleplaying and character development in **Werewolf**.

Rites are the spiritual touchstones through which Garou interact with Gaia's creation, the spirits and other werewolves. They serve to keep werewolves in touch with the spirits with whom they enjoy pacts. Rites also provide Garou with a structured social interaction. All the members of the pack or sept may partake of rites, and are in fact expected to do so. Garou from other tribes or areas can meet together bound by common rites to a common purpose regardless of other differences they might have. Finally, rites are the tools with which werewolves remain in accord with or restore balance to the natural world, their caern, the Umbra and the spirits as well as giving the Garou a means for punishing transgressors and acknowledging accomplishments. Considering how many activities rites encompass, it would be strange if Storytellers couldn't find great roleplaying hooks in performing them. Likewise, it should be easy to look for places where rites would fit into your storyline and encourage your players to play out the appropriate rite.

Involving the Pack

While Garou usually turn to a ritemaster to lead their ceremonies and most often involve the sept performing the rite at their caern, it is possible for a pack to enact rites on their own so long as one of them knows the rite and the others participate. Some packs even create their own personal versions of rites to help define their role in Gaia's creation. Storytellers who want to involve their players in creative endeavors to enhance their roleplaying should encourage them to take the rites they know and find specific items, actions and words for invoking the rites that are particularly significant to their own pack. You might even want to decrease the difficulty level of the rite as a reward for their creativity as well as excellent roleplaying. When doing so, the players should consider that rites serve as religious or spiritual experiences as well as being invocations that bring about magical effects.

If players seem initially resistant to doing rites, you could introduce such ceremonies by having the characters be required to attend and participate in rites performed at the caern by their sept. If Storytellers undertake the part of the ritemaster and make the resulting rite truly interesting, players may become more willing to try playing out other rites on their own. And once they're interested, your players could learn to enjoy taking a break from rip-tear Crinos form foe-bashing to perform the rites that define the more civilized and spiritual side of werewolves.

Jazzing It Up

So how do you generate that interest? Take it out of the ordinary. Most players (with a few exceptions) tend toward being extroverts of one sort or another and usually enjoy getting to grandstand for a little while or garnering attention for their cool ideas. Encourage them in this. While Philodox and Theurges are typically considered the most appropriate auspices for becoming ritemasters and leading rites, any Garou possessing the appropriate rite may lead it. Thus any pack member can become the star of the moment. Still, Theurges and Philodox are particularly schooled in performing rites as an expected part of their development. Making certain they have scope within the game to use those skills makes it more likely they will choose to learn more rites and round out their characters more fully. It also gives them more roleplaying opportunities, something few players find objectionable.

While you shouldn't push your troupe beyond boundaries they're unwilling to cross, many methods exist for encouraging more interaction and creativity from the players. Some players find it uncomfortable to experiment with live-action roleplaying and they may need a little more persuading than others, but the real key to pumping up rites is to play them out. We don't mean you should perform some sort of pseudo-Satanic ritual complete with animal sacrifice. But lighting some incense, drawing some symbols in the dirt or eating something symbolic of the rite can all help establish the mood and help players envision the ceremony.

Bringing props appropriate to the rite, drawing a circle, and lighting candles are all options. So are playing background music or chanting. Think of ways to involve the players in the rites. Do any of them particularly excel at wordcraft? That player's character may be the one to invoke the spirit that powers the rite. Musically inclined players might want to write their own accompaniment or play rhythmic drum parts.

The main thing is to get your players involved. While all these methods have been suggested before, they are usually used as background techniques designed to enhance mood. Here, we're recommending that you use them as part of the rite itself. Consider how effective it could be to hold your game outside around a campfire or think about holding a cleansing rite in a sweat lodge or pool. Even if you do no more than consider what elements might make for an interesting rite, then describe it to the players, it should generate more excitement than simply saying, "And you do a rite of contrition."

Hobnobbing with the Spirits

The pact made at the beginning of their existence between the Garou and the spirits requires the werewolves to serve them in exchange for the spirits' empowerment of the Garou's rites, a bargain Gaia's warriors have kept throughout time. Thus, rites serve to link the Garou with spirits they may call upon for aid and who may, in turn, ask the Garou for help. Storytellers whose troupes conduct many rites (roleplayed or not), should keep track of what rites the characters use and how often. Certain types of spirits act as the usual conduits between the Garou and the mystic energy that powers different types of rites. Pacts or septs that repeatedly perform a given rite over time may come to realize an affinity with the spirits that empower those rites (at the Storyteller's discretion). This could potentially create a situation in which the specific ritemaster or group attains a lowered difficulty level (by one to two points depending on the strength of the bond) when performing that rite. It should also open them up to demands from some of the spirits whose aid is given. This is an often-overlooked source for story material — a spirit requesting aid from the characters in return for past services and continued support. It also gives the Storyteller an interesting supporting cast member to portray when the troupe enacts a rite appropriate to that spirit's domain. Below are some of the most significant rites associated with spirits in the Garou arsenal. Feel free to extrapolate and use these suggestions to enhance other rites not detailed here.

Rite of Summoning

While any Garou that knows the proper rite may attempt to summon spirits, it's not always easy to do so, nor is their cooperation assured when they arrive. After all, they have their own agenda and aren't just hanging around waiting for some cub to snap his claws and whistle up a spirit to help him out. Granted, totems and spirits who have a particular interest in whatever task the Garou wishes them to perform usually arrive more promptly and evince less hostility when they come, but even they may be called at an inappropriate moment or a time when they are busy elsewhere. As they are required to attend once successfully summoned, even the most affable spirit may react with something less than joy — especially if the spirit considers the task the Garou summoned it for to be demeaning, frivolous or particularly dangerous to the spirit's continued existence. So too will they react more favorably to a serious, well-thought-out summons to aid in the preservation of Gaia's handiwork.

As the Storyteller, you must place yourself in the spirit's shoes, so to speak, and judge how well the characters performed their summoning and to what use they intend to put your services. Then react appropriately. Although there is a specific chart given in the Rite of Summoning's description, feel free to modify it to reflect the roleplaying that surrounds the enactment of the rite. After all, if you had an important appointment you'd been awaiting for months (one that could well determine your future), and some jackass forced you to miss it in order to demonstrate to his buddies that he could make you bring a pizza over to his house, you'd be pretty irate. You'd be even more pissed off if that same idiot then forced you into his basement at gunpoint and chained you up down there with the intention of making you clean his house every week. On the other hand, if you received word that a humble and appreciative student wished to learn martial arts from you and offered both heartfelt praise and tangible, valuable tokens of respect to you in return, you'd probably enjoy the experience and feel honored by the interest. Keep that in mind when reacting as the summoned spirit.

While spirits may initially be hostile, it should be possible to change that through good roleplaying as well. Characters might offer praise or extremely heartfelt thanks for the spirit's generosity in appearing (okay, so they're *compelled* to appear, but they might like the flattery anyway). Or the characters could ask the spirit what it would like in exchange for its aid. Those who plan ahead might even stock certain things the spirits are known to like and have them on hand as an offering when the spirit arrives. It's only courteous since the Garou have interrupted whatever the spirit was doing and often called it into an inimical place to perform some task the spirit doesn't relish. Be sure to demand such treatment when playing a hostile spirit if necessary to get your troupe thinking along the right lines.

From this, it's easy to see how important it is for you as the Storyteller to set the tone by playing the spirit to the hilt. (Some thoughts on doing this are given in Chapter Two.) In like manner, you should encourage the players to have their characters develop strategies for attracting the spirits they need to summon. Discovering an item, scent, intricate drawing, dance, series of praises, color or other element that each spirit finds attractive and compelling may even serve as the focus of a storyline leading up to the rite. Encourage your players to think symbolically; a fire elemental might appreciate it if its summoner wore a gold clasp shaped like a salamander, while a pain-spirit might appreciate the summoning circle being drawn by a blade, or in its summoner's blood. Whatever else they do, the characters should *at least* plan out the ceremony they intend to perform to summon the spirit and the players should present it to you before making rolls for success. Obviously, the more powerful the spirit to be called, the more elements are necessary and the greater the amount of time spent either in performing intricate steps or beseeching the spirit's help.

Rite of Spirit Awakening

In many ways, this rite should emulate that of Spirit Summoning in terms of player participation as they share a similar purpose. However, as this rite specifically calls for performing a rhythmic piece on some sort of instrument, that should be the primary focus used in the rite. You might consider actually providing a drum or other percussion instruments for the players to use. Maracas, tambourines or even two sticks or lids of pots to clack together might serve for this purpose. There's something innately primitive and exciting about pounding out rhythms, especially ones that grow in intensity or speed when performed. Adding other instruments (according to the players' talents) can add the dimension of melody. In essence, you're making an alarming noise to awaken the spirit just as your alarm clock summons you from sleep or a siren alerts you to an emergency in more mundane circumstances. If you have the room and the troupe is inclined to do so, pacing out the dance around the instrumentalist(s) and howling or growling as appropriate can also get the blood moving and give greater scope to roleplaying the rite. Of course, nosy neighbors may call the nuthouse or the exorcist in their ignorance, so keep it discreet.

Again, as Storyteller, it's your job to enact the personality of the spirit that has been awakened. It's your unique challenge to try to impart a recognizable trait or two to inanimate objects your troupe wants to awaken. In the actual rite description, awakening a VW bus is mentioned. So, how do you play a bus anyway? Is it even necessary for you to? The object will appear in the Umbra, true, but remain stationary unless used in the physical world. So, let's say someone drives the bus in the physical world and you as the bus spirit move through the Umbral landscape. Do you need to make bus sounds? How about giving out the impression of straining to get up hills many VWs experience? While this can be fun and entertaining to both Storytellers and players, you need to ask yourself if going that far defeats the mood you're trying to set in your game. Gasping as if releasing the bus' exhaust may cause more laughter than appreciation of your roleplaying expertise. On the other hand, playing a weapon used repeatedly to give death in the physical world as an aggressive, bloodthirsty and conscienceless entity can send chills up your players' spines if done correctly. And it might make them stop a moment or two and consider exactly what it is they're trying to awaken and why — especially since awakening a spirit does *not* grant any control over it.

Sanctification is the name given to the practice of awakening plant-spirits. As most plant-spirits are benevolent, you shouldn't have to enact any seriously hostile spirits. Such spirits give of their powers as if they were talens, granting one use of their particular abilities. Each plant grants a different ability. Some of the most common plants and herbs are detailed below, but Storytellers should feel free to create their own at need. The suggested personality traits consist of an opinion concerning their suitability. If you don't like the personality given, simply change it. It's your game. The most often awakened plants are those with medicinal qualities.

• Basil

Noted for its use in cooking (especially in pesto), basil becomes a potent magical herb when sanctified. It grants either of two uses: The first use is in curbing the effects of poisons inflicted by vermin such as snake or insect bites or stings, removing the toxin from the victim. The second use involves mixing the sanctified herb with horses' dung. This produces a horde of magical scorpions, which have a game effect similar to the Bone Gnawer Gift: Infest (although rather less potent). Last minute rescues from fatal poisonings or great scenes of

A Note Toward Balance

Some of the game effects suggested as powers for Awakened plants might seem a little powerful, allowing a ritemaster to pull off tricks that would be difficult to accomplish with Gifts. However, remember that you have an inordinate amount of control over the Rite of Spirit Awakening — you set the power level of the awakened spirit, to say nothing of its willingness to use its powers for the Garou in question. Don't worry too much about the power levels involved; if your players seem to be gaining too much for too little effort, it's an easy thing to start having the spirits become a little less effective, particularly if some of the characters possess high Rage. Plant-spirits have a history of preferring low-Rage Garou to those with more supernatural anger, something that works very well against the more fervent characters in a group. And above all, remember that you want to reward them for participating in rites — after all, by so doing, they're drawing nearer to what it means to be Garou.

scorpions overrunning obnoxious villains can easily ensue. But how should you act when portraying awakened basil? (Even asking the question sounds a little weird.) Since it can grant both poison immunity and create poisonous arachnids depending on how it's used, basil might be a very ambivalent personality (and perhaps a little vain about its growing popularity with chefs). And if the players decide their characters should also awaken the horse dung, you're on your own.

• Catmint

Acknowledged as a means to bring on late menses, catmint has traditionally been used for birth control (not always terribly successfully). It also has a strong attraction for cats, hence the name. When awakened, this second power is substantially broadened, making it irresistible to felines. Feline creatures, including Bastet or feline fomori, must make a Willpower roll to avoid falling prey to the herb's lure. The number of successes they achieve equals the number of actions they can take before being rendered harmless (due to rolling, licking, eating the catmint, purring and striking silly, drugged poses as a result of ingesting it). The difficulty of the roll equals the Gnosis of the plant. So how do you play catmint? At the risk of sounding facetious, the mint part suggests being fresh, while the other calls for… a more catty mindset.

• Foxglove

Foxglove grows wild or may be cultivated in gardens. It's best known use is to produce digitalis, a drug used in treating heart disease. Its lesser-known properties as a sanctified magical flower involve protecting against faerie magic (adding two to the difficulty roll of any faerie spell or supernatural power used against the wearer). Its spirit might appear very calming and down-to-earth to reflect its properties.

• **Peyote**

A sacred plant to many Native Americans, peyote is a cactus found in the Southwest. Protrusions on the plant, called buttons, are chewed or boiled into a tea and drunk. In its mundane use, peyote has a hallucinatory effect. It's awakened version is considerably more powerful. Few Theurges beyond those of the Uktena or Wendigo know the rite to awaken peyote; perhaps a good thing since few beyond those two tribes tend to use it wisely. They tend to use it even without sanctifying to promote vision quests and dream walks.

Sanctified peyote has several uses. First, it allows someone who ingests it to step into the Umbra (without rolling or effort involved) and remain there for a number of hours equal to his Gnosis. Additionally, the infusion created by boiling allows someone who is deranged to ignore his Derangement, again for as many hours as she has Gnosis. Finally, someone who drinks the tea may achieve restful sleep, ignoring disturbances until awakening refreshed. Peyote should be played as quite mystical, somewhat difficult to follow and a little spacey. Lying underneath this trippy façade, however, should be hard-won, visionary wisdom.

• **Woundwort**

Also known as plantain, this plant provides powerful healing when awakened. When used as a poultice or brewed into a tincture, it heals all damage taken or disease inflicted from frenzied combat or spirit travels. The sanctified plant heals as many levels (including aggravated damage) as it has Gnosis per use. Only one such poultice can be used in any twenty-four hour period, however. Taken as a tincture, woundwort heals internal injuries. For each dose ingested, one Wyrm-inflicted ill can be healed. Thus if a Garou had eaten tainted meat and taken two health levels of damage from it, one level could be healed by drinking the woundwort tincture. Woundwort should most probably be portrayed as a caring, nurturing healer eager to erase damage taken in battle.

• **Yaupon**

Found in the lowlands of the Southeast (as far west as Texas), Yaupon's leaves provide its power. To be awakened, the leaves must be browned in an oven or over a fire, then boiled in water. This creates a bitter, black brew that allows its drinker to ignore fatigue for up to a day per dose, performing tasks without sleep and at no penalties for the lack thereof. Naturally, pushing oneself so hard eventually takes its toll (three days should be the absolute limit) and the imbiber must sleep out her fatigue to the number of hours she "borrowed." The brew imparts no immunity from needing to eat and imbibe fluids, nor does it give any abnormal strength beyond the drinker's own natural amount.

Yaupon is also used in divination. A Theurge who drinks the brew can see any Wyrm taint on his own soul and the souls of any others who share the cup with her. Thus, it is also used to unmask enemies within their midst or sept members who may be straying too close to the Wyrm's grasp. Yaupon might appear to be breezy and confident as it imparts so much energy, yet also insightful.

Obviously, there are far more than these few plants and herbs to choose from. Feel free to consult herbal sources or books on plant mythology and lore to help you develop special properties and personalities for these spirits. Keep in mind that no one plant should be an automatic cure-all or solve the characters' problems with a quick fix. You might also consider whether these spirits ask anything in return from the characters that make use of them. Who knows what plants might need? Fertilization? Cross-pollination? Weeding? Perhaps they simply want the characters to take cuttings from them and start new growths elsewhere to assure their continued survival. Try to envision what each might request in exchange for its far from insignificant aid. Then roleplay the bargaining. And remember, scent, pose or color, placement in the sun or shade or any other weird plant-centric element might help or hinder communication. Have fun!

Rite of the Fetish

As with the Rite of Summoning, Garou utilizing the Rite of the Fetish must once again force, flatter, bribe or cajole spirits into aiding them. Rather than asking for a one-time effort, however, this rite creates a permanent magical object imbued with a spirit. This means, of course, that the spirit must give up its freedom in order to enter into a material item. While some ultra-generous spirits might readily agree to such a plan, most are less than thrilled by the prospect. As this is the case, Storytellers should ask their players just how well they are preparing said object. Unless the item is reverently cleaned and cleansed as detailed in the description of the rite, any spirit asked to enter it should automatically refuse. After all, this is going to be that spirit's home for the foreseeable future (which could encompass centuries); it certainly doesn't want dirty dishes in the sink and grime in the bathtub!

Your job begins once the characters have made the item suitable for habitation. You should really make them work for this one. Playing a spirit being asked to semi-permanently enter a prison and work for the jailer in perpetuity can be a real challenge. You have to argue your own point of view, even fight to maintain your freedom if you're being coerced into this, but you must also be willing to be swayed by good enough arguments or impassioned pleas to serve Gaia's chosen, if that's what the spirit would eventually do. As always, however, there might need to be a haggling session wherein you as the spirit make known your demands and conditions under which you'll agree to become a fetish. Whether spirits have a large enough scope of interest to allow for counter offers remains in your hands. Play it as you see it.

Don't think that after you've given in (or been beaten into submission) you have no more personality and become merely an object to be used at the characters' whim. Fetishes should be created for specific purposes and ought to have unique properties. Otherwise, they lose their mystic aura and become just another tool like a wrench or a broom. Further, players usually enjoy having something truly different rather than just a ho-hum fetish like any other. So why not have a fetish that pompously offers advice on how to best use it just when an elder Garou happens by or pontificates concerning combat strategies at the most inopportune times? Naturally, if you bedevil the characters with such behavior, you'd better make sure the fetish is useful enough that they can't bear to just chuck it away. Remember also (and remind the players at need) that the pact the Garou hold with the spirits requires them to always treat a fetish with honor bordering on reverence.

Some Garou bind unwilling spirits into fetishes, which almost always results in a fetish that is difficult and rebellious. At their discretion, Storytellers might portray these fetish spirits as uncooperative at the most crucial times or have them make demands the characters are loathe to grant in order to function properly. Though the Garou consider such fetishes cursed, the pact still requires that they show honor to the spirit inside such an object. It's somewhat ironic (and this may be played upon) that forcing a spirit into a fetish permanently against its will can hardly be considered honoring it. If your troupe's characters insist on doing so, you should exact a heavy price and make certain they do it only out of extreme need and sincere desperation in order to serve Gaia's cause. If they're making the fetish just to acquire another cool toy for themselves, Garou deserve

what they get when a horde of spirits allied to the one they're harassing turn up to beleaguer the upstarts who are standing a hair's breadth from breaking the time-honored pact. This action would spell disaster for all Garou everywhere so make sure the players realize the severity of what they're doing.

Although almost all spirits who inhabit fetishes are Gafflings, what happens when they aren't? Imagine, for example, the chaos that could erupt through some yahoo somehow managing to bind a totem spirit into a fetish. Would that fetish them take on all the powers of the totem? Would a pack or sept dedicated to that totem lose its connection and powers until the spirit was freed? And just what might happen in the vicinity of the fetish as the totem spirit becomes increasingly hostile the longer it is pent up? Could the totem summon lesser spirits or Garou dedicated to it to aid in its escape? Would its particular job go undone while it was captive? This could become the basis for an entire chronicle culminating in a showdown with the owner(s) of the fetish and the pack determined to rescue their totem. And if a totem spirit might cause difficulties, how about something even more powerful, such as an Incarna or Celestine? These great beings might cause untold destruction (assuming someone was powerful, persuasive or tricky enough to force them into the thing in the first place).

As fetishes are rare and treasured items, they aren't just found lying around waiting to be picked up. If your game isn't brimming with potent fetishes spilling from every generous elder's pockets, or falling by the bucketload from every defeated foe, sooner or later one or more players will want to create their own. Obviously, they can or we wouldn't be having this discussion, but how do you judge how to determine the Gnosis level of the item the player plans to create? The fetishes detailed in second edition Werewolf all have a Gnosis rating somewhere between five and eight, with most having a rating of 6. Each fetish usually does only one specific thing (with the notable exception of grand klaives). As Gnosis is literally the life force of the spirit bound into the fetish, the more powerful the spirit, the greater the Gnosis level of the item. In general, if the fetish is intended for protective or defensive purposes or for general usefulness (such as the Spirit Tracer) Gnosis should be five or six. Those that disguise Garou or hide them from scrutiny as well as basic weaponry (such as klaives) call for a Gnosis rating of six to seven, depending on usefulness and rarity. Many Garou have klaives, for example, but few have Phoebe's Veil, making the veil of higher Gnosis due to its rarity. Fetishes that are extremely rare, affect more than one opponent in an aggressive manner or

hold more than one power might rate a seven or even an eight. Additionally, if a greater spirit is bound into a fetish, the Gnosis level ought to rise appreciably. Then again, if you allow your player's characters to bind such powerful spirits into fetishes, you'd better be prepared to play out the ensuing weirdness with all the Gnosis at your disposal.

As for the level of the fetish itself, this isn't *quite* as necessary, as the player needn't spend Background points on a fetish gained in play. However, what if you like the fetish so much you want to make it available to later characters? Or if you'd like to create your own fetishes, but are unsure as to what level they should be? Although far from scientific, the following advice may be of some help:

Level One: Useful. A fetish with a power that is useful, but not overpowering, in a specific situation.

Level Two: Reliable. A fetish that is potent in limited situations, or generally helpful much of the time; also, a fetish weapon no more useful than a werewolf's claws.

Level Three: Potent. A fetish weapon with a minor blessing, or a fetish reliably useful in dangerous situations.

Level Four: Powerful. A fetish weapon with a secondary power that is either consistent (such as a klaive dealing silver damage) or powerful and requiring activation. Also, a fetish with a very useful power.

Level Five: Legendary. A fetish weapon with multiple powers, or a fetish that is exceptionally powerful or versatile. Most fetishes of this level are great treasures, and much honor is attached to them.

Level Six: Beyond legendary. Fetishes with powers beyond that of mortals. One-of-a-kind artifacts worthy of the greatest heroes that ever lived.

Rite of the Totem

In many troupes, the Storyteller and players consult to determine which totem the pack wants. Sometimes they try to figure out which seems most appropriate to the tribes or personalities of the pack. At other times players just want whatever totem is strongest or gives them the most advantages. In a few cases, players choose based on whether it seems "cool" rather than "too fairytale" or even choose a totem that won't require too much work from them to remain in the spirit's good graces. Depending on what you and your players want from the game, these are all valid reasons for choosing a particular totem. It's usually preferable to have a totem the characters feel comfortable with and one they feel they can serve without having to bend their characters' personalities to fit.

The actual rite calls for a pack to anoint their eyes with a holy substance in order to grant them the magical sight to find the trail of the spirit to whom they wish to dedicate themselves. While it calls for mugwort or tobacco or some similar substance, creative Storytellers might have their troupes search for a particular herb associated with or attractive to the specific spirit and use it instead. At the Storyteller's discretion (depending on how hard it is to acquire this information or the rarity of the substance) using this element in the rite could make the spirit in question become better disposed toward the pack, accepting them more readily as its children. Naturally, even using special ingredients is no substitute for good roleplaying. Members of the pack should still be required to present their case to the totem through both speech and actions.

While the rite may require the characters to undertake some sort of quest to prove their worth to the spirit, the Storyteller could help the pack improve their chances of being assigned an easier task or needing no special assignment at all by wowing the spirit on first meeting.

How? By doing their homework. Which spirit are they seeking? Is it a totem of respect or war? Custom designing their approach to impress the spirit with their maturity, prowess or whatever the spirit stands for should be rewarded. By arriving on the scene with appropriate gifts, proof of their skills or of successful hunts, battles and what have you, the pack can prove to the spirit that they are both worthy and serious and that they have a lot to offer the spirit in return for its patronage. Of course, its your job as Storyteller to play any spirits the pack might have encountered before with such skill that the players will realize the gravity of asking for a totem's favor. When they actually meet, you must also play up the totem's majestic presence so the characters feel as though they've received a great honor in allying with it. Totems should embody the principals of Respect, War, Wisdom or Cunning and should require those whom it adopts as its children to behave in a similar fashion. It's up to you as the Storyteller to portray the spirit in such a fashion that the players (and their characters) aren't confused by it. A pack member showing his wisdom in defeating an enemy without the need for combat to a totem of war should receive little or no interest from the spirit. Those Garou who approach a totem of war after having won a difficult battle through both good tactical decisions and personal bravery, however, ought to be flattered by the amount of attention the spirit lavishes on them.

So what happens when the players don't really know which spirit they ought to choose as their totem or when you want to introduce a spirit into the game that is appropriate to your setting, but not detailed in the main rulebook? The rite calls for the characters to be able to track specific spoor and distinguish it from any other. In this case, though, the characters don't have a clue what they're looking for. In such cases it falls even more to the Storyteller to point your troupe in the proper direction. Since they don't know what they're seeking, you need to have an entire adventure in the Umbra ready for the characters. Rather than following a specific trail, the substance rubbed into their eyes should let them see the area of most need, leading them in the direction they need to go to perform great deeds that will attract the spirit you've chosen for them. Alternatively, you could present the troupe with several choices and note which one they feel is most important, then use that as a guide for selecting which spirit offers its patronage. Finally, you might have their sept assign the pack a task in the Umbra culminating with a rite to acquire a totem for themselves. You could have an interesting session involving several spirits that evince interest, who each offer the pack their nod in return for completing the quest. Playing each spirit presents quite a roleplaying challenge for Storytellers, especially if you really want the pack to choose one totem over another. Actually having the various totems played out for them, however, may be instrumental in helping the characters choose the one they feel best suits them.

Becoming Garou: The Rite of Passage

No cub is accepted as a true Garou until she undergoes her rite of passage. Although the cub's tribe isn't established either until this seminal rite is performed, it's pretty obvious which tribe most cubs belong with. Those that are born to a Garou parent of Silver Fang stock could hardly be considered a Child of Gaia or Uktena. In like manner, most tribes keep track of their Kinfolk whenever possible and perform a Baptism of Fire on newborns if they are Garou. This marks such children with a spiritual brand, the pictogram that identifies the child's tribe. It isn't that difficult then, to design a rite of passage to incorporate elements that are important to the cub's tribe-to-be. While the tribe may not yet acknowledge that the cub is part of their society, they usually don't deny that the cub's genesis lies within their own tribe. A notable exception exists with the Black Furies, who do not accept male cubs.

It's up to the Storyteller to devise a true rite of passage for the characters that will test them and prove their honor, wisdom and courage to the tribe so they may gain acceptance. As when dealing with spirits, there is little point in sending an Uktena pack into a head-on confrontation with Wyrm creatures. The tribe won't honor them for it and may even wonder if they truly belong elsewhere. A quest to uncover secret knowledge guarded by Wyrm creatures that must be defeated, bypassed or tricked into surrendering their secrets, however, is imminently suitable and can gain the characters instant respect for successfully completing it. Playing the elders that send the cubs off to complete their rite of passage requires Storytellers to assume roles that impress upon the cubs just how serious — and deadly — rites of passage are supposed to be. After all, if they cannot complete a difficult, but not impossible quest, they hardly deserve a place within the tribe.

But what occurs when the cub's parentage is not known? Kinfolk may move around, a Kin-Fetch sent to watch over the baby may falter in its duties or something else could happen to leave the newly changed werewolf as a lost cub. In this case, the rite of passage becomes the best means for discovering what tribe the cub actually belongs with. The tribe that performs the rite will not necessarily end up with a new member. The rite may prove that the cub is destined for some other tribe entirely. Depending on relations between the two tribes, the one giving the rite might demand that the cub foreswear her natural tribe and join theirs instead or might assist the cub in locating and joining the tribe to which she actually belongs.

Scent of the True Form can tell that a young werewolf is unquestionably Garou, but it does not convey a sense of "tribe"; only genealogy and research can provide that. (Pure Breed goes a long way as well.) Tribe is a matter of acceptance; birth is not always proof of one's worthiness. Indeed, a male born to the Black Furies might prove during his rite of passage that he has the greatest affinity for the Get of Fenris and their creed, but might not be offered a place within their ranks. He would then have to apply elsewhere and take whatever tribe accords him welcome. While this is a rarity, it's surprising how many players want their characters to be mysterious and unknown, to have secrets the other characters don't know about them. As the Storyteller, you need to accommodate that and not give anything away to the other players, yet still create a rite of passage that will identify the character's tribe (at least to that character's player) so he may receive the Gifts he should have. If the player herself is unsure what tribe she wants her character to have, you need to watch how she deals with the challenges of the rite you've set up and make your best guess based on her actions and words which tribe is the best fit. If the player is unhappy, ask her to make a choice for herself and create situations appropriate to the tribe.

Sometimes, no matter what you do, characters simply refuse to fit into a tribal stereotype. This is fine!

Each tribe is a diverse community, not an inbred pack of clones. Some of the best roleplaying opportunities arise from uncomfortable juxtapositions, such as an Amish cub born to the heritage of Get of Fenris Ahroun — to be sure, the love of family is there, but sparks will surely fly as the cub's philosophy of non-violence runs headlong into the Fenrir's warlike ways. Naïve Shadow Lords and apparently ultra-sane Silver Fangs also provide endless fuel for story fodder. Just make certain the Rite of Passage reflects what the cub has been up until now, challenges them physically, socially and mentally, and gives them a good glimpse of what they can expect from the future. If you do so, you can't go far wrong, even if your potential Black Fury turns out to be a sweet tempered Child of Gaia.

Seasonal Tribal Rites

All Garou perform at least some seasonal rites to honor Gaia and mark the turning of the year. All the tribes know these great rites (though each tribe places its own stamp on the performance of them). Every Garou who can attend such rites is encouraged to do so. You, as Storyteller, can maximize these rites in your players' minds by making them truly elaborate affairs where Renown can be won or lost for their knowledge and performance or their lack thereof. No Garou in his right mind should disrupt the seasonal rites unless failing to do so would bring down destruction on the entire sept. By making these rites so important to your players' characters, you can also encourage them to perform some of the seasonal tribal rites each tribe observes. It's especially fun to convince a mixed pack or sept that *all* their tribes' seasonal rites should be observed by everyone (pack or sept) and see the fall-out as a member of one tribe attempts to understand why his pack or septmate's tribe would even bother celebrating in such a manner. Though these rites first appeared in the original **Storytellers Handbook**, they have been streamlines and reworked for inclusion here. Storytellers should feel free to create their own seasonal rites as some packs and septs may observe such rites as often as once per month. Obviously, these rites are performed only at the appropriate times of year they were designed to celebrate. Only a few seasonal rites are presented here for lack of space, but many others exist or can be created especially for a single tribe, sept or pack.

• The Mysteries (Level Three)

Performed by the Black Furies at the time of the first new moon after the Winter Solstice (December 20, 21 or 22), the Mysteries hark back to ancient times. Greek females would gather to celebrate the mysteries associated with the female sex: birth, death, renewal and questioning of their place in the ongoing cycles of life. The Furies meet within caves, often with trees atop the tor that houses them, during this dark of the moon. Those too old for childbearing unwind black string and tie it to a rock or tree. Those who have borne children use red string, while those who are still virgin utilize white string, symbolizing the threefold aspect of the goddess as maid, mother and crone. The ritemaster shares a tale of a great heroine who has walked a path through darkness to knowledge and the Furies dance, intertwining their stings into a pattern, then share a cup of blood and wine. The rite ends at dawn.

• Superbowl Sunday (Level Two)

Every year on Superbowl Sunday (in January) American Bone Gnawers gather to listen to or watch the game. Bone Gnawers in other areas of the world perform similar rites for World Cup soccer matches and the like; in a World Cup year, the Gnawers may be performing this rite for weeks. During the pre-game show, all who are gathered tell each other what they think the sept ought to do post-game, such as help out someone who is down on his luck, rescue people from abusive spouses, check up on their Kinfolk or hunt down Wyrm creatures. Other suggestions might also be tendered. The ritemaster passes around an old hat and each Bone Gnawer throws in something he considers valuable (a CD, an old watch, even an Indian head penny), then predicts which team will win and by how many points. No one can predict the same score, so popular guesses go early. As the hat passes, it becomes a temporary fetish. Worn by the winner, it acts to point that Garou in the exact direction she needs to go to accomplish what she earlier stated she wanted the group to do. The rite ends at dawn or whenever the goal of the winner is accomplished. For this reason, no Bone Gnawer ever tries to say they want to do something post-game that will take more than one night.

• Memorial Day

While American Glass Walkers enact this rite on Memorial Day, others world-wide do so on days their own countries designate as a time to honor their dead. Before dawn, Glass Walkers gather on rooftops, in office buildings or even within parks and grieve for their fallen comrades and ancestors. The rite honors those who have fallen in Gaia's service or in an attempt to gather new technological information or devices. As dawn breaks the ritemaster calls the Glass Walkers into their Hall of Honor, a special room or area where the names and deeds of the honored dead are written. New additions are made to the rolls to honor new martyrs and the ritemaster summons a City Spirit to guard and protect the room for a year in return for a single favor from the Garou.

• Rite of the Impergium

Red Talons hold the Rite of the Impergium on June 28, one week after the Summer Solstice. On this night, they gather and howl the Song of the Impergium, which tells the history of this once-sacred duty and the subsequent decision among Garou to stop enforcing its dictates. This howl is so guttural and derisively chilling that anyone not of the Red Talons tribe inevitably flees its sound. Humans who hear it may try to run, but rarely escape the Talons' sweep when they disperse outward, culling whatever humans cross their path for this one night. While entire towns are not subjected to it, lone travelers, groups camping, ranches and rest stops become their targets if within the Talons' territory. The werewolves continue their terrifying song as they slaughter those caught within their bounds, reiterating that this is a sacred trust they should be performing and lamenting that they no longer serve Gaia in this fashion. At dawn, the Red Talons return to their territories far from human habitations, leaving chaos and terror in their wake.

The Beast Courts

Gaia wears many masks. Or, rather, Gaia has many faces, each a true manifestation, simply not the entire truth. In the eastern half of the world's largest continent and in the oceanic realms surrounding it, the Changing Breeds deal with each other and with the world around them very differently than they do in Europe and the Americas. This section summarizes how the Asian shapechangers live. For a great many more details, see **Hengeyokai** and **A World of Rage**. This is an introduction for those who don't want to immerse themselves in the full complexity of the situation just now, and an update in light of recent developments like the Stargazers' departure from the Garou Nation.

History

Originally, according to the myths of all the Changing Breeds, the various shapeshifting races existed harmoniously. Gaia, whom the *hengeyokai* (shapeshifters) often refer to as the Emerald Mother, gave each kind of

---

The Middle Kingdom

The term "Middle Kingdom" refers to an area of shared spiritual influence. China sits at the center, providing the oldest traditions and the greatest population. From there, the kingdom of the soul extends to include Japan, Korea, the Philippines and other islands of the Pacific and Southeast Asia. There's overlapping authority and in some cases outright conflict along various borderlands in the north (Siberia and eastern Russia), west (the central Asian republics and nomadic territories) and southwest (India).

shapeshifter a particular role to play. Unfortunately, the various kinds fell into quarrels and then into war.

In the lands of eastern Asia, the Middle Kingdom, this war did not become the total catastrophe known as the War of Rage. Changers did fight each other, often bloodily, but no single kind drove another to extinction, and through it all the kinds retained some common purpose. The Beast Courts of the Emerald Mother were, and are, literal courts, formal gatherings of the elders of each kind with authority to give orders and dispense justice. While the Courts have sometimes been greatly strained and in some places cease working for a while, there is a more or less continuous tradition of governance in the midst of chaos.

The Beast Courts' sages present a much more complex view of history than their Western counterparts. The prevailing view among supernatural denizens of the Middle Kingdom features a great Wheel of the Ages. It begins with the consummate perfection of the First Age and progressive descent into decadence, confusion and woe. Some stories say that the world itself changed shape in the catastrophes that ended the Second Age, though nobody can say for sure. The world now stands poised on the brink of the Sixth Age, the era of greatest darkness. Old lore says that the wheel will continue to turn, into a Seventh Age of somewhat better conditions all the way back up to a Twelfth Age of restored perfection. It's hard for most *hengeyokai* to believe that now, and many fear that history will grind to a halt with the Sixth Age. There may be endless misery or simple annihilation ahead, depending on who tells the tale, but hope is scarce.

The Wheel of the Ages isn't just a matter of interpretation. Elders of the Beast Courts can document specific changes in their relations with the spirit world, the operation of familiar Gifts and even their ability to draw on the Rage within themselves. When one age gives way to the next, it matters in practical, tangible ways, at least to changers attuned to the conditions of the Middle Kingdom.

Court Fundamentals
The Shen

One of the most obvious differences between the Middle Kingdom and elsewhere is the relations between the *shen* or supernatural races. Some members of each race keep to their own kind and follow a system of rank and renown like that described in **Werewolf**, the various Breed books and other source material. Most band together across Breed lines, as described in more detail below.

Things are far from smooth in inter-Breed relations. Every Breed has its own history, its grudges and jealousies. The bond of shared nature competes with

Asia or Everywhere
Very few individuals have the connections and inclination to pursue detailed comparisons between the historical accounts provided by various supernatural communities. In particular, anyone who knows the lore of the Beast Courts thoroughly is unlikely to be much good at coaxing information out of suspicious western Theurges, let alone out of Mokolé and other observers. There's no stock Werewolf answer as to whether and to what degree the changes created by changing ages of history affected the world outside the Middle Kingdom. Whatever answer you settle on for a chronicle, if in fact the question seems to need answering, should be hard to uncover and even harder to verify.

the bonds of community. The Courts host politicking of all kinds from subtle intrigue to overt violence. It's just that the bonds of community have yet to become as irrevocably shattered as they were in the West.

The Beast Courts also deal with other sorts of *shen* beyond the ranks of shapeshifters. The most numerous and influential of these are the *Kuei-jin*, the so-called "Kindred of the East." These strange vampires have a complex history of their own, which **Kindred of the East** presents in detail. The first of their kind, in the Second Age of the world, were mortal men and women given special power by great spirits and assigned to guard society and the world, overseeing humanity much as the Garou once tended the natural world. Gradually they succumbed to the temptations of power and the lure of corrupt, evil spirits like those who empower the Black Spiral Dancers. The spirits that originally created them turned their founding gifts into curses.

Now the Kuei-jin exist in a peculiar undead condition. A human soul which escapes from its afterlife in one of the many hells of the Middle Kingdom's Dark Umbra can sometimes reunite with its body, when driven by a sense of unfinished duty. Unfortunately, the dead body cannot make the vital energy that sustains all living creatures — what the Beast Courts and other *shen* call "chi" — and must feed on chi from other sources. As it happens, the blood of living people contains chi in particularly concentrated form, so that hapless Kuei-jin begin as blood-suckers, until and unless they master the art of drawing chi from less conveniently potent reserves.

Unlike most Western Leeches, the Kuei-jin claim an extreme sense of moral duty. They exist precisely to do the good and necessary deeds they didn't in life. This gives them a point in common with the Beast Courts, though there remains much tension between those chosen by the Green Mother to protect life and those who must prey parasitically on life. Shapeshifters and vampires do not pal around, nor do they often go on vacation together. They do have common enemies, like the spirits that would annihilate the world or paralyze it in the dark chaos of the Sixth Age, and mutual concerns, like the decline of spiritual understanding or moral ambition among human beings. So they sometimes cooperate on matters where their interests overlap, and otherwise they mostly stay out of each other's way.

Even this limited interaction startles unprepared Garou from the West. On occasion, a favored outsider has come in on the (careful, etiquette-bound, tense) conversation of a Kuei-jin and one or more *hengeyokai* and launched into an attack on the vampiric menace. Such efforts never go well, whether they end in a dead Kuei-jin, a dead werewolf, grave injuries all around, or some other outcome. Thoughtful *hengeyokai* warn their guests beforehand, but the actual spectacle carries a shock that no amount of calm discussion can. Garou who see the sight and return to their home almost always end up reinforcing suspicions about Wyrm-tainted Asian changers. In turn, members of the Beast Courts tend to find the Garou reaction proof that the West is mired in willful ignorance and self-destructive superstition.

Other sorts of *shen* appear less frequently. The ghosts of the Middle Kingdom exist in a highly organized society of their own, presided over by the Jade Emperor of the dead, Yu Huang. (In recent years there's been substantial turmoil in his realm, but the empire persists. If you really want to get into details about Asian ghosts, see **Dark Kingdom of Jade** and **Ends of Empire**. For most purposes it suffices to say that the equivalent of a classical Chinese empire rules over all the Middle Kingdom's lands of the dead.) The *hsien* are something like Western fae and something like guardian angels, and spend almost all their time concerned with their own matters.

The Sentai

The Beast Courts' equivalent of the pack is the *sentai* or war party. Tradition calls for precisely five members, though sometimes a smaller force's members must each take on multiple roles and occasionally several individuals each take on one of the roles to form a larger band.

• **The Lantern:** The Lantern leads the sentai, making overall decisions about how best to carry out their mandate; it is a role most comparable to the Philodox.

• **The Fist:** The Fist exercises authority over martial matters, providing tactical guidance and taking the lead in combat; the Fist is comparable to the Ahroun.

• **The Mirror:** The Mirror deals with the spirits, keeping the sentai in touch with their totem and other

sustaining powers; it is a role with much in common with the Theurge.

• **The Leaf:** The Leaf goes ahead of the sentai to scout, then back to report, specializing in arts of stealth and information-gathering. A Leaf is most like a Ragabash.

• **The Pillar:** The Pillar provides support for all the other members of the sentai in their respective duties. It can be likened to the role of the Galliard, although the differences are many.

Sentai often form for specific missions, rather than as lifelong bonds — though shapeshifters who find they work well together are likely to continue doing so, on the very sensible grounds that the Courts and the Green Mother need all the successes they can get.

The Court

Tradition also establishes roles for each Court. In practice, most Courts lack enough members for each role to be filled by a separate individual, but they do what they can. Ideally, each Court takes responsibility for a separate caern, though the press of numbers often forces a Court to oversee two or more caerns.

• **The Regent:** The Regent holds highest authority in the Court, resolving disputes, issuing decrees and interpreting the Traditions and the dictates of the spirits. It's not a position many *hengeyokai* volunteer for, as it involves huge responsibilities and, in time of crisis, great risk. Courts do not choose regents lightly, and if it becomes necessary to remove a regent, everyone involved usually suffers loss of renown.

• **The General:** The General, or warmaster, performs duties much like those of a caern warder, training the Court's members in the arts of war and ensuring that the caern itself is properly guarded. The general usually enjoys substantial prestige, but this can vary widely depending on the particular circumstances.

• **The Seer:** The Seer oversees the performance of rites and summonings and other interactions with the spirit world, like the Master of the Rite. The seer must be personally skilled at dealing with the spirits, though some seers delegate specific kinds of tasks to subordinates. The seer always exerts a great deal of influence over the life of the Court. Wherever possible, the seer has at least one student, preparing to step in should the seer become injured, lost in the Umbra or otherwise unfit for duty.

• **The Historian:** The Historian keeps the lore of the caern and Court for future generations, and instructs the other *hengeyokai* in all that has come before them. This is partly a matter of mastering myth and folklore, but also eminently practical; the historian is the master of scouts and spies as well as tale-spinners. Zhong Lung, the Asian Mokolé, often fill this role, but others are by no means unheard-of, and necessity dictates some very unlikely assignments on occasion.

Honor

The changers of the Middle Kingdom talk a great deal about honor — and engage in many acts to maintain and increase it — but they seldom offer full explanations to outsiders. As Storyteller, you need to know what the Middle Kingdom changers your players' characters encounter are thinking about.

The eastern Asian tradition of honor is, first and foremost, about meeting one's duties to the people with whom one is bound by oath and tradition. An honorable leader seeks the well-being of those serving her and the triumph of their shared cause. An honorable servant seeks the greatest good for her master, ideally acting without needing instruction so that the master is free to tend to other duties. An honorable warrior fights not just bravely but intelligently, protecting the other members of the community and showing integrity and ingenuity in prosecuting the battle most effectively.

Honor requires the individual changer to uphold the well-being of her family, her community, and the Beast Courts as a whole. Whether her innate capacities are great or small, what matters is that she uses them well. Honor may call upon her to sacrifice herself if the sacrifice will win something important for the groups to which she's bound; it may also call upon her to endure when self-sacrifice would be easy, if she remains necessary to the life of her groups.

However, honor does not impose any obligations whatsoever to outsiders. Garou and other visitors from outside the Middle Kingdom do not belong to the Courts. They have a different (and, from the Asian point of view, flawed) understanding of Gaia, history and the present moment. By definition they do not belong to Asian lineages or communities. If they choose to submit and take oaths of obligation, then they become part of the system. Otherwise, they're to be used as appropriate and discarded when irrelevant.

At least that's what honor requires. If an individual chooses to act out of other concerns, like a love of scholarship or a personal sense of benevolence, that's fine. Noble and kindly action earns praise among the Beast Courts just as it does in the West. Such action is, however, always a matter of individual choice rather than general duty, and there's no disgrace among *hengeyokai* for sticking with honor as their guiding principle.

High War and Low War

Tradition identifies two general categories of conflict that the changing breeds may engage in.

• **High War:** High War is the reality that most closely compares to Western stereotypes of noble Asian warriors. Its participants agree to binding conventions and an overall concern for honor. They make explicit declarations of war, and they fight with limited means. While on the battlefield they may slaughter each other (and sometimes do; it's not unknown for a battle to end with no survivors at all), they seek the blood only of their fellow warriors. Acts of general terror and rampant slaughter of bystanders or civilians are strictly out of bounds. High War happens openly.

• **Low War:** Broadly speaking, all other conflict is Low War. Anything goes. Espionage, assassination, kidnapping and terror all occur in Low War. In modern terms, so do acts of genocide and regional destruction, or at least they can if the participants choose to use such weapons. The only principle that guides Low War is the determination to destroy one's adversaries. It's possible to fight Low War with honor, but once the war begins, nobody should expect anything but utterly ruthless determination.

The werewolves and weretigers of Asia are the greatest masters of High War. Their respective traditions have practically refined it to an art form, full of ceremony and great dignity. There's an elegance to the total commitment of mind and body to the task of combat within boundaries, a terrible and cruel beauty that speaks to something very deep in wild changers' hearts. The Ratkin are, in Asia as elsewhere, the consummate masters of Low War. They do whatever they deem necessary, and expect nothing of their enemies except that they should obligingly die once killed. They don't care what others think and respect nothing but success in the endeavor.

High War includes the notion of worthy failure, when one is true to one's code even while overwhelmed by superior force. Low War does not.

The Shapeshifters of the East

Hakken

The Hakken are a tribe of werewolves found only, as far as observers know, in the Middle Kingdom. They've sometimes been described as "Shadow Lords, only like samurai." The Hakken share the Shadow Lords' driving ambition to exert authority and refusal to submit to the leadership of inferiors, but they combine it with equal dedication to a complex code of honor. As is usual with Garou, the resemblances to human culture only go so far — the Hakken aren't just samurai, and were never precisely bound by human notions of honor. Their distinctive code of *bushido*, the warrior's way, has both influenced and been influenced by the human communities all around the Hakken, but it takes into account the distinctive realities of Garou life.

Family lineages provide the foundation for Hakken organization. Noble families preside, and lines of retainers serve them. In the classic Hakken formulation, the *daimyo* or lord is the heart and mind, the warriors the hands and feet; the elders are the senses, the juniors the body. It all adds up, when things work right, to a single transcendent organism aware of and capable of more than any of its individual members.

Hakken serve the Beast Courts and seldom feel much conflict between their duties to court and to clan. Providing excellence in military or other service to the Court, thereby ensuring its success and prosperity, serves the clan as well, bringing glory to the community which produced such worthies. On the other hand, the Hakken distinguish between service to the Court and service with other *hengeyokai*: they work reasonably well with the Kitsune and Tengu, both of which have long histories in areas of Hakken strength, but are generally unhappy about being assigned to sentai with other breeds. They strike to excel in such situations, as always, they just don't like it and seek any opportunity for honorable change.

The Hakken are among the most numerous members of the Beast Courts, in no danger of extinction. When a Court's elders know that contact with Westerners is coming, they generally aim to include at least a few Hakken among the sentai who'll deal with the outsiders, since the Hakken have some shared nature with the Garou Nation despite very different outlooks.

Khan

The Khan, weretigers, are the only Bastet who take part in the Beast Courts in significant numbers. The other breeds of changing cat find the life of the Courts uncomfortable or unappealing for various reasons. The Khan, however, combine their breed duty to gather the secrets of their enemies with a duty as warriors on behalf of the Emerald Mother.

Khan exist outside the Middle Kingdom as well as inside, but the lineages on opposite sides of the divide seldom trust each other. There's a legacy of betrayal and warfare that leaves both sides unwilling to expect anything but more conflict from their distant cousins. This deep suspicion reinforces the Khan's naturally solitary nature to ensure that few *hengeyokai* or outsiders ever encounter more than one Khan at a time. Many members of the Beast Courts, let alone those from other lands, never encounter a Khan directly at all, except perhaps at a great distance on some special ceremonial occasion. The global population of Khan may be less than a hundred, and every one is special.

Experienced Khan serve the Courts as generals and strategists. Outsiders who come with rank and prestige enough to warrant dealing with the Courts' great leaders may therefore encounter Khan and perhaps even fight alongside them against some grave mutual threat. Otherwise, Khan will remain matters of story and court legend as far as visitors are concerned.

Kitsune

The werefoxes are unique to Asia, and occupy a distinctive position among the ranks of the changing breeds. They don't have a history that runs back into myth and legends. Rather, they emerged as a breed within the scope of human history, within the last age or two of the world. They combine a wit to match the Tengu's with the ruthless determination of the Nagah and Nezumi, acting as, in one description, "laughing assassins" of those who threaten the Emerald Mother and Her works. Their version of the Litany denies them the right to attempt to exterminate humanity or to make war upon other changers, but they generally have a very free hand when it comes to wiping out forces that menace creation.

Most of the Kitsune keep to themselves, but enough of them belong to the Beast Courts that outsiders may well encounter them, particularly at courts attached to particularly large caerns or in particularly dangerous areas. The Kitsune thrive on clashes with danger, and serve bravely where other changers may make excuses to avoid the risk. They simply don't show enough respect or concern for minutiae of etiquette for most *hengeyokai* to feel comfortable with them. This informality would make them particularly suitable companions for Western changers, except that Kitsune don't feel obliged to treat strangers with much respect, either.

Dealing with Kitsune is a little like dealing with Nuwisha, but although both are tricksters to some degree, the Kitsune are also consummate diplomats with a taste for sorcery. They strive for a refinement that the earthy Nuwisha care little for.

Nagah

The serpent people of the Middle Kingdom are almost as scarce as the Khan: the whole realm holds only a few hundred of them. Some press on in the manner of their breed without reference to any other changers' concerns, but most serve the Beast Courts as quiet, unobtrusive ministers of justice. Whereas the Nagah are altogether unseen in the West, in the Middle Kingdom they're known and respected (usually feared) as valuable participants in the behind-the-scenes life of the Courts.

So far the Nagah remain a matter of rumor as far as the favored few outsiders allowed into the Courts are concerned. The Nagah remember and remind each other of the War of Rage, and do not care to risk fresh conflict

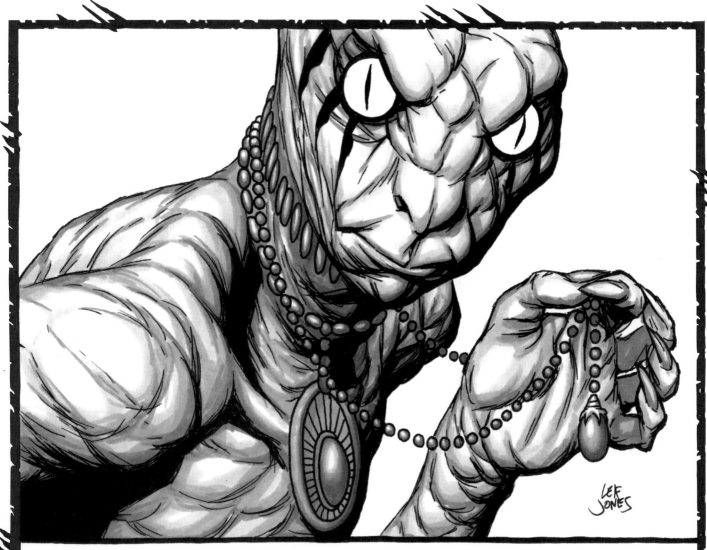

now. Their allies in the Courts readily provide conflicting rumors and misleading accounts in the rare instances when an outsider starts asking the wrong questions.

Nezumi

The Ratkin of Asia live on the fringes of the Beast Courts. In theory they are just as valued as any other Breed, created by Gaia and carrying out their duties as best they can. In practice they're almost universally looked down on and condescended to, lowborn and untrustworthy.

Thus the Nezumi are simultaneously the most populous of the Changing Breeds in Asia and among those outsiders are least likely to encounter. They're busy with their own concerns, and have little more use for court formalities and mingling with the other Breeds than the others have for them. Strangers in the Middle Kingdom almost always come to the attention of the Nezumi, at least if the strangers spend any time in large cities, but the Nezumi see much more often than they are seen.

Like the Ratkin in the West, the Nezumi regard themselves as the Emerald Mother's last line of defense against humanity run amok. Where honor and battle-field bravery and the majesty of other breeds fail, the rats wait with the terminal gifts of disease and death. Indeed, some warrens of Nezumi have already taken it upon themselves to start reducing humanity's numbers drastically: not all "industrial accidents" and other mass disasters in Asia are quite as accidental as they seem. Garou who stumble on Nezumi operations are far more likely to disappear quietly than to receive a generous welcome and expository lump of information.

A few Nezumi elders work with other Breeds, teaching them the arts of Low War. They do this quietly, usually secretly, and it shows only when the others begin using surprising tactics.

Same-Bito

The weresharks of the Middle Kingdom wear the same forms as their kin elsewhere, but lead tremendously different lives. As creatures of the sea, they naturally cannot participate fully in the land-based routine of the Beast Courts, but they do belong to the Courts and do serve with honor and distinction. They're seldom sophisticated, and they have very little use for the intricacies of court politics or highly detailed status systems. They are not just brave but determined and persistent, and they seek to act with sound judgment as well as the tremendous force that comes naturally to them.

The seas of the Middle Kingdom face many challenges, both natural and supernatural, and the Same-Bito do not suffer for want of reasons to stir themselves into activity. Often they must fight by themselves against maritime foes. When the challenge is closer to shore or involves foes on land as well as sea, then they join with other Breeds in sentai dedicated to sea-related missions.

Garou who stay on land are very unlikely ever to cross paths with the Same-Bito. Garou who sail the seas of the Middle Kingdom are much more likely to encounter them. The Same-Bito take a very practical approach to outsiders. Anyone who fights against the Emerald Mother's foes is an ally, even if a stranger. Anyone who supports the Emerald Mother's foes or who interferes with the fight against them is an enemy, even if familiar.

Tengu

The wereravens have more in common with their Western cousins than most hengeyokai do. After all, they can fly (both on Earth and in the Umbra), and they're accustomed to long journeys. They certainly must take account of the barriers posed by mountains, deserts and oceans, but they can overcome them more easily than other changers.

Like Western Corax, the Tengu work hard to gather the world's secrets and to share them with all that also serve the Emerald Mother. They also enjoy their labors in ways that most other changers don't, often attracting a reputation for frivolity despite their frequent sacrifices and the great risks they face. They find not just satisfaction in doing their duty honorably, but real pleasure in it, and whenever the Courts gather there's usually some argument about the appropriateness of such a reaction.

Outsiders in the Middle Kingdom usually come to the attention of the Tengu first. Whether the Tengu contact them depends mostly on what impression the outsiders make. The Tengu are most likely to make friendly contact with Garou or other changers who show courage and cluefulness, most likely to harass particularly arrogant, ignorant or pompous targets. If outsiders come on missions that require dealing with the masses of Asian humanity and make a good impression on their hosts, Tengu are generally best-positioned to guide them to suitable contacts.

Zhong Lung

The Mokolé of Asia hold places of special honor among the Beast Courts. Few in number, their gift of memory makes them uniquely valuable in a society that places so much weight on tradition and propriety. They say that they were the first hengeyokai created by the Emerald Mother's favored servants, and the other changers generally agree.

The Zhong Lung differ dramatically from their Western counterparts. Their auspices are tied to the seasons rather than to the behavior of the sun itself, and their dreams tap into the mythic lore of the region about dragon princes. In their reptilian Archid form, they generally resemble the sinuous whiskered dragons of Asian art, and some take on truly tremendous proportions. The giant lizards and weird creatures of popular monster movies reflect, in highly distorted fashion, the mythic presence of the Zhong Lung.

Zhong Lung seldom engage deeply in human society, or even pay much attention to its details. For much of history they could do that without serious consequence; now they're constantly caught off-guard by the destruction of precious Kinfolk habitat and other calamities, but they remain psychologically unable to rouse themselves to the sort of quick and nuanced response the situation calls for. Thus they depend on the rest of the Beast Courts to help them protect themselves, in exchange for their access to the wisdom of the ages and their personal power.

Garou who come on scholarly tasks are quite likely to end up visiting with a Zhong Lung sage if they make a good impression and behave well. Others won't, not so much out of deliberate aversion as because there's simply little other common ground.

Kumo

The werespiders of the Middle Kingdom do not take part in the life of the Beast Courts; they remain tenuous allies at the best of times and bitter enemies at the worst. The great families of the Kumo all serve the Wyrm, and vigorously destroy any individuals who work too fervently to further the welfare of the Emerald Mother or Queen Ananasa. Whether a particular Kumo lives alone or as part of a village of werespiders, all give themselves to the task of plunging the world into perpetual oblivion.

Into the Sixth Age

The Beast Courts have been busy in recent years, with wars and rumors of wars. This section surveys some major developments and their current conditions.

After the Week of Nightmares

In the summer of 1999, beings of godlike power went to war in the fertile lowlands shared by India and Bangladesh. Their magical conflict killed hundreds of thousands of people and blighted the land. The Gauntlet actually disappeared altogether for several days over hundreds of square miles, allowing in unprecedented destructive force. In the end… somebody won, presumably, since the battle came to an end and the work of covering it up began. *Everyone* seems interested in burying the truth the matter deeply. Human governments talk about terrorists and psychoactive chemical warfare, while the *Kuei-jin* speak cryptically of the sacrifices of their elders and technophilic magicians occasionally allude to super-weapons in the heavens.

Most of the cover-up and related debate pass by the Beast Courts without comment. Some sentai focus on what they see as the really important task, which is healing the land. Akosha's Eye, a Red Talon Theurge from her tribe's stronghold across the subcontinent in western India, took the early lead in direct action and in organizing others, both of the Beast Courts and outside. Her clashes with strange Wyrm creatures on both sides of the Gauntlet have left her a legacy of wounds which will not heal properly, and after two years of great physical exertion, she had to cut back and concentrate on training her successors. A Theurge from the small Bangladeshi population of Hakken, Syeda Strikes-the-Side, now takes the leadership role in the field, working with a dedicated and highly diversified little community. With varying mixtures of affection, admiration and disdain, observers sometimes call it the Court of the Great Hole.

Most of the worst contamination is now gone. The last hundred miles of the Ganges' riverbed as it flows into the sea remain heavily polluted, and crops can grow safely and healthily only in scattered pockets where the clean-up has been most successful. Elsewhere in the three-hundred-mile-wide war zone, life goes on at a reduced pace, with small regions of still-intense corruption. Monsters do still roam the land, but not with such strength as they once had and not in anything like their former numbers. Humans see the area as about what they'd expect a few years after a brief but nasty war. Garou and other shapeshifters see more. The Gauntlet remains low, not rising above 6 even in the midst of areas where it would normally rise much higher, and spiritual force leaks through… for good as well as ill, in some cases. There's a renewed quiet respect for spiritual realities among the human survivors of the nightmare war, a fresh appreciation for the complex needs of the land and its inhabitants. They seldom talk about it for fear of sounding superstitious, even to themselves, but *hengeyokai* who deal with humanity find their work a little easier these days.

Spirits gain 1 extra Rage when in the region between Calcutta and the Bangladeshi city of Dhaka,

and must make Gnosis checks against the local Gauntlet rating each night to avoid a brief fit of mad desire to slaughter anyone they encounter. (Sustaining a single Essence level of damage suffices to bring a spirit back to its senses, and the fit expires in any event at the next sunset or sunrise.) Ghosts suffer extra temptations from their dark sides, urges to slaughter and random acts of degradation, and the southwestern regional guards of the Middle Kingdom's underworld empire try to keep all ghosts well away. Slowly shrinking Umbral storms, now usually a mile or so across, sweep through the area at 1-3 miles per hour. They inflict one or two dice of aggravated damage along their periphery, more inside. The best observations suggest that pieces of the soul of the thing responsible for the Week of Nightmare power these storms, and that as its soul goes beyond the realms known to Gaia's children, the storms collapse in on themselves.

The Camp of Shiva

A radical faction among India's Garou take a stance related to that of the Ratkin: Garou defend the world at large, and have precisely no obligations to humanity whatsoever. Humans can get out of the way when Garou fight the world's enemies, or humans can die. Shivans don't much care which. Humanity at large knows that wolf attacks have become more frequent and more deadly in western India. Few humans know how lupus packs of Black Furies, Children of Gaia, Red Talons and Shadow Lords have led their wolf Kin into well-organized assaults on humanity, nor how sympathetic Glass Walkers and Silver Fangs have quietly interfered with human efforts at organizing a response.

Their critics among the Garou Nation and the Beast Courts say that Shiva the Destroyer is, as these wolves venerate him, merely another face of the Wyrm. Shivans say that their critics can no longer properly distinguish the world's real needs and are blinded by their own mythology. Every so often a very tense council moot occurs, so far without any satisfactory results. Recently the widely respected Theurge Akosha's Eye spoke critically of the Shivans for the first time, and this may rouse the Beast Courts into more coordinated action to rein in Shivan excesses. For their part, the Garou of India outside the Beast Courts worry that public pressure will favor the widespread slaughter of potentially dangerous wolves, thereby costing everyone precious Kinfolk.

The Stargazers

Most Garou know in a vague sort of way that the Stargazers lost their most prominent caern, felt abandoned by the Garou Nation and have collectively given their allegiance to the Beast Courts. It doesn't much matter to most Garou, so more recent news makes it way around slowly, if it all.

In principle, the elders of the great Beast Courts are glad to have the Stargazers among them. The practice is somewhat more complex. The Stargazers are held by most to be long-lost brothers who have lived along the barbarians for too long — welcome, and in many cases properly members (by the Courts' standards), but outsiders nonetheless. It will take generations to teach them right thought and right conduct and for these principles to become innate to the Stargazers as they are to the Hakken or Zhong Lung. Elders with an interest in teaching the newcomers flock to courts throughout western and southern China, running special academies with courses in history, tradition and the spiritual realities of the Middle Kingdom. Few Stargazers take much comfort in the thought that they get very special schools all their own; they regard themselves fully as mature and civilized as any of the Courts' established breeds, and more

Not all *hengeyokai* welcome the new arrivals with the same degree of enthusiasm. The Kitsune are very much in favor of having new and refreshing company among the Courts, strangers that they might dazzle with their cunning, beauty and repertoire and who in turn have valuable insights to offer about the Wyrm's activities on the fringes of the Middle Kingdom. The Tengu likewise find the Stargazers' experience very interesting, and very much deserving of remembrance and repetition. The Zhong Lung began with general indifference, but changed their mind when it became clear that many Stargazers would settle in the Yangtze Valley. Some of the newcomers immerse themselves in the struggle to save land and spirit from the disruption created by the Three Gorges Dam, and have earned the heartfelt gratitude of the Zhong Long.

The Hakken have little use for their cousins and would prefer to see the Stargazers kept on the margins of the Courts, if indeed they must belong at all; some argue that the Stargazers cannot be trusted to defend the Courts, considering their history with the Garou Nation. Since the Stargazers joined, Hakken have goaded each other into ever-greater displays of prowess and noble correctness, setting an impossible standard

for werewolves unfamiliar with Beast Court ways. Every court with Hakken elders hosts very complex games of intrigue behind the scenes, with efforts to maneuver the Stargazers into situations where they must become disgraced. The Hakken would be perfectly happy to see the Stargazers wander elsewhere, anywhere else but the Courts.

The Hakken's caution is doubled among the Khan, who have heard the ancient stories of other tribes of Bastet being slaughtered in the Wars of Rage. Though they are willing to accept new allies to fight alongside their own dwindling numbers, the tigers are a proud, proud race. Similarly, the Nagah have great reservations about the Stargazers, and most are unwilling to divulge their true nature around any Stargazer — after all, what if the werewolf returns to his old sept and starts gossiping? As for the Nezumi and the Same-Bito, both groups seem to think little of the change; after all, the Stargazers are unlikely to come assist or hinder them along their own battle fronts.

And the Kumo, it's said, await the chance to welcome their new neighbors… properly.

Chapter Two: The Battlefield

Once again I lost myself in the moment, in the everlasting now of my wolf-life. It's as though I live with a separate notion of time when I'm a wolf, in a perpetual present renewing itself constantly, and I have no concept of tomorrow or yesterday, no sense of a time other than the very night of my transformation. My whole memory is tied to the physical, the tangible objects of my desire. My only future is the hunger I feel that causes me to stalk.

— David Holland, *Murcheston: The Wolf's Tale*

The City: The Weaver's Playground

Let's be real. There are only so many games you can run in the great outdoors before your players want a taste of something just a touch more… sophisticated. Whatever their characters may feel, most players are from urban environments and so are most Storytellers. After all, it's difficult when living down on the farm twenty miles from anywhere else to get a weekly game going, and few of us make our homes in a national forest or pristine mountain setting. That's why there probably exist many more urban **Werewolf** games than might normally be the case. It's familiar and we all know what cities are like. Or do we?

From the average werewolf point of view, cities are crawling pustules of the Wyrm's corruption set within the labyrinthine soul-deadening webs of the Weaver. The Glass Walkers and Bone Gnawers remain notable exceptions to this viewpoint, of course, but the majority of Garou experience an unsettling cross between revulsion and morbid fascination when forced to function within the city.

So the question is as follows: How do you get this point across to the players and by extension, their characters? Unless the characters are based in a city setting, Storytellers have their work cut out for them adequately portraying the city and its denizens in such a fashion that you evoke the disgust-seduction reaction. Some of the ideas presented below can help bring home the alien allure of forbidden territory.

A Note for Our Urban Readers

We know, we know. The city isn't *that* bad, and not all Garou are as repelled by an urban environment as we may suggest from time to time. But, this being the World of Darkness, we do tend to accentuate the negative — the crime rates, the racial tensions, all the things that sell newspapers and "details at 11." Don't take it personally; it's not like a **Werewolf** chronicle is going to focus on the cleaner, safer areas of town, anyway. There's just not as much for Garou to *do* there, you know?

The City as Foreign Environment

We are never as comfortable in a strange place as we are at home or in a familiar setting. When introducing rural or wilderness-based Garou to the city (even if they were originally born and raised there), Storytellers need to stress the oddities found there. Things seem bigger, more threatening, grimier. Corporate behemoths, steel and mirrored glass skyscrapers seem to invite Garou to step sideways, but the Umbral landscape is draped with the Weaver's choking webs. The people all rush by, few paying attention to anyone else, pushing, their faces tight with stress, anger and hatred. Any greenery seems sickly, either caught within strangling webs of concrete and steel or formed of too-green, sterile plastic. The stench of oil, gasoline, garlic and onions, stale urine, spilled semen and unwashed bodies overlaid with cloying perfumes and effluvia should be enough to leave most Garou sick and shaking. Food and water reek of chemicals and taste of equal parts ashes and taint held at bay by unnatural preservatives. Horns blare, sirens shriek, radios and CD players compete incessantly to top one another with ever-louder offerings while people scream to be heard over the din. With their keen senses, all these sensations and the fast-paced motion occurring all around them can easily overwhelm Garou. And this is in the daytime! Nighttime brings its own horrors, with the never-lessening neon glare and the enmity of the Leeches on whose home territory the Garou now tread. And overhead, more garish lights redden the air and block the natural illumination of the moon and stars.

As you can see, description and word choice go a long way to establish how the characters would view the city. Although not everything about a city environment should be bad, the first impression a werewolf — a creature designed to defend Gaia at her most pristine — is probably going to have an overwhelmingly negative. Feel free to emphasize the most revolting, lurid and corrupt aspects of the urban environment. The residents seem both crazed and mysterious, obsessed with trivial things, charging around at top speed like frenzied herd animals. Think of times when you've been most uncomfortable somewhere and translate that into your descriptions of the city.

The City as Home

Some Garou who live in the city may, in fact, feel that it's as unnatural a place as their country cousins do. They've simply learned to adapt. They often find pockets of greenery or unspoiled areas to inhabit and prowl the streets in search of Wyrm-tainted prey. These werewolves may force themselves to remain in this alien environment in order to hunt down enemies or in an attempt to clean out the filth they find there. Some have bonded with packmates that cannot function well outside of an urban environment and choose to endure the city's discomforts rather than abandon a packmate. Many are doomed to failure as the tension of surviving and preserving the Veil in such a place gradually poisons their minds or souls, sending them into Harano or berserk rages. Some fall to the city's allure, losing themselves to the fascination of the ever-changing, throbbing patterns of life and death found there.

Others, such as the Glass Walkers and Bone Gnawers, actively embrace the urban environment, reveling in the technology or living on the leavings of others. No less devoted to Gaia, the urban Garou realize they can serve Her best within the very clutches of the Weaver's tapestry. Unlike the more extreme of their country cousins, urban Garou can see the value in some of the city's features.

Obviously, to those Garou that think of the city as "home," devastatingly gruesome descriptions of the horrors there seem woefully inappropriate. What country Garou find "deafening and overwhelming," urban werewolves may enjoy as "upbeat and exciting" or even "commonplace and dismissable." Many urban werewolves take a more human-friendly perspective, enjoying the spiritual warmth of a talented musician playing for an audience because he loves his music, or of a block where neighbors still treat each other like family. While rural werewolves may choke on noxious air or suffer from the reek of Wyrm and Weaver, city Garou have long been adjusted to it, associating it with the smell of home. City dwellers probably find the air in the country too complicated with the scents of unfamiliar animals or the aroma of farm fertilizers. Not that Garou frequenting cities dismiss or avoid areas where the Gauntlet is thinner and Gaia's natural features shine through. Most truly enjoy parks and small stands of woods. They simply don't feel Gaia's presence recede from urban settings so keenly as do others of their kind. Storytellers whose troupes are city-bred and associated can concentrate on good general descriptions of the setting without the need to characterize it as threatening, frightening and alien. That way, you can save those aspects for the truly bizarre and obviously sick, damaged or corrupted things such Garou may encounter.

The City as Hunting Ground

Of course, to some werewolves, the city is not a place to be shunned or cherished — it's simply a territory for the hunt. If your game emphasizes the horror aspects of roleplaying werewolves, you may want to portray the city as an urban labyrinth teeming with prey. Even if the characters limit their predation to "enemies of Gaia," the city environment offers a multitude of potential victims… ah, targets. Drug pushers, corrupt policemen, violent street gangs, sexual predators, paid leg-breakers, pimps and arms dealers and arsonists — the pack could hunt a different target each week and not see a fomor, vampire or Black Spiral Dancer for a year. (Of course, even though such restraint is feasible, it might not be preferable….)

Although werewolves are not as susceptible to their hunting instincts as vampires are, you still might want to borrow a few pages from the average **Vampire** chronicle and at least throw temptation in the players' paths once or twice. If a werewolf shifts into Crinos in the middle of a crowd, the stampede of panicked humans might tug at the lupine instinct to chase down fleeing prey. The thick smell of musk and sweat at a dance club might cause a hungry Garou's stomach to rumble; after all, instinct knows no Litany. And although wolves don't hunt for sport, people do — and for werewolves, being half human as they are, the appeal of stalking an enemy (or even a normal by-stander) through the hostile urban environment might strike a chord. Try teasing the characters' instincts just a bit; after all, they don't *have* to decide that their characters succumb, but one of the most powerful elements of a werewolf story is the idea of a beast in human form that classifies humans as potential prey, just like cattle or deer. It would be a shame to ignore such a vivid image, wouldn't it?

Descriptions of the City

Because some of your players' characters may come from rural areas and others from urban settings, it isn't always easy to give each an equally accurate picture of what he is encountering. Somehow, it just isn't fair to say to the rural crowd, "You enter a seething den of corruption, penetrating what seems a darkened bowel luridly lit with hellish red light. A reeking, squirming mass of writhing bodies gyrate wildly in the fetid, smoky air, emitting scents of rotting grain and desperate sexual longing," while turning to the urban crowd and saying, "It's a dance club." Just because they're

used to it doesn't mean the city characters should be shorted. They have the same senses as their country counterparts and since they aren't distracted by what's already familiar to them, they may actually pick up on *more* clues — or more subtle ones — than their shell-shocked cousins might. While the outsiders deal with the assault on their senses, trying to work out if everyone in the room is so tainted they all need to be exterminated, the locals may notice the actual fomori moving through the crowd and get first crack at them. In this case, you also wouldn't simply tell the characters, "You notice the fomori," but would perhaps say something like, "Your rural visitors seem overwhelmed by the sights and sounds common to the Furies, a local dance club notorious for the number of women who disappear after a night's dancing. You note — and dismiss — most of the couples and trios grinding together to the pulsating beat. What catches your eye against the backdrop of crimson-tinged lamps are the three shapes moving through the dancers like sharks circling blood-soaked prey."

Whatever description you give should be both evocative and factual at the same time. If you're simply reporting what's there, you're missing the opportunity to emphasize the mood you want or to subtly guide the characters in the direction you want them to go. It's the difference between telling them, "You look around at all the amazingly tall buildings and know you're in the Weaver's clutches." Instead, try to picture how such a setting would unnerve you if you'd never seen it and knew it was considered enemy territory and use that to color your description. Then you might explain, "Thousands of soulless eyes glare down on you from the glass and steel towers that surround you on all sides like a limitless maze. The Weaver's sterile children loom overhead and crowd around you as though awaiting the signal to grasp you in their gaping maws and suck you in."

The main trap many Storytellers fall into, however, is trying to tell the players how their characters are feeling rather than using emotionally charged words and letting them draw their own conclusions and decide how they feel for themselves. This is just as dangerous a practice in an urban environment, if not more so — after all, not all Garou hate and shun the "scabs," and you don't want to force that opinion on your players. If you're telling them, "You feel chilled by the sight of the mangled bodies," you're denying the characters the right to have the reaction they would normally experience. Maybe some of them aren't at all chilled by what they see. Though the circumstances leading up to the statement aren't explained, it's entirely possible that some of the characters feel relieved to have their worst fears confirmed. Others may be sad that they failed to prevent such a thing, while still others may be angry to have missed the battle. If you want your players (and the characters) to feel something, you're going to have to lure them into it through your presentation. You can't say, "You experience revulsion when..." but you can state, "The clotted mass blocking the sewer grating writhes with crawling maggots..." and let them decide if that disgusts them.

Write down a list of all the words you can think of related to things like horror, beauty, purity, corruption, death, nature, fear and anger. What about concepts like honor, loyalty, cowardice and love? Use the list in your portrayals to make things come alive in your players' imaginations. Consider how different types of words make you feel. Words carry emotional charges and can be used to convey negative or positive feelings and even create associative images in people's minds. Good Storytellers know how to find these kinds of words and use them when they craft a tale, sprinkling them through the telling at important junctures.

What sounds make you feel secure? Which ones make you feel nervous? Play to that in your game by using sound effects tapes or nature sounds CDs. Try jacking up the volume on really high energy music when you take the characters into a club and make the players try to talk over it. This is also a form of description. You should also remember that the characters' environment is more than visual. Dampen that Crinos' character's fur with depictions of pouring rain or a dank fog (we don't recommend actually dousing them with water; it tends to annoy the players). Talk up the scents or flavors the characters would notice. It's been said that just mentioning certain scents is enough to trigger sense memory of them and call forth memories of a time when a person experienced that aroma. When describing a place or thing, think what scents might be present and use them to heighten the reality of your narrative. If they touch something, is it smooth, corroded, slimy, cold? They may need to know that. Think about what colors or sounds make you feel safe or create nervousness or excitement. Look up odd, evocative words in a dictionary or thesaurus and sprinkle them into your descriptive portraits. While pictures can help, it's hard to find photos that depict exactly what you need. So mostly what your players have to depend on to envision the setting are your words. Don't waste them.

Setting as Background

Having primed you to choose each word with the care of a novelist, we now need to take a moment to say exactly the opposite. All the detail and evocative wordplay should be used only to highlight really important points, and a little goes a long way. You're here to involve the players in a shared story, after all, not to perform a tour de force of your pithy prose. If every step the characters take is described in lovingly crafted detail, the players will never get a word in, much less have anything to actually do or initiate. Give them an initial idea and reiterate the point from time to time. Save your best words for major encounters.

It's fine to let the setting become the background against which the story is played out. In real life, we pay attention to some things that we find important or that catch our attention while ignoring thousands of distractions every day. In Storytelling, we need to give the story room to move and evolve. We do that by taking shortcuts. Once you've established a general description that piques the players' interest, they'll continue playing to that until you give them something else to react to. It gives them roleplaying clues they can hang their hats on and players are great at running with whatever they're given and even taking it a few steps beyond the original. They'll fill in their own details. If, for example, you've shown them the tawdriness of the poorer sections of town, then simply say, "You move down the dank, garbage-strewn alleyway," they'll picture the urine patches, broken glass and used condoms themselves. Some may even ask for additional details, like inquiring if there's a dumpster there or if any homeless people use the space for sleeping. So feel free to do set-ups, then concentrate on the action. The background will take care of itself.

Setting as Metaphor

You're already trying to evoke a sense of mood with the words you use to describe the city, so you may as well use them to outline your theme too. Dozens of aspects of the city lend themselves to good themes for city-based stories anyway. Think of the decay most cities experience. Neighborhoods abandoned by all but junkies and whores, broken down stripped cars, graffiti smeared along the walls, jumbled and broken building ruins in overgrown, trash-littered lots all call to mind the decay and soul-sickness Garou can experience in response to the city's atmosphere or to an encounter gone very wrong. If your theme concerns truth versus appearance or the masks even other Garou wear, emphasizing the artificiality of the city can mirror this. Concrete and asphalt take the place of stone and dirt. Plants seen inside a restaurant through a window on closer inspection turn out to be replicas made of plastic. Thinking about running a story about the allure of the forbidden? What better place exists to portray that theme than the seductive, taboo city? If your troupe is into the truly dramatic or has gone through prior stories that have left them feeling wretched and empty inside, bring them to the city. Show them how the crowded space, lack of privacy and tedious, repetitive jobs most people endure combine with governmental control and the depersonalization and callous indifference that characterizes large urban areas speaks to the characters' feelings of loneliness and worthlessness. Consider how violent and perverse city life is. The Garou are used to being the baddest muthas around. Show them how relatively tame they are with gang warfare and terrorist bombings. Let them witness children murdering other children in a school or watch as a hate group burns a church or synagogue. Present them with a serial killer. At least the violence the Garou unleash seems to have a point and occurs to serve a good cause. Still, making the characters consider their use of excessive violence gets a boost from witnessing the insanity that prevails within the city.

Why Garou Loathe the City

To creatures who spend their time defending the natural world from the Weaver's and the Wyrm's incursions, the city seems like the most loathsome, soul-deadening cesspool imaginable. The Wyld occupies only a tiny fraction of this landscape. Most of Gaia's defenders find it difficult to think coherently or even breathe in this domain where the Weaver rules all except the places the Wyrm has wrapped in its coils of decay.

The Weaver's Power

Until they enter a large urban area, few Garou even realize the power the Weaver holds. They are so used to fighting the Wyrm and seeing its minions as their main foes that Garou hardly consider the Weaver's works as anything more than an inconvenience and a blot on Gaia's creation. Then they come to the city and encounter the endless, looming buildings. The sheer immensity of the skyscrapers, their overwhelming presence towering above the Garou, brings home the incredible power of the Weaver to such a degree that some werewolves surrender to despair. The Penumbra crawls with webs and Pattern Spiders. On both sides of the Gauntlet, the Weaver's works are inescapable. Even those Garou that don't feel cowed, experience a sense of uneasiness that leaves them vulnerable to making mistakes and overlooking vital clues. If nothing else, Garou hate to feel weak for any reason.

The Wyrm's Blight

Though the Weaver's strength is undeniable, the Wyrm occupies most areas of the city. From the filthiest slums to the most elaborate, yet corrupt, corporate headquarters, its coils writhe throughout the city. The Wyrm's taint lies on the myriad instances of degradation that characterize the city. Prostitution, the proliferation of child pornography, rape and torture-deaths are only the most obvious. Garou, attuned to the Wyrm's presence, feel it all around them, just as they do the Weaver.

Constantly surrounded by the enemy, with few places to which they can retreat for renewal of their energies, many werewolves go berserk. Even those Garou that usually have no major difficulties with humans begin seeing all city dwellers as creatures of the Wyrm. Junkies, winos and other down-and-out victims reek of the Wyrm's taint, while gangs, dealers, corrupt cops and hate-mongers spew forth the Wyrm's corrupt venom. These are the obvious targets of Garou Rage, but any human that seems even momentarily on the path toward corruption might find himself facing an enraged werewolf in Crinos. Though such unfortunates might suffer for only a moment, the werewolf's fall continues unabated. Many Garou, trapped within the city, still need an outlet for their natural tendency to hunt. Lacking other prey, they turn to hunting humans, with some of the more desperate even falling into the practice of feeding on humans, laying themselves open to becoming the creatures of the Wyrm they once battled. And once they've descended that far, making their way back is almost impossible — if they even care to try. Other Garou, encountering these deviants, must often destroy them, further weakening their race and leaving Gaia with ever fewer defenders.

Why Garou Love the City

Despite the stereotype of Garou as raging eco-warriors wholly devoted to defending the Wyld and Gaia's creation from the Wyrm's corruption and the Weaver's obsessive constructions, some werewolves fall in love with the city. Rather than seeing the city as a trap or a blight upon the land, these Garou think of it as either "home" or an unparalleled opportunity.

A Spiritual Connection

Glass Walkers and Bone Gnawers need no excuse to embrace the city. Some see the Weaver as their ally rather than a foe. They understand the Weaver's use as a weapon, using the technology available to them against their enemies. Garou who do so have some congress with city spirits and are able to work with and command the Weaver's minions. There also exists another spiritual link than many Glass Walkers feel. Because they feel such closeness with the spirit of the city, they act as its protector and are, in turn, protected by it to some degree. Some come to believe that the city is a more spiritual place than any wilderness area; after all, so many humans' hopes and dreams are tied up in a city that great things are just waiting to be born. To these Garou, city spirits may become pack totems. The Bone Gnawers in particular are keenly aware that the Wyld can be strong well within the most urban environments; some places are rich with the Wyld's energies, despite the concrete all around.

Abundant Opportunity

Some rural Garou find that the city fascinates them. The city's excitement, constant motion and sheer size combine to draw them in and set their hearts pounding. Some find that after their exposure to the city's rhythms, they can never be happy leaving it for good. Many rural Garou see the city as a curiosity. They study it as a way to learn about humans and the Weaver's works. Further, being in the city provides Garou with their best opportunity to encounter the enemy face-to-face on a daily basis. The main problem Garou must deal with in tracking their enemies and battling them is picking a target. So many possible targets abound, it's sometimes difficult for Garou to prioritize which to take out first.

Urban Patterns: The Penumbral Cityscape

When Garou enter the urban Umbra, they confront a strange landscape that assaults all their senses. The Umbra reflects the spiritual side of the physical world, and many cities suffer from a great spiritual sickness. As a Storyteller, you need to bring home to your Garou characters the fact that the urban spirit world reflects the unease and disease that lies close to the heart of most cities. Careful attention to description can recreate the sense of discomfort and alienation that marks the Umbrascape of the city for most Garou.

Getting There: Crossing the Gauntlet

The ease with which a Garou can enter the Umbra depends on the strength of the nearby Gauntlet. In general, stepping sideways poses greater problems in the city than in the wilderness due to the unnaturally high Gauntlet. In game terms, the Gauntlet within the urban environment presents characters with a higher difficulty to their dice rolls. Storytellers can bring this higher difficulty to life for their players by using evocative words and images.

For example, Cara's character Darien Farwalker, a Silent Strider Theurge, tries to step sideways in a darkened alleyway. Cara rolls Darien's Gnosis (four dice) against a difficulty of 8 and achieves only a single success. Her Storyteller makes this marginal success real through the following description.

Your body touches a sticky film dense with a griminess that clings to your skin and attempts to hold you in place. Thousands of tiny web-like strands grab hold of you and try to keep you from pushing your way past the barrier between the worlds. Finally, you emerge, soiled but intact, in the alley's Penumbral reflection.

Cara can feel her character's struggle just to do what would come so easily in a wilderness setting. The difference between the pristine Umbra near Darien's caern and the dismal spirit world of the city becomes more real and sets the tone for the encounters to come.

The Weaver's Domain: Urban Constructs

Once in the urban Umbra, Garou find themselves in the world as envisioned by the Weaver. Pattern spiders scurry busily from place to place on unfathomable errands. Everywhere, the hum of machine spirits provides a constant drone painful to the sensitive ears of Garou in Lupus or Crinos form. Dark shadowy forms indicate the presence of buildings, dead matter that intrudes on the spirit world. The colors that dominate the landscape tend toward neutral, dull tones — various shades of grays, dull greens, browns and blacks. Though found in nature, these colors in the cityscape seem like perversions of the hues found in trees, stones, sky and earth.

And don't forget the webs. The Weaver's mark blankets the urban Umbra like a cloying film of static. Besides providing a graphic visual reminder of the Weaver's presence, webs also possess tactile properties. Thick ropy webs act like heavy vines, tripping up Garou who try to pass them, lashing out to grab arms and legs. Thin cobwebs cling to the skin, clogging eyes and noses and providing a constant irritation. Storytellers may allow Garou to replenish some or all of their Rage from sheer frustration at dealing with the pervasive presence of the Weaver's toys and creations.

Where the Wyrm Turns: Urban Blight

The Weaver's cold immobility pales in comparison to the true horror that lies deep within the urban Umbra. Places exist within the city where the Weaver's sway has given way to the tyranny of the Wyrm. Crack houses, Pentex offices, factories that produce Wyrm-tainted goods, abandoned buildings that provide homes for clutches of fomori all fill the city with the stench of corruption.

Garou should feel the hopelessness and despair that emanate from these hubs of Wyrm activity. Describe the darkness and oiliness of Wyrm-taint, the fetid odors that cluster near these foul centers. Wyrm creatures and Banes haunt these places where the Wyrm's control has overtaken the Weaver's careful constructions.

Pockets of Hope: The Urban Wyld

Despite the sometimes-overwhelming presence of the Weaver and the Wyrm, the Wyld exists even in the most alienated of cities. Parks, nature preserves and zoos that make use of environmental habitats provide necessary relief for Garou. The Umbra in these places should reflect the relative freedom from restraint and corruption they offer in the physical world.

The Customary "Of the Wyrm" Warning

Players who rely too heavily on the Sense Wyrm Gift to discern between "evil and needs to be killed" and "not evil and should be protected" are SOL in the city. Wyrm-taint is a pervasive spiritual force, and it clings to victims as well as abusers, the violated as well as the violator. Although certainly not everyone in a city is going to smell of the Wyrm, using Sense Wyrm in any crowded area will probably register multiple instances of taint. In a nightclub, that taint might belong to a few frat boy date rapists, the bouncer who augments his bulk with Magadon "nutritional supplements," the young lady who unintentionally sipped a little vampire blood during her "hot date" last night, the drunk who's attracted the attention of a tiny Bane of despair, the habitual drug user on the dance floor, the "special" bottle of King spirits behind the bar, and yes — any fomori that might be present. How does the Garou discern which instances of taint are a direct threat, which need slightly less immediate attention, and which are probably beneath his notice?

He uses his head, like any werewolf who wants to survive in the city does.

Don't make it too easy on your players. Give them the evidence to make them realize that they need to pay attention to their surroundings, the better to recognize and prioritize the threats facing them. Show them that the city is the ideal environment for the spread of Wyrm-taint, and that they can't rely on Sense Wyrm alone for that very reason. The Garou didn't survive two Wars of Rage and millennia of battle against the Wyrm because they attacked everything that smelled funny — they survived because they're wolves, and wolves know how to *hunt*.

Use contrasting images to highlight the differences between the exotic urban Wyld pockets and the more familiar provinces of Wyrm and Weaver. Think of finding an oasis in the middle of a desert or coming upon a garden hidden behind a high wall. Describe the Umbra of a city park in terms that portray it as a respite from the onslaught of the Weaver and the Wyrm. Beleaguered Wyld spirits cluster in these havens, fearful of treading too far afield. Garou should find a few allies in these spirits.

Lupus in the City

Wolf-born Garou find cities almost unbearable. The most extreme of them refuse to enter cities of their own accord. Unfortunately, the war isn't going so well that a pack can always choose their battleground. Lupus have to make do in the city just as the other breeds do — but there they face problems all their own. Storytellers should not hesitate to use the plight of the lupus Garou to flesh out and add depth to her chronicle.

Animal Control

Lupus Garou find their birth forms the most comfortable ones to assume. Few lupus willingly spend a lot of time in human form. City life, however, does not favor animals that run around without human "owners." Lupus Garou on their own can attract unwanted attention from the authorities.

Dogcatchers, known in the modern world as animal control agents, answer reports that "wild animals" are roaming the streets. When Garou in Lupus or Crinos form confront fomori or Black Spiral Dancers or Leeches or any of the other antagonists, the ensuing conflict usually leaves behind a detritus of blood and pieces of flesh. To the unsuspecting mortals who come across the aftermath of such a battle, these effects indicate the presence of a pack of wild — probably rabid — dogs. Most Garou can elude normal procedures used by animal control officers. Tranquilizer darts respond to the ultra-healing properties of Garou, while most nets or traps provide only minimal obstacles to lupus Garou.

Not all animal control agencies serve the best interests of humanity. Pentex has trained groups of elite "dogcatchers" to look for the telltale signs of Garou interference. These experienced agents come equipped with silver bullets, dart guns loaded with Wyrm-toxins and other devices tailored to capturing Garou.

Zoos

Zoos provide both good and bad encounters for Garou. On one hand, they usually contain at least some natural-seeming vegetation and the best zoos — ones that employ habitat-based environments rather than cages — just might offer Garou a rare chance to replenish Gnosis, a commodity hard to come by in an urban setting. Occasionally, Garou end up as prisoners in zoos — and trouble usually comes calling shortly thereafter.

A few lupus Garou don't understand the purpose of zoos and see only places where creatures of the wild languish in captivity. Homid pack members sometimes find themselves forced to restrain their lupus companions' desires to liberate all the animals in the local zoo.

City Stories

Stories that take place in an urban environment deal with different manifestations of the eternal battle between the Garou and the enemies of Gaia. While Bone Gnawers and Glass Walkers may understand and appreciate the many faces of city life, most Garou find cities unpleasant at best, downright evil at worst. Storytellers can use this ambivalence to good purpose in designing stories set against the urban backdrop. From the initial culture shock as the Garou from the wilderness arrive in the big city to the eventual discovery of the true horror that lies concealed beneath the streets of the metropolis, city stories provide Storytellers and players with a constant barrage of challenges and sensations.

Country Cousins Come to Town

The hardest part of telling city stories may occur at the beginning. Why should your pack of Garou come to the city in the first place? Finding a convincing reason to bring the characters to town can provide a challenge for Storytellers. Depending on how long your want your characters to remain in the urban environment, you might want to consider some of the following reasons to bring wilderness-based Garou to the land of skyscrapers and cobwebs.

• **Born to Be Wild** — An inner city teenager has just undergone her First Change. The characters' pack receives a summons from a spirit, asking them to go into the city and bring out the new pup; or perhaps the cub is from a bloodline tied to a tribe with no members currently living in the city. Once the pack arrives, however, things may not be as simple as they seem.

• **Call for Help** — If the pack has contacts among the Glass Walkers or Bone Gnawers, one of these urban werewolves may request outside assistance for a problem they can't handle on their own. Of course, they probably don't admit the seriousness of the problem or that they have any trouble at all. They may simply call in a favor.

• **Following a Trail** — The pack defeats a group of Black Spiral Dancers but a few members escape to the city. The Garou must travel there to track their enemies down, where they discover that the Dancers have their own allies peculiar to the urban environment.

• **Jail Break** — The pack discovers that some lupus Kinfolk have fallen into the clutches of an urban exotic animal collector and must go to the city to locate and rescue them.

• **Umbral Accident** — The pack makes a mistake traveling through the Umbra and ends up deep within the center of the city instead of at a distant caern. This is particularly appropriate if the pack tries to travel on the Weaver's webs.

Surrounded on All Sides

Once the characters have arrived in the city, you need to immerse them immediately in the sights and sounds, scents and flavors of the urban environment.

Lupus or metis Garou, accustomed to living in the wilderness or within the confines of a rural sept, should experience the impact as a shock to their system. Describe the blare of automobile horns, the ceaseless background noise of traffic and machinery, the sight-obscuring haze from pollution, the reek of factory smoke and car fumes, the wail of sirens and the overpowering press of humans crowded together in an unhealthy land of narrow concrete streets and towering buildings. Homid Garou should also feel beset by these sensations, but they may also feel twinges of guilt for their human relatives' deeds, or a shade more sympathy for the humans in this oppressive environment.

City Encounters

Now that you've gotten your characters to town, what are you going to do with them? What sort of trouble lurks around the corner and down the alley or in the sewers waiting for your pack to stumble upon? The suggestions presented here should give you a starting place for your own ideas.

• **Affairs of the Heart** — One of your packmates falls in love with a city girl and asks you to accompany him on a journey to convince her to leave her urban life and move to a smaller town. When you arrive at her apartment, however, she is gone and the scent of blood is strong in the air.

• **Challenge** — In order to achieve a new Rank, one of your pack must enter the city and live there for a month. During that time he must achieve a series of tasks that include creating a fetish containing an urban spirit and discovering the location of a secret Black Spiral Dancer Hive.

• **Diplomacy, Garou Style** — A pack of Glass Walkers wish to end their long-standing feud with a rival group of Shadow Lords. Each pack claims the same territory within the city. Your pack, as outsiders, has the joyous task of arbitrating the peace talks and preventing them from devolving into carnage. In the meantime, a third party wants to see the feud continue.

• **Hunting for Cadavers** — A group of Red Talons has made a foray into the city, determined to rid it of all traces of vampiric influences. They have not returned and your pack has to find out why, even if it means talking to the walking corpses.

• **Renegade At Large** — A former member of your sept has succumbed to the wiles of a mage who has lured him to the city for her own unsavory purposes. Though the renegade Garou has abandoned his sacred duty and has received censure by the sept, you still need to prevent him from causing more harm by pursuing his foolhardy course of action. First, though, you need to find him.

• **Still Waters Run Deep** — Something is polluting the river that runs through your protected territory and the cause lies somewhere within the city. The pack must journey into town and try to discover who or what is fouling the waters and stop the problem at its root.

Wilderness and Werewolf

Werewolf is a game about man-beasts, half mortal and half nature spirit, created for the service and defense of Gaia, the spirit of the world and all that lives in it. Half animal, they are forever creatures of the wild, even when they walk the paved streets of the Wyrm-tainted modern world. Only the Weaver-trapped Glass Walkers are uncomfortable in the wilderness. Yet many **Werewolf** Storytellers will be considerably less comfortable with the topic than the characters they portray. This section is written to serve as an aid to Storytellers in setting stories in the wild. It covers primarily the sort of environments that **Werewolf** characters are likely to find themselves in — woods, mountains and the hot deserts of the American Southwest.

A Sad Disclaimer

This section of the **Werewolf Storytellers Handbook** is an incredibly abbreviated summary of actual useful information about wilderness survival, a sort of crash course in the topic so Storytellers won't be totally at sea trying to set a game in the wild. For those who hadn't already figured this out: Please, don't try to use this to really hack it in the wild. There are a number of excellent survival guides available (the United States Air Force survival manual is particularly good for covering all the basics in a simple and very readable fashion). Use one of them, or better yet, several different ones and a lot of advice from someone who has done it before. You can really die a miserable death trying to be Grizzly Adams if you don't know how.

More likely, you will make dozens of volunteers risk their lives and force the government to waste tens or hundreds of thousand of dollars to find you and retrieve your soaked, hungry self from the middle of nowhere. This disclaimer isn't just for your protection and watching the company's legal back — every time some clueless goof goes out to "rough it" and needs rescuing, it encourages legislatures and park services to consider regulations that restrict access to wilderness areas and limit the enjoyment of people who actually know what they're doing. Don't be That Guy.

The Truth About the Wild

The truth about the wilderness is this — life is hard. There is no "dying of old age" in the woods. If you are an animal, your life will almost certainly end either when something makes you too slow to run and a predator eats you, or you something makes you too slow to hunt and you starve. It could be arthritis, hunger, sickness, or plain old bad luck, but you get off your game and that's the end of it.

As a Storyteller, you have two major challenges. The first is to get the hostile nature of life in the wild across to players who probably don't know. It's not that you have a moral obligation to do this, but it's an absolute must if you want your players to take wilderness situations as serious challenges to their characters. If you can't get across the fact that the struggle for survival is quite pressing, and that failure has the direst of implications, you'll be hard-pressed to get the players involved enough to make it interesting.

Secondly, this is the view of the wilderness that Garou society not only accepts, but embraces. The Garou see nature not as a static backdrop, but as an ongoing system; a system of which they are a part, and whose hard edges are not meant to be conquered but critical features the Garou must maintain. The Litany embraces the ruthless nature of the world, urging the Garou not to burden the young with the toil of maintaining the old. Likewise, the Impergium was an intervention by the Garou as a people to prevent humanity's use of tools from allowing them to overturn the natural order. Even if the characters have a more modern, idealized version of nature, the vision of nature as a ruthless and entirely necessary struggle is the social context for a character raised as part of the Garou Nation.

What the Wilderness Offers

The wilderness is a perfectly viable venue for stories about the Garou — and given the tone and subject matter of **Werewolf**, it's probably best described as the primary venue. As a venue, it has strengths and weaknesses, and rewards certain approaches.

The wild's strength is the fact that it is a hard place, and one that rewards a certain skill set which most Garou possesses in abundance. Out in the woods or up in the mountains characters are cut off from all the benefits of a consumer society. They can only have what they can carry, and if they don't have it with them, there's no real running off to get it. Characters are also cut off from the benefits of the information society. Cellphone coverage is limited at best; data transfer rates are atrocious even when characters can achieve a link. There is no instantly calling in allies or looking up the answers on the Internet. The deck is

stacked for a Storyteller who wants to make the characters operate on wit and careful preplanning, and not on their ability to use their Resources to conjure up a solution to the problem.

At the same time, while they are cut off from technology, they are also in their natural environment. Though they may not have manmade tools, they have the tools that nature gave the wolf. Where mere humans are unable to find food, the characters can sniff out edibles or hunt as wolves. Where humans have to worry about exposure, the characters can endure even the harshest conditions, and find shelter much more easily. Where humans often find the wilderness tough going, characters can assume a fleet-footed quadruped shape with a body form that makes slipping through dense underbrush easy. This is one of the great strengths of the Garou. They have all the natural tools of a wild beast, and all the man-made wonders and intellect of the human race. This is your chance to highlight the true strength of the Garou's dual nature. Not only are they at home in the concrete jungle of human society, they are also at home in the nature's jungle as well. Take time in the wild to show how effective those natural tools are, and to highlight how the skinchanging of the Garou is more than just the ability to assume a war form, but also to gain an entirely new set of strengths that complement those of humanity. Confront the characters with challenges that would be impossible for normal humans, but that are a snap for them with their wolf forms. Have them pursued by trackers who *don't* have helicopters and thermal vision rigs and every other improbable piece of technology, and then let the characters run rings around their opponents.

Wilderness adventures also serve as an excellent opportunity for intra-pack bonding and roleplay. Characters in the wild will have only one another for company, and teamwork is critical to any sort of wilderness endeavor. People who take long backpacking trips together get to know each other very well indeed. Adventures like this are a time for forming and affirming bonds of friendship and respect among the members of the pack. Animosities may be laid to rest or fanned to open hostilities, and care and respect can blossom into forbidden love.

Storytellers who have been having problems getting members of the pack to roleplay can easily set up situations where the characters are compelled to interact. Face the characters with a challenge in one scene, and then set the next scene as the characters sitting around their camp or temporary den talking about the situation they just overcame. You can even just take two characters and say that, while performing a task together, they have a conversation, and then turn to the players and ask then what they're saying. If your players are used to roleplaying, they probably take to it well, but you can also use this to provoke less-experienced players to roleplay. Set up the circumstances, let them perform a few acts to lead into the conversation, and then indicate they should talk. If it works, you'll get one-on-one interaction. Don't pressure the players beyond the necessary nudges — if the conversation isn't going to catch, it isn't going to catch, and sometimes a halting conversation is the kind that really should occur. Keep alert, and when it ends, cut gracefully to the next scene. As a bit of additional advice, don't make it so that Bob and Joe talk, then Joe and Jane talk, then Jane and Bob talk. That's patently contrived and feels more like a scheduled rap session than genuine roleplaying. It's okay to have everyone interact, but try to make it seem naturalistic and break it up with action or group roleplay.

The bonding is equally easy to inject — there's a reason that wilderness experiences are used as a way to teach troubled youths teamwork. There are countless situations where several characters will need to work together. Anything from clearing a rockslide to climbing a cliff to fording a river. Even dividing up and accomplishing the day-to-day chores is accomplishment when you're living out of a rucksack. Present problems that the characters can't solve alone, force the players to devise solutions *in character*, and then let them carry the plan out. Use all of the crazy "group effort" and "helpers" rules from the Systems chapter of the **Werewolf** book, and genuinely make overcoming the obstacle as a group into an important and rewarding challenge in the game. Make the characters work and plan together, and they'll soon develop the sort of bonds that are supposed to typify Garou packs.

Wilderness Concerns

At the same time that the wilderness can provide lots of story hooks and has strengths that a Storyteller can exploit, there are also weaknesses to a story set here, and pitfalls worth avoiding.

The first obstacle is that unless you've done it a lot before, you're probably not experienced with describing wilderness situations in an exciting fashion. Before you run your wilderness epic, practice a little ahead of time, or run a number of short one-or-two scene outdoor situations to get the feel of it. Try to learn to describe static challenges in an exciting way. Read some books on wilderness survival to learn how it's done. Scout locations — go out in the woods or up into the mountains and look at the kind of potential obstacles a party might face. How could they bypass them? What are some valid ways to attack the obstacle and overcome it? What you're looking to do is give the situation a naturalistic feel. If you don't describe it well and make it feel like a genuine obstacle or a real problem, it's really just going to be you calling for a Dexterity + Athletics or a Wits + Survival roll, and the players trying to roll enough successes. Don't be afraid to use the dice, but rolls should be used to determine if the characters are able to carry out the solution they devise, rather than being something you determine ahead of time. If it's just a matter of making a bunch of predetermined Ability tests, the players could have stayed at home, because you could run the adventure with just some dice and the character sheets.

Also, one of the most effective things about the wilderness as a setting is that when the environment becomes an enemy, it is genuinely terrifying. It is implacable. It doesn't even realize or care that it's killing you. But at the same time, people don't come to roleplaying games to be killed by impersonal forces beyond their ability to influence or control. In trying to emphasize the harsh, uncaring side of the wilderness, it's very easy to accidentally create an adventure that puts the characters in an unsurvivable situation to demonstrate that they cannot conquer Mother Nature. That's really not the point, that's just a more elaborate version of the character opening up their coat closet and finding a Nexus Crawler waiting for them. Even if the situation is designed to beat up the characters, make it something more than just a beating. Let them learn or increase Abilities, or gain a spirit ally, or get something out of the experience. Otherwise you're just brutalizing the characters under the guise of adding verisimilitude.

Finally, keep in mind that that one of the defining aspects of being out in the wild is the inability to get to anywhere else quickly. This can prove quite troublesome if the adventure you planned turns out to be duller than you expected, or the characters are clearly not up for quality time with the snakes and the bugs. Try to think out ahead of time how long (in terms of session time) the wilderness trek you're planning on will take. It's a rare gaming group that wants to spend their third straight game session walking through foothills of the Rockies. Get a sense of how long your group can tolerate fairly mundane challenges. If that's an hour, then make sure the wilderness excursions don't last much longer than that. If it's one or two sessions, then set that as your upper limit. Be sure to underplan a little, because things will naturally take longer than you expect, and you don't want to have everyone coming back to the next session for "just one more hour of slogging through the bayou!" Also, if you're pre-planning events, make a list of what encounters or events are must-happens, and which are luxuries, that way if things seem to be dragging, you can know what to cut out and what to keep when you're speeding things along.

Wilderness Stories

The great outdoors is a natural setting for many **Werewolf** stories — but just what kinds of stories? The list below is a beginning, not a comprehensive catalog of possibilities. Use it as a catalyst and jumping-off point for your own work.

Spiritual Retreat

While the wilderness of the World of Darkness is under attack and tainted in many places by the corruption of the Wyrm, it is also a holy place, a place of primal power far greater and far older than the Garou.

It is the body of Gaia and the face of the world, and werewolves are its creatures. In these increasingly dark and tumultuous times, they must often find it necessary to seek shelter and solace in the arms of the great forests and mountains that have been haunts of their animal cousins since the dawn of time. Not all gatherings must be part of the sept's caern rituals. Alone in the wild or running with their pack, they can reflect on what it is that they're defending, regaining their sense of purpose and renewing their ties to the land.

Garou may go into the wild simply to rest from their warring. They may go to find a wolf mate. They and their packmates may stake out a territory and defend it as their own — those Garou whose mortal lives force them toward a life of rootless travel probably find this to be immensely satisfying. The skin-changers may need to seek out the spirit guardians of their Gifts, or to contact spirits strange to them and find new Gifts for their people, or to seek out a totem for their pack.

As a Storyteller, such adventures can provide you with the same break the characters seek — a chance to get away from ongoing continuity and return refreshed, and to challenge the characters with simple situations, or just allow them all to roleplay freely.

Parables and Homilies

And it may be that nature presents the Garou with wisdom unsought. When in the wild, the wolf-men are open to spiritual influences, and those influences may well speak to them uninvited. A character in the wild may learn lessons from nature as nature intends, not as they wish.

Doubtless, many of these lessons are simple ones, and really no more than the reassuring touch of the wild, encouraging the Garou to breed while they may, to accept a death in stride with the natural order, and to bond with their packmates. Yet others may be more complex — don't be afraid to make the wilderness a mystical place. They may be obvious messages; a stream speaking directly to a Theurge with Pulse of the Invisible, and telling her the identities of those beings that have polluted the stream, or a forest conspiring to arrange for a pack to come upon something that will teach a lesson. They could be more elaborate, though. Many spirits can provoke visions — who is to say that a werewolf's time in the wilderness is entirely lucid, especially if he willingly throws himself into Nature's embrace. It could be that a pack experiences genuine religious visions at the behest of nature and ancestor-spirits, or their totem. The characters may gain great insight from witnessing natural events. Like a martial arts master learning new forms, the Garou may come to understand new strategies from watching a fox stalk a pheasant, but the lessons could be far deeper than just fighting styles. What if a character looks back on a

<hr />

Wolf Versus Man

Werewolf poses an interesting dilemma to Garou characters by forcing them to make certain critical decisions about how they'll be using their shapeshifting abilities in advance of any wilderness travel. The very small number of items that can be dedicated by a given Garou mean that if the werewolves plan on using their Lupus form to cover ground quickly, they are very limited in the amount of equipment they can carry with them. Even if they employ the sort of packs designed let dogs haul their own food on camping trips, modified so that they can be removed by other Lupus-form Garou, the amount of supplies they'll be hauling is minimal. They'll probably have little more than a few days worth of wolf food, survival necessities like a knife, compass / GPS, a cell phone, map, some plastic tarping and stakes to form a temporary den, and a set of clothes so that when the Garou must assume Homid form, they needn't risk hypothermia.

By the same token, if the Garou plan to take advantage of the Homid form with its large carrying capacity and tool-use, then their ability to use the Lupus form to cover ground is severely limited. While the wolf-shape is still useful for scouting or escape, the burden of human gear essentially locks the werewolf into Homid form, with its plodding pace and inability to slip efficiently through undergrowth.

Obviously, there are ways to bypass this incompatibility — the characters can cache supplies themselves or have others cache the supplies. They can abandon their camp and move as Lupus, scavenging as they go. Whatever the solution is, it requires planning, just like all successful wilderness treks.

sojourn in the wild and finds that the problems he faced were exactly like the ones he confronts in his life now?

As a Storyteller, this is a chance to have spirits who would otherwise be setting elements and plot or clue dispensing machines become active parts of your game. Those ancestor-spirits are no longer just a mechanical edge; now they're putting the character through her paces. The spirit patrons of the characters' caern aren't just potential totems, but active entities who touch the characters' lives and influence their doings. It's also a chance for you to directly steer the game through the intervention of your Storyteller characters. If you see the characters heading toward a fight they can't win or just falling off the tracks of smart thinking, it's a chance to give them a message without breaking the illusion of free will by taking them aside and telling them what's best.

Infiltration and Evasion

It isn't true that we've made the world a smaller place. We've just made it very easy to move through some extremely narrow corridors. The vast majority of North America is sparsely populated or totally unpopulated. While a permanent residence would probably attract notice given time, the wilderness provides an excellent highway for small groups of individuals who need to avoid detection. While the going is painfully slow compared to cars or planes, and in most places you can't travel a day without crossing a road, a group traveling lightly and mindful of covering their tracks can cross long distances

without any real fear of detection. This can be quite useful for the Garou, who may often be avoiding human authorities in order to preserve the Veil, or approaching an area where anyone or everyone they meet may be able to detect their true nature.

For Storytellers, a travel story — particularly a tense one as the characters try to evade pursuit or spend weeks sneaking close to a heavily guarded installation — can be an excellent interlude in a chronicle. In this role, they don't just serve as roleplaying interludes and reinforce the game's wilderness overtones. Infiltration can also serve as a tense lead-up to a dramatic confrontation or as a second climax to an assault or espionage mission, as characters who penetrated a sophisticated defense network must evade pursuit to make a successful getaway.

Survival Situations

Finally, characters can be tossed into a situation where they're genuinely unprepared. They may be Kinfolk or even Garou in some sort of traumatic situation like an airplane crash, a moon bridge mishap or an attack on an isolated caern that sets them to unprepared flight. Whatever the case, the characters are left with only their wits and what they can gather. This probably isn't much of a threat for the Garou, but it can be, if the conditions are harsh or the pack is largely hopeless city-slickers. This is a very legitimate challenge for Kinfolk, and can win them a lot of positive prestige among their skin-changing relatives, even serving as a chance to try out or learn Gifts without being totally overshadowed by the full-blooded members of the family.

As a Storyteller, this is a chance to put the characters in a bind and force some quick thinking. They probably don't have all their weapons and gear, and they're probably off their home turf. The characters may be wounded or on the run, and Glass Walkers and other urban characters will probably be in an alien world. Storytellers that feel the pack is drifting into too much of an urban/civilized mode might want to throw such a story at the characters purely for shock value. While qualified for the challenge, are the Garou really at home? Are they panicking just because they're off the asphalt? It might not be outside the realm of possibility for a pack's totem or ancestors to arrange such an event just to get the message across. If the characters are smart and adaptable, they'll live and learn, if the characters are unwise and foolish, they'll probably die, and that's one of the lessons the wild teaches best.

Wilderness Survival

This section deals with the necessities of wilderness survival, and provides a brief overview of how exactly you hack it in the wild. It is general, but should serve to give Storytellers with no woodsy background a fairly good understanding of the mechanisms involved. Although some of this could technically be construed as "player information," ultimately it's most important for you as Storyteller to know the important parts of wilderness survival, so that you can relate important information to the players that require it — or use the ignorance of an over-citified pack against them. After all, it's much more involving for the players to learn these techniques over the course of a dramatic story than to read it out of a book.

Plan

Planning is the number one survival rule. Any character going into a situation where she and her companions are on their own had better know exactly what the hell she's doing, and she should know ahead of time. A wise character preparing for a wilderness journey will worked out every day's walk ahead of time with a map and an almanac, using the map to find good campsites and estimate travel times, and the almanac to determine the start and stop times for the day's travel. The stop time is critical — it is very difficult to set up a camp after sundown. Without the ambient skyglow from streetlights, it gets *very* dark at night. Characters trying to set up a tent and cook a meal in the pitch dark will quickly find it both exhausting and prone to damaging valuable gear. When planning travel times, wise characters will be sure to allow

generous margins for a member of the traveling party turning an ankle, or for the group to find that the trail was washed out a year ago or has become totally overgrown with blackberry bushes.

Meals should be planned ahead of time, with attention paid to making sure everyone in the traveling party gets the right number of calories for the sort of heavy exercise wilderness travel entails. Water is also a major planning issue. It is heavy, bulky and indispensable. These facts combine to force traveling parties to restock their water supplies frequently; every 2 to 3 days at the most. In temperate or tropical areas, this generally isn't a problem — it's hard to walk a full day without hitting some sort of running water. In arid regions, however, the location of water typically dictates the course of travel.

Characters should also plan for what to do in case of injury, including a well-stocked first aid kid and all the gear necessary for a travois to haul an injured member of the group out. Everyone should know how to do all of the important first aid tasks — it's no good to have the one person who's a walking medical dictionary get knocked unconscious by a falling rock. The first aid kit can obviously be dispensed with when the traveling party is all Garou, since between Mother's Touch and regeneration there's not much that can keep a werewolf down, but it's still critical if there are Kinfolk along, or the Garou wish to present a façade of normalcy.

Characters' plans should include an objective — aimless wandering without worrying about what comes next is a luxury that our modern society affords us. Once you leave the land of convenience stores and shopping malls, you have to keep your goals in mind and try to marshal your resources toward them, because those resources are limited. If you don't spend them well, they'll be gone and you'll have nothing to show for it, and in the wilderness "nothing" means you don't have any food to eat or a place to sleep. Characters who are traveling toward a destination have reaching the destination as their ultimate goal, and all their plans must focus on that. Characters stranded in the wilderness due to accident or other happenstance have their return to civilization as a goal. Even characters who have gone out into the wilderness to live as hermits have a goal; to achieve a sustainable state of living, where they're gathering at least enough food to balance the amount they eat, while still having enough time to maintain their dwelling and advance any other personal projects.

Avoid Cold

The second most important rule of survival, beyond planning, is to control your temperature. The human and lupine bodies are both immensely flexible machines, capable of regulating their internal temperature to allow them to survive in a broad range of conditions. However, the human body is mostly suited to fairly warm temperature — anything below 60 degrees Fahrenheit is uncomfortable without clothing, and temperatures below that can cause hypothermia. In hypothermia, the body loses heat faster than it can generate it, until its core temperature drops below that at which the human body can function. For a naked human, hypothermia can be a risk at even 50°F. Hypothermia is characterized by severe shivering, replaced by a sense of warmness and physical weakness as the body fails. If it remains uncorrected, the victim will eventually go into shock and freeze to death.

The remedies to this hazard are simple. First, the character can move vigorously, which causes his muscles to generate heat and warm his body. This is only effective at relatively warm temperatures, or in conjunction with other forms of protection. Second, the character can remove himself from the wind. As a character radiates heat, it warms the air around him. Since the amount of heat transferred between two bodies depends on their relative temperature, this slows the rate at which the character's body loses heat. Wind constantly pushes new air against the character, causing his body to lose heat quickly. This makes it seem much colder than it is, and high winds plus subfreezing temperatures are a combination that can rapidly sap the strength of characters exposed to them. Characters trapped in high, cold winds should seek the shelter of any sort of structure that can function as a windbreak. Huddling also works, and several characters huddled close together can stay warm by minimizing the amount of surface area any given character exposes to the cold.

Third, the character can surround himself with some sort of material that absorbs his radiated heat and retains it, rather than letting it flee into the surrounding air — winter clothing, for example. However, arctic weather gear is not the only effective form of protection. Anything that breaks the wind and traps air helps — pine boughs covered by a tarp, for example, will provide some protection. Snow is an excellent insulator, and the best thing a character trapped in a snowstorm can do is burrow her way into a snowbank. This shuts out the wind, and the burrow temperature can go as high as 50 degrees Fahrenheit, allowing even poorly protected characters to stay warm.

If the pack's cold weather gear is inadequate for the temperature, and they will not go to ground or cannot go to ground (for example, if they are stranded on open ice) then they will almost certainly die of hypothermia. This will fell even the Garou unless they have Gifts to protect them from the cold. Their astonishing powers of regeneration cannot protect them against the chilling effects of winter. (In game terms, Garou

> ## The Wolf in Winter
>
> Wolves have fur coats, and are well protected against winter cold. Arctic wolves can survive in temperatures as low as -70 degrees Fahrenheit, though they are a specialized breed. Hypothermia isn't much of a concern for most characters in Crinos, Hispo or Lupus until about -20° to -30° F, at which point most wolves will start thinking about huddling in the snow somewhere. The weakness of a wolf's insulation is that, like goose down, it relies on its fluff to trap air. If the wolf becomes wet, the insulating properties of its fur are greatly diminished. A soaked wolf in sub-freezing temperatures is an animal in dire straits.

who do nothing to defend themselves against the elements start taking aggravated damage when the cold gets too intense. This damage should accrue slowly enough that the players feel that werewolves are still better off that humans would be in such a situation, but quickly enough that freezing to death remains a real danger; a health level of damage every couple of hours spent without sufficient warmth should suffice.)

Characters in cold conditions also have a second danger to face — frostbite. While hypothermia comes from the character's core body temperature dropping below safe levels, frostbite comes from the temperature of the surface tissue dropping so low that actual damage occurs. This normally occurs in the farthest reaches of the characters' extremities first: fingers, toes and the like. They're the farthest away from the character's body core, and their small size means there's a great deal of radiating surface for only a small amount of tissue.

However, this is not the only place that frostbite can occur, and characters exposed to high winds can suffer frostbite effects all over their face and other exposed skin areas. In its first stages, frostbite is simply numbness and a sensation of cold. As it progresses, permanent circulatory and neurological damage accrues — the flesh will never again have full sensation or proper blood flow. Very severe cases involve tissue necrosis — the affected flesh simply dies, and will rot off, with all the associated health complications. While frostbite is obviously a minor concern for Garou, it is a serious danger for Kinfolk and other normal mortals exposed to cold.

Avoid Heat

Heat is not as great a threat to the human organism as cold. The human body has a phenomenal cooling system that, if provided with enough water, can sustain it in the hottest of conditions — unsurprising in a species that evolved near equatorial Africa. The body secretes water, which evaporates, transferring heat into the surrounding air more efficiently than simple radiation. Other than the very old, the very young, the sick and those with breathing ailments, very few humans need fear death from heat exposure. Nevertheless, heat-related equivalents to both hypothermia and frostbite do exist.

The equivalent to hypothermia is hyperthermia, or heat prostration. Heat prostration occurs when the character's core body temperature climbs above the level at which her internal organs function properly. It is most common when the character has no water to drink and thus stops sweating, but can also occur when individuals — especially individuals not acclimatized to hot conditions — exercise in hot weather and direct sunlight for long periods. Hyperthermia is very dangerous because a stubborn individual can often remain upright until after the point where she cannot naturally recover from the condition.

The first stage of hyperthermia is common called heat exhaustion, and is typified by a feeling of nausea, light-headedness and by clammy skin. The victim will, at this phase, generally improve if moved into the shade and given water, preferably water lightly laced with salt and other electrolytes. In more extreme cases, commonly called heat stroke, the skin becomes dry, and the victim will generally not recover naturally, though Mother's Touch will probably improve him, as will natural regeneration if he's removed from the light and allowed to rest.

Normal mortals are generally treated with a warm water bath and a saline IV. Victims that are not treated properly can die from brain or organ damage, and many survivors of extreme cases suffer kidney and other renal system problems afterwards. While werewolves are resilient enough to recover from the systemic damage, they are still vulnerable to overheating, fainting and even death if they abuse themselves enough that they become dehydrated and fall unconscious of sun poisoning too far from water.

Sunburn is the heat-related equivalent of frostbite. This occurs when the skin is exposed to direct sunlight for extended periods. Radiation penetrates the dermis and damages the tissue beneath it. Depending on the severity, sunburn can range from mildly uncomfortable to life threatening; although it occurs slowly, sunburn is an actual burn.

All humans naturally secrete a skin pigment with radiation-blocking properties — melanin — in varying amounts based on the area of the character's ethnic extraction. Some solar radiation exposure is catalytic for a healthy metabolic process, so human groups that have adapted to cold, dark environments often have relatively low level of melanin compared to the norm for the species. These subgroups — from whom many Garou are descended — are most susceptible to sunburn. All humans will secrete additional melanin to

block radiation as an automatic reflex if they're exposed to sunlight, but this process is slow and cannot prevent immediate burns. Contrary to popular mythology, however dark your skin is, you can still suffer sunburn — the threshold for injury is simply higher. Characters in sunny conditions should cover as much of their skin as possible. If disease-carrying insects are not a threat, light-skinned characters in very hot conditions will probably want to adopt a program of progressive exposure to darken their skin and allow them to minimize the amount of clothing they wear, since bare skin is far more efficient at radiating heat than skin covered in cloth. Garou that are severely sunburnt can of course simply regenerate the damage.

Protection from heat is generally easier than protection from cold. The characters should avoid direct sunlight, avoid heavy exercise during the hottest hours of the day (typically the period from 1 p.m. to 4 p.m.) and drink plenty of water. It is only when they begin to violate these rules that they run a serious risk of injury from heat — the human body is just that good at dissipating heat. Unless the characters ignore the basic rules of hot weather survival or end up stranded on the floor of Death Valley or some other flat, shadeless plain in high summer, survival is probably assured.

Stay Dry

It is critical that characters in the wild attempt to avoid getting wet, at least in the sort of cool-to-cold terrain that wolves favor. This seems like a relatively minor matter, but it's actually quite important. A wet person is effectively covered in a torrent of icy-cold sweat, leaching their heat away. Even after the immersion is over, wet clothing transmits heat efficiently, speeding the onset of hypothermia. A character caught in driving cold rain may succumb to acute hypothermia, or be so weakened by the experience she develops pneumonia or some other opportunistic ailment. The obvious solution is to find shelter from rain, particularly cold blustery rain. Characters that have been soaked should attempt to dry off and dry their clothes as best as possible as soon as possible.

The second reason to stay dry is trench foot. Human tissue isn't entirely waterproof — when you expose it to water long enough, it softens, bloats, and eventually splits. Obviously, boots are the worst culprits for retaining water (hence the ailment's name) but damp cloth rubbing against any tissue can cause very serious chafing injuries.

In the case of true immersion, however, the foot turns blue and becomes covered with blood blisters, all accompanied by agonizing pain. If treated promptly, it can generally be reduced, though the character will certainly suffer a loss of feeling and periodic pain in the

The Wolf in Summer

In hot weather, all the phenomenal insulating properties of the wolf's coat become something of a liability. It only sweats from its nose, tongue and toepads, and while the rest of the beast's body can radiate heat, it is insulated by fur and doesn't have sweat glands to raise the efficiency of radiation. This is not so much a survival hazard as a major limitation on the animal's activity. While very hot temperatures are not incredibly healthy for wolves, they are not directly fatal so long as the wolf has shade and water. However, if the animal indulges in any sort of strenuous activity for any period of time, it risks hyperthermia, as its body will be producing heat as quickly as or more quickly than an active human, and has a far less efficient system for dumping it. Storytellers may wish to begin imposing penalties on Hispo or Lupus-form characters in extremely hot conditions after as little as ten turns of activity.

The Crinos form is slightly better adapted, thanks to its "war form" aspect. A werewolf fighting in Crinos can generate a lot of heat, between the furnace of Rage and the incredible metabolic furnace that drives regeneration. The Crinos form is thus equipped with more sweat glands than usual (though not quite as many as the human body), allowing it to vent off excess heat during or after an intense fight. An exhausted Crinos might be in a slight lather, like an overworked horse — which is good for short-term cooling, but not so great for fighting dehydration.

extremity. This is not unlike the tissue damage caused by frostbite, and, as with severe frostbite, there is a strong tendency toward necrosis. The dead flesh often becomes gangrenous, necessitating amputation.

Trench foot is a terrible ailment, and very easy to catch if you don't take care of your feet — trench foot was responsible for over 20% of medical evacuations in World War 2. The solution is to change your socks several times a day. Characters unable to do so should dry the socks and shoes they have thoroughly after an immersion. Characters who do not do so will develop trench foot, and possibly lose their feet. While a Garou or Fera could heal the damage after the episode has passed, it is unlikely that she can prevent the bloating itself.

Drink Water

Characters may wish to avoid getting wet, but they certainly don't want to avoid water. As mentioned above, water is both heavy and bulky. Water weighs about eight-and-a-half pounds per gallon, and is incompressible — you can't easily make it occupy less volume by pressurizing it. Unfortunately, it's also the supply characters can never

afford to run out of. An exercising character can use over a gallon of water a day, and that includes characters exercising in cold weather, and going without water for more than two or at most three days is quite likely to be fatal. People have lived for longer, but there's usually renal system damage, and brain damage and other organ damage is also quite possible.

Normally, water is obtained from surface sources — streams, ponds and rivers. Gathering it is as simple as making sure there isn't a dead fish floating nearby and filling your container up. Surface water quality is a critical issue — just because it looks clean doesn't mean it's safe to drink. Much of the water in the wild is contaminated with natural parasites or contains minerals poisonous to humans. Waterborne parasites are nothing to laugh at — they can cause anything from diarrhea (with the consequent dehydration and waste of calories from food the character is unable to digest) to serious long-term organ damage. This is probably nothing that Mother's Touch can't cure, but it's still a serious inconvenience. In general, running water is safer to drink than still water, but you still shouldn't drink it unless you have no choice.

There are excellent filters and purification kits available that make drinking wild water safe, and they're quite light. Characters should be aware that modern water filters become ineffective after straining a certain amount of water, and bring extra filters with them. Characters without such advanced kits will have to rely on more traditional methods. Parasites are susceptible to boiling, but water must be distilled to remove its mineral content. Since stills of any size are bulky, most mineral-contaminated water is effectively undrinkable. Characters should also be aware that commercial filters, like those sold in supermarkets to "purify" residential water, are typically geared toward removing minerals that cause water to taste odd, and not actually purifying it — they are not necessarily useful against parasites.

Characters in cold areas may have to melt snow or ice for water. Snow is not good for you to eat in any kind of volume — you really must melt it first. Characters in arid areas may not be able to find surface water of any sort. It may be possible to dig for water in "creases" in the terrain (where steep slopes meet a flat surface) and, of course, the presence of plant growth indicates water. Likewise, seasonal streambeds often carry a year-round sluggish current through the sediment. Characters in arid situations will normally require a solar still to gather enough water to survive. Such a still is little more than a fairly large hole — preferably one dug in damp earth. The hole is filled with chopped vegetation if any is available (the roots of desert plants work best), and a bowl, cup or other wide-mouthed container is set at the bottom. The mouth of the hole is covered with a sheet of polyethylene or other rugged, flexible plastic, with a weight in the center to tent it downward to form a downward-pointing cone whose point is directly over the cup at the center of the hole. The sun shines on the still, heating the air inside up and causing moisture to evaporate from the moist earth and chopped roots. The water condenses on the plastic, beads into droplets, flows down the sloped polyethylene, and drips off the point of the cone and into the cup. Every morning, after the dew has formed for the day, the character simply lifts the edge of the polyethylene and gets the water out. If there's a plastic hose available, the character can even slide it down into the container when they're constructing the still, and drink from the accumulated water whenever he's thirsty. It's hard to get enough water to drink from just one still, but several can sustain a character and refill his canteens over the course of several days.

Eat Food

There are no grocery stores in the middle of the wilderness, so anything the characters need to eat must come along with them, or be picked up from the terrain they cross. Foraging for food is generally slower, but it's fairly certain and you don't need to carry food that you gather as you go. There are very few places in North America, other than above the snowline and perhaps the deserts of the American Southwest, where a determined individual can't find enough food to eat. Note the use of "determined" — this word implies a willingness to eat mice, bugs and wild plant food including soft tree bark and possibly even grass. A character that will only eat large, obvious food items can quite easily starve. Training and a handbook or good knowledge of the area in which the characters are trying to subsist is a must for foragers. Usually only certain parts of various different plants are edible, and they must often be prepared certain ways.

Most foraged food will consist of wild plant food and small animals trapped with snares. Hunting larger animals, for people traveling through the wild to get to a destination, is a bit problematic. First, it typically requires guns and bows. Local law enforcement is quite alert for this sort of thing, not because they worry about mad snipers — most rural law enforcement professionals aren't from a culture that assumes everyone with a gun must be a violent lunatic. They're alert because they're watching for people doing exactly what the characters are up to — poaching game. Hunting out of season is illegal, and every state has full-time employees, called game wardens, who patrol for illegal hunting. While characters in survival situations obviously won't care, characters trying to use the woods to get

Survival Tips

The body of this section contains the primary keys to survival. What follow are some other helpful tips that didn't fit in elsewhere.

• **Always carry a sturdy knife and a waterproof lighter** — These two items are the key to survival. If you have a good hunting knife and a waterproof lighter, survival is about two to twenty times easier than if you don't. If you don't have those tools, you'll need to make the stone-age equivalents as your very first task, and the original stone choppers and firebows just cannot compare to the 5,000 years of refinement we've applied to the concept. If there's any chance you're going to have to hack it on your own, have those two things, and you are much more likely to survive, and survive comfortably.

• **Civilization lies downstream** — If you find a watercourse and follow it downhill, and keep following the bigger and bigger watercourses it joins, you will eventually find human civilization. This is just as handy for avoiding civilization as finding it.

• **Don't trust what animals eat** — Animals, especially birds, lizards and amphibians, often have very different metabolic processes and digestive systems than humans. Just because animals eat plants doesn't mean they're safe for human or werewolf consumption; mistletoe is just one example of something that birds find edible but that would poison a Garou.

• **Rain and watercourses don't mix** — Characters who camp in or near creekbeds, even "dry" ones, may find themselves in for unexpected surprises. Rain twenty or fifty miles away can suddenly swell a placid creek into a torrent, just in time to wash away all your irreplaceable gear. Likewise, there are canyons in arid areas carved by water action. These often have fifteen foot diameter rocks wedged firmly between the walls at a height of twenty feet or higher. Think for a second about the fact that this indicates how high and hard the water flows when the gulley fills. You probably don't want to be in there when that happens, because it is not a gradual process. In general, if there's any real risk of rain, stay away from low-lying areas.

somewhere probably don't want to leave an obviously dressed, obviously poached carcass laying out in the woods for the wardens to find.

Secondly, hunting is time-intensive. The game must be stalked and killed. The killing part is quick and relatively easy for someone with a rifle or a bow, or werewolves using Hispo form; Garou have many hunting advantages over their wolf and human relatives. But unless the characters are willing to leave the bulk of a kill there to rot and take only a few cuts, the carcass must be dressed and the meat prepared. Take some meat out of your refrigerator and leave it on the table. It doesn't take very long until it gets smelly and generally inedible, does it? It doesn't take any longer just because you're out in the woods. Characters have a day or two to smoke, salt or eat the meat, with maybe another day or two after that if they're willing to go into Lupus form and exploit the tougher canine digestive system to stomach the ripening meat.

So in general, unless the group is traveling very light, it's probably wise for Garou to bring along some or all of their food rather than hunting, because hunting takes time and draws attention. In any case, modern survival foods generally engineered, have a better calorie-to-weight ratio than wild food. Meal planning for characters that don't intend to hunt must focus on light, high-energy foods — food bars, nuts, chocolate and fatty meats. Lightness of food is critical for wilderness sojourns of any real length; two pounds of food a day doesn't sound like very much, but it sure is a lot when you have to carry twenty days worth on top of twenty pounds of water and your camping gear. Food should be stored in waterproof containers, and hoisted into a tree away from camp every night. Characters should not store food in their tents, because most of god's animals are extremely hungry most of the time, and Mister Bear will not take no for an answer when he tries to stick his nose in your backpack. Sure, werewolves can beat a Kodiak in a fistfight, but do you really want to have that fistfight on top of your campsite?

The Lupine Diet

Characters in Lupus may "go native" and survive as predators. Wolves must eat about 2.5 pounds of meat a day to survive, or about 5 pounds to stay reproductively fit, which also means they need that much to stay in "fighting trim". This equals one large groundhog or other similar animal per wolf, per day, or about one white-tailed, antelope or other game animal of comparable size every 4 days for a pack of five wolves. Wolves can eat over twenty pounds of meat in a sitting, allowing them to "fuel up" for a multi-day dry spell, but 20 pounds of meat doesn't sit easily in anyone's stomach — wolves that gorge will spend at least a day sleeping and lazing it off before they're ready for action again.

Human Cultures and Myths

The world of **Werewolf** is very much not what modern Western civilization teaches its people. It's a world of spirits and sacred struggle, in which everything has an aspect of holiness and the world seems quiet only because we lack the knowledge to hear its many voices. It is, therefore, a world in which a great many tales people have told each other over the millennia may be partly or wholly true.

Certainly, **Werewolf** owes its existence to the variety of myths and stories told in the real world. Without the American Indian stories of animals that act as messengers from the spirit world, without the South American stories of jaguar-people or the African tales of Anansi the spider-trickster, without the popular legend of the "mokolé-mbembe" or the Indian stories of the naga, without the Norse Fenris and the Amerind Wendigo and the Greek Furies, where would Werewolf be? Given that **Werewolf** is based on the idea of such myths having a bloody "reality" in the World of Darkness, it's obvious that a little attention to other myths can only benefit the crafty Storyteller. Any myth, legend or story can be inspirational for a **Werewolf** chronicle; all it takes is a little forethought.

Changing Stories

In the real world, of course, there are no Garou. Therefore, no real-world tale accurately reflects their influence. When you bring in an element of the real world and explain it in terms of the game's realities, you are changing its meaning. It's very important to be clear about this at the outset, so that you can think clearly about when and how you want to go about it.

Is it okay to explain real people's experience of the world and their efforts to make sense of it in terms of fantasy creatures? The answer must be a resounding "sometimes, depending on how you go about it."

Note that the idea of stories that exist in fixed form and carry a fixed meaning is itself by no means universal among the real world's peoples, past and present. The myths of a living culture, the exemplars and symbols which express people's hopes, fears, values, devotions and enemies, change over time, just as individual people grow up, mature and grow old. Few cultures have ever developed the notion of "canon" in the sense of texts and interpretations that ought not change. (Nor does the notion of canon actually keep things from changing; it only changes the way changes express themselves.)

As an example, consider Uncle Sam. Uncle Sam's general figure, the tall and lanky man in red, white and blue suit and white hair, first appears in political cartoons in the middle of the 19th century. He's been used to recruit soldiers and to represent the spirit of the nation admonishing warmongers, as a symbol of America's benevolent leadership and with evil leer as the demon of American aggression, as the endorser of commercial goods and as the noble critic of commercialism degrading the country. His proportions vary, because whatever real person or people inspired the original illustrations are all long dead and he now reflects archetypal features.

Other cultural heroes serve similarly diverse purposes. Confucius has been invoked, just within the last century, to support imperial government and to attack it, to anchor Communism in the Chinese tradition of philosophical leadership and to justify the rejection of tradition in favor of reformulation, to beam down on the masses as the primal wise scholar and to glare down at them as the scheming justifier of tyranny. He's been saint, hero, villain and demon, and will continue to play all those parts and more as long as anyone remembers him. The real struggling scholar of the 5th century BC who taught the principles at the heart of the *Analects* doesn't matter much to these cultural functions, either; they deal with Confucius the symbol.

So you aren't doing anything unprecedented when you offer a new explanation for some aspect of a society, or choose to ascribe a different meaning to one of its symbols. Indeed, since in real life many tales are told for simple enjoyment as well as for didactic purposes, you're just doing what people around the world and through history are already doing. The particular mythology you apply from **Werewolf** may be now, but the process of adapting existing material to suit one's own purposes is as old as stories themselves.

Archetype and Stereotype

The act of reinterpretation is itself neither good nor bad. What matters is how you go about it. One of the easiest ways to make a travesty of someone's outlook (from your own culture or another) is to lose track of the difference between archetype and stereotype.

Archetypes point to what the people in a culture value, or feel that they ought to value. In his heroic persona, Uncle Sam represents straightforward "square dealing" and concern with facts and plain speaking over pretty appearances, while Confucius illustrates the combination of personal humility with piercing intelligence and sense of duty. But no individual American is Uncle Sam and no individual Chinese is Confucius. The statement "Americans tend to praise forthright honesty as more important than polished formality of presentation" talks about an aspect of the culture, and doesn't state or imply that all Americans have that feature or even that every single American wants to. "No American can understand irony" is a

bigoted put-down; "few Americans learn how to appreciate irony" is closer to a statement of fact — it may or may not be true, but it can be discussed reasonably objectively and it doesn't try to force every single individual into a particular mold.

Stereotypes strip away individuals' identities in favor of a collective identity. Stereotypes that the speaker intends as positive do this just as much as stereotypes intended as derogatory: "Gypsies naturally understand the spirits" and "Celts have a special innate understanding of the Goddess" are just as confining, inaccurate and depersonalizing as "all African-Americans are lazy" and "all Jews are greedy." The positive stereotypes impose goals and priorities on the people they're about without regard for what the individuals in question may want or regard as important.

Positive stereotypes make it easy to slide into paternalistic attitudes. After all, if this girl belongs to a group with a special affinity with the spirits, wouldn't it be a disservice to let her adopt a religion that denies the spirits? And if that man has the mark of a particular aptitude for communing with the force of nature, shouldn't we steer him away from anything so tedious as business or science?

In American history, the romantic notion of the Native American as free from the tyrannical shackles of Western rationalism and possessed of a deep affinity for the wonders of nature played a major part in the development of programs and laws that denied Native Americans opportunities to join in the life of less romanticized, mainstream society. The belief that Native Americans were innately superior therefore helped keep them poor, ignorant and in unnecessary misery from disease, bad sanitation and other problems that the mainstream had addressed for its own members long before.

Archetypes speak of hopes and fears within a society. Archetypes embody truths and principles that can manifest in many ways, allowing for growth and development (and loss and decay), while stereotypes speak of values that can manifest in only one way, allowing for no movement. Remember that individuals and therefore societies change, and do not commit yourself to inflexible, constraining visions of what people in the game world must be, even if you mean well by it.

The Werewolf in the Story

Opportunities and pitfalls travel in pairs through the landscape of potentially useful real-world stories and beliefs. As usual, this is not an exhaustive list, and the categories are necessarily somewhat arbitrary. They're intended to help you achieved a balanced outlook. There's very seldom one uniquely right answer to any question about whether a particular piece of reality belongs in your chronicle, but there are concerns you should keep in mind as you see what feels right for your specific circumstances.

Details

• **Rich, complex, varied environments are fun to play in.** One of the major reasons to set a game in a fantasy version of the real world rather than one completely made up is precisely that humanity has done a lot of your preparation for you. As a World of Darkness Storyteller, you can draw on the actions and thoughts of billions of people over thousands of years, in addition to much wider-ranging natural phenomena.

Once you know where your chronicle will be taking place, you can go to the local library or bookstore and the World Wide Web and look up all kinds of supporting details. The meaning of colors varies from culture to culture, for instance: white is the color of mourning in many Asian societies, while red is a color of good fortune. What the characters wear can therefore create impressions they don't intend, for good or ill. Every culture has its own ideas about what foods are suitable for consumption by upper classes and lower ones, what's healthy and desirable and what's nasty and should be avoided. The snacks characters bring with them from a long-distance flight could fascinate, appall or just confuse the people on the far end.

Details matter when the characters are at home, too. How close is too close to stand when talking to someone you don't know? How much public show of emotion is appropriate? And why are these things so? This kind of nuance keeps players thinking about how it feels to be their characters in the game world, and that's good.

• **Roleplaying the encyclopedia is not fun.** **Werewolf** is at heart a game about courageous characters tackling the impending end of the world. It works with broad strokes as well as subtle, elegant ones. Don't keep your players afraid to go someplace interesting or do something risky in the expectation that they'll run into a morass of details which add up to inevitable embarrassment and failure. Choose a few illuminating details, but be prepared not to get to use some of the nifty stuff you uncover in your research or extrapolate on your own. The game session shouldn't turn into an extended lecture with brief improv exercises to illustrate some points; it's about adventure, with the research there to enrich and support the game's themes.

Game Ideas

• **Werewolf** concepts provide neat fictional explanations of many real things. **Werewolf** is a game about hidden truths. There are forces at work that people (and most animals and plants) don't know

about. So you have a great deal of freedom to say "this aspect of the game world really accounts for this interesting thing I found in history or current affairs."

One of the key features of an animistic world is that things exist on several levels. You as an individual person are yourself, and also a manifestation of the spirit of your community, and of your tribe, and of humanity. You partake of the spirit of your environment, sharing some part of your soul with the life and land and air and water around you. Other sorts of identification may also come into play. This means that an explanation based on something working a particular way because it's part of one group doesn't rule out the truth and relevance of explanations based on the thing belonging to other groups as well.

The coexistence of multiple meanings allows you to use real-world myths and legends to speak of **Werewolf** matters *as well as* the real-world concerns they address. Reducing everything to a single meaning of any kind stereotypes it, and you shouldn't rush to do so. You should go particularly slow when interpreting real people's beliefs and customs in a fictional light. When you approach the real world as fodder for your game, you should think of it in terms of adding meaning, not taking away the meaning that's already there.

Uncle Sam embodies the national pride in vigor and ingenuity. These are what they are, reflecting the real and diverse heritage of pioneers along with a generous dose of mythologizing and nostalgia in the face of changing social conditions. All of this (and a great deal more) is true, and moving it to the World of Darkness doesn't make it false. Rather, the move makes other aspects also true. To a Triatic scholar, Uncle Sam might show how the Wyld's principle of boundless creativity continues to operate in industrial societies. Technology past the late Iron Age doesn't make the Wyld irrelevant; it opens up channels for birth and the productive chaos from which all things come that tribal peoples may not recognize.

Likewise, Confucius is the symbol that those evoking him intend him to be. He embodies the essence of scholarship in the service of society and the protection of social order through diligent pursuit of virtue. This is as true in the World of Darkness as it is in reality. Confucius also comes to symbolize something more thanks to the Triat: he manifests the "benevolent tyrant" aspect of the Weaver. This aspect of the principle of equilibrium and continuity isn't mad, but its morality is open to interpretation depending on the priorities of observers. Just as in the real world, Confucius becomes the example by which rival visions of society may illustrate themselves, so in the World of Darkness he can serve as an example for Garou and others who debate the desirability of the Weaver's

actions in long-lived societies like China. Nothing becomes false here; more things become true.

Draw on the full range of concepts **Werewolf** offers. Not everything flows directly from the Triat, or from the tribe found most often in a geographical area. What interesting people and natural phenomena reflect the influence of a particular Incarna or Celestine? What somewhat mysterious phenomenon can be accounted for through the temporary manifestation of a connection with one of the great (or small) Umbral realms? Who are the unwitting Kinfolk of other Changing Breeds, and who has a family history that keeps bringing them up against the edge of the Delirium? If there's an aspect of the game that you've been wanting to bring into play, a bridge with real folklore often leads players where you want them to go not just willingly but enthusiastically.

• **Werewolf-specific concepts don't explain everything.** While it's good for your players to feel that their characters move through a landscape with unexpected dimensions and endless interesting revelations, be careful not to trivialize real-world concerns. Not every story is secretly about the **Werewolf** setting, and you should include attention to stories that really are about what they seem to be about.

Indeed, a certain level of apparent contradiction is thematically sound in **Werewolf** terms. The Garou don't understand the whole universe. They don't know much about how the magic of the Namebreakers works, for instance, nor do they have a good grasp on the complexities of the lands of the dead in the Dark Umbra. They don't know what all lurks in the depths of the Wyrm's realms — nor those of the Weaver or the Wyld. There are secrets in the natural world not revealed to them, either, in places where neither the spirits nor other Changers choose to share with the Garou. These limitations apply to all the Breeds, no matter how much any of them would like to think they know it all, too.

So it's appropriate to introduce a myth from time to time whose explanation seems true and yet does not fit smoothly with the forces Garou venerate. Many mythic creators combine elements of two or even three aspects of the Triat. Some cultures ascribe different personalities and responsibilities to the spirits of the planets. Totemic animals don't have consistent natures, and afterlives vary wildly. The Garou as a race suffer from arrogance and self-blinding pride, and it's no bad thing to show characters that sometimes there is, irrefutably, more than they can account for. Don't do this often enough to make them feel that their beliefs are trivial or profoundly broken, because in the World of Darkness the Garou understand (or can understand, if they pay attention) much of the cosmic order. It's just that there's always something more.

The World

• **The world is marvelous**. Like the real world, the World of Darkness contains breathtaking beauty and wonder. The Garou see more of it than human beings can, too — there are places no human eye will ever see, far from civilization, and beyond the Gauntlet there's far more. There are the glories that strike the unaided Garou eye (and ear, and nose, and skin), and then there's more to see on other scales, from the evolution of a healthy ecosystem over the centuries to the ritual dance of symbiosis among creatures too small for the eye to see.

When Robert Ballard and his crew discovered the wreck of the *Titanic*, they found it festooned with stalactite-like extrusions that were clearly the remains of metal features after iron-metabolizing bacteria had done their work. Ballard's science team dubbed the features "rusticles," invoking their nature as a deep-sea manifestation of rust and corrosion. Several years later, multi-disciplinary scientist Charles Pellegrino and his colleagues actually brought rusticles to the surface to study more thoroughly, and found wonders. Each rusticle is actually a complex community of up to two dozen different bacteria species, each with its own particular feeding requirements, and they form layers and even crude circulatory systems so that the excretions of one species feed the next ones in line. The bacteria involved in this amazing synergy come from, literally, all over the world, carried by deep-sea currents until they find a suitable home.

Most Garou would think of a shipwreck at the bottom of the sea as not very relevant to them. And yet, here is a whole thriving network of life, whose remains strongly resemble long-mysterious fossils of some of the very first living organisms. The Wyld is at work in a place where the sun never shines, in and around the *Titanic* as in the volcanic vents along mid-ocean ridges and other deep havens.

Here is an occasion for a moment of mystic appreciation that owes its existence to modern science. The theme of unexpected beauty in the midst of difficulty, struggle and death is a potent one. Don't overuse it, but reward your players from time to time with a moment of awe and satisfaction along with the more conventional and accessible forms of beauty.

• **The world is terrible.** The natural world is not *nice*, and a key theme of **Werewolf** is (or at least can be) that simple answers do not suffice. Any species that produces offspring must include some provision for its members to die, or it'll overrun the world, destroy its habitat, and then become extinct. For that matter, extinction is a fact of nature: the overwhelming majority of all species that have ever lived have become extinct, and nature does not hesitate to destroy species individually or by the thou-sands. Sometimes the survival of any life on earth at all has been a matter of chance.

Nature makes no provision for rights as people define them. Predators hunt their prey without regard for the hopes or aspirations or dreams of the creatures they kill. Seeds and eggs and live young alike are all created in much larger numbers than can possibly survive, and most die young. Just as there are dazzling instances of harmonious mutual support in the wild, so there are horrifying instances of parasitism, with creatures whose whole existence depends on the ongoing pain of others.

Remember that darkness and destruction are part of nature. While the Wyrm has gone mad, the principle of dissolution existed before it did. Not everything the Wyld ever brought forth was cuddly and friendly, and the equilibrium achieved under the Weaver has often been something less than kind. One of the most potent uses of real myths about the origins of the dark side of the world is to bring it into comprehensible form for your players, to integrate it with the rest of their characters' understanding.

Roleplaying Animals

Animals are a vital part of **Werewolf**, more so than they are in any other White Wolf game. Whether it's the wolf Kinfolk that stirs up trouble for the sept, a deer the pack pursues or a guard dog the group tries to make friends with, animals are a common sight. **Werewolf** has an added dimension in that, unlike most roleplaying games, it isn't uncommon for characters to be able to converse with the rat in the drainpipe or the hungry tiger. Good Storytellers should treat animals with at least as much respect as they do the other characters under their control. Let's face it, there are times when speaking to an eagle is as pivotal to the plot as pumping the local crime boss for information; it should be at least as dramatic. But where to begin?

Perception

A key point in representing animals is to understand how they perceive the world — or more appropriately, how we think they perceive the world. Take a wolf, for example. Her view is low to the ground, so the top of a table is unknown territory. She can see moderately well, but is better at noting movement than identifying stationary figures. Like some color-blind humans, she has a hard time distinguishing shades of red and orange; they blend in with green foliage. She sees farther into the blue spectrum than we do, and can see much better in dim light. When focused, the wolf's hearing is quite keen, and she can pick up tones in a much higher pitch than a human can detect. And of course, her nose opens an olfactory world we can only imagine, revealing to her who and what is upwind, the sex and health of the wolf who marked a tree and how long ago he passed by, and any number of other clues about her environment. Finally, she has whiskers that help her feel around her in the darkness of a den — and possibly which way the breeze blows.

Many critters discover their world through senses that are more than a little alien to us. Some bats and dolphins use focused sound waves to navigate. Many fish (notably torpedofish and sharks) hunt by sensing the electricity generated by the prey's own muscles. The compound eyes of bees register far into the ultraviolet spectrum. Hawks have a narrower range of hearing but can easily pick up movement and focus on a rabbit while soaring high above. Some birds, sea turtles and fish can travel hundreds or even thousands of miles annually to find a specific tree, beach or stream, using navigational aides that are often beyond our ken. Even dogs have been known to journey incredible distances to return home. Sometimes we just don't know how animals know what they do, a good example being dogs that sense the change in their epileptic owners up to half an hour prior to a seizure.

But it's more than just having keen senses. Wild animals are quite simply more adept at using what they have than the average human, who spends his life in a kind of sleepwalk of half-awareness. Survival in the wilderness depends on well-tuned senses with which to find food and avoid predators or other hazards, and those whose nose or ear isn't as good as the rest will find themselves evicted from the gene pool.

All In the Mind

Thought and Instinct

Animal behavior is a mixture of reflexive instinct and conscious thought. To say that animals "think" like us does a disservice to the critters; millennia of evolution have endowed creatures with the smarts they need under normal circumstances. Because we can only guess what goes on in the mind of a non-human, how critters think has been a controversial subject for a very long time.

Animals seem to think in terms of "if, then": "If I choose the left path, the floor will hurt my feet." "If my human is in the room, I can't get food out of the can." Making the leaps of understanding that connect "if" to "then" is the basis of learning. For example, the alligator that happens to be in a part of the bayou when the truck comes to dump bodies, if it makes the connection between truck and food, will swim towards the sound of the engine, expecting a meal. A sea bird that notices a dropped shell cracks against a rock will seek out large rocks to break open mussel shells in the future, assuming it connects the rock and the fall with an easy meal.

At the lower levels of the animal hierarchy, instinct is the basis for most behavior, but as one moves up the evolutionary ladder, so to speak, there is more room for individuality. A flatworm is a flatworm is a flatworm, but any two bears will react differently to a situation based on a combination of instinct, experience and individual personality. Higher-level animals can more readily adapt to new situations and take advantage of novelty. Suburban or park deer grow quite complacent when there's nothing to fear, until they can hardly be bothered to move out of the way of cars; in the countryside they tend to be much more watchful for slow-moving vehicles or people on foot, even from hundreds of yards away.

Yet even in "higher mammals" we see "hardwired" reactions, instinctive behaviors that are overcome with difficulty, if at all. Some are benign, like the dog that scratches the floor and turns in circles before lying down. Others are more dangerous; even a zoo-born, well-fed cougar will leap up and rush towards a child running along the other side of the fence. Some animals, particularly those usually considered prey species, have strong "fight or flight" reactions; if held restrained and subject to prolonged handling or even proximity to humans their systems are overcome by the stress, resulting in death at the scene or within a few days after capture, even if they weren't physically harmed while captured.

Now and Then

Most animals live in the "now;" their attention is focused in this place at this moment — how different from the average human, whose mind is on yesterday's argument, tonight's dinner or any number of entertaining or philosophical distractions. That's not to say animals have no past or future. Usually, the past is a vague place where associations spring up at need. For instance, a puppy abused by a tall blonde woman may grow up to be a friendly dog that snarls at tall blonde women. A coyote nearly caught by a trap baited with fish may avoid anything with a fishy smell.

The future is a much more abstract concept. Instinct covers a lot of ground, timing wise — readying a nest when the time for egg-laying approaches, or swimming from the sea to a mountain stream to spawn — but the specifics may allow for some thought on the part of the individual. For example, some birds plan nesting sites by scoping out potential food sources that don't yet exist. Even bees can compensate for a moving food source by heading towards the expected new location rather than the last known location.

And just as they make intuitive connections between an action and a positive effect, they can also discern negative repercussions, provided the effect happens soon enough after the cause. When a bird becomes ill after eating a bad-tasting butterfly, it will avoid all similar butterflies in the future. The longer the time between cause and effect, the more tenuous the connection in the mind. If a wolf experiences a painful electric shock when it bites a sheep, it connects sheep with pain and may avoid them for a while; if the wolf bites a sheep and three days later a party of bounty hunters appear to harry it, the wolf will see no connection between the cause (stock killing) and effect (men with guns).

Predator and Play

When you look at animals, you can usually tell the predators from the prey. Prey species such as turkeys, rabbits and deer tend to have eyes and ears placed for a wide angle of view — often better than 270 degrees around – to watch for danger. Predators (foxes, cats, hawks and of course wolves) look more forward to focus on the hunted. Predator brains tend to be larger (it takes more brainpower to outwit a deer than a patch of grass). To human eyes, these hunters are often more "clever," and more likely to try new approaches to achieve a goal (said goal usually being a snack).

Though they don't hold a monopoly on extracurricular activity, predators have more of a propensity for play. Even as adults they toss bones, sneak up on their fellows and play tag. Otters are among the most accomplished players around, but coyotes and ravens have a well-deserved reputation for fooling around with others without regard to species. Like humans, these critters seem to need to work their minds and bodies in "recreational" activities. Without novel stimuli to occupy them, higher animals kept in captivity grow increasingly neurotic, resorting to stereotypic movements such as endless pacing or head tossing, biting the bars or even self-mutilation. This is why many zoos have expanded and "naturalized" animal habitats, as well as hiding food so animals may forage rather than simply eating.

From Heath to Hearth

Another distinction that should be made is the difference between wild and domestic animals. When humans domesticate a species, they selectively breed them to accentuate the desirable traits and diminish or eliminate the undesirable ones. That's why a dairy cow produces far more milk than necessary to raise a calf while at the same time being docile enough to handle, seeing as any aggressive or protective tendencies were bred out. The upshot is that the creatures in Man's keeping are often quite unlike their wild relations. The wild turkey is a canny, wary bird, while the white domestic turkey is stupid with a capital S.

The same is true with dogs and their wild wolf cousins; both are mentally very alike, yet with key differences. For example, as a rule dogs have been bred to retain certain juvenile traits into adulthood. Friendly acceptance of other humans (dogs often seeing humans as packmates) is a notable one; wolf cubs are open to others for the first few weeks of life, but after this period of socialization they form additional attachments with difficulty. A related juvenile characteristic is the submissiveness and eagerness to please that many dogs express, even to friendly strangers. People that raise wolves find they must remain ever vigilant lest their charges "challenge" their leadership.

Communication

Most unpleasant encounters between man and beast are the result of misunderstanding and miscommunication on both sides. Through color changes, posture and other subtle visual cues, animals communicate their mood, status and even intentions. People are notoriously lousy at seeing and interpreting the body language of other species, and often, said species are no better at understanding us. That's why injured hawks fight those who try to save them, why otherwise-friendly dogs snap at intruders and why bison kill people who wish to treat them like friendly cattle.

That's not to say that animals can't read other species' non-verbal languages, only that the interpretation isn't a sure thing. A gazelle uses a lion's body cues to distinguish between a hungry hunter and a recently-fed loafer, yet assumes a safari hunter is dangerous because it can't read the human's intent in his movements.

In Your Game

We aren't suggesting that you dive into behavior textbooks and scientific journals to plan out each animal's potential reactions (though you're certainly welcome to do so). But it's helpful to have a general idea about how a creature will interact with the Garou.

Here are a few (not exhaustive) points to consider:

General Temperament

Take your cues from the general behavior of an animal. A highly-socialized black Lab puppy that wags its tail at passersby will be more likely to be friendly than a mistreated, isolated junkyard mutt will. Depending on the species, domesticated animals as a rule will tend to be a little more docile and not as mentally swift as their wilder cousins are (that doesn't mean you should try to pet a fighting bull or outsmart a border collie). Domestic animals raised by humans often desire to be near people, whereas wild-born horses and dogs can be just as fearful of humans as any wild beast.

Reactions to Garou

Garou are powerful predators who fairly radiate their primal rage. Prey species, including rabbits, deer and even horses, will likely form a poor first impression of a pack of werewolves, no matter how big the latter smile. Predators see Garou as competition rather than comrades — and sometimes even as creatures that would kill *them* for food. Large, tough beasts such as bull elephants or grizzly bears might be less inclined to run than a rabbit, may take a belligerent stance. On the other hand, a blue whale probably feels no particular threat at all.

Besides reactions to the Garou-ness of a character, there may be behavioral differences based on the character's form. The dog that is more inclined to be friendly to a human will probably bristle at a wolf; a young wolf might have the opposite reaction.

What's in It for Me?

Animal altruism (assuming it exists — another controversial topic among ethologists) doesn't extend outside a species. Aesop's fables aside, you aren't going to find a mouse helping a lion. Even the amazing African honeyguide, which leads humans to beehives, expects a share of the spoils; if it doesn't get rewarded, it eventually stops bothering. There needs to be some tangible (or at least perceivable) reward for any action taken on a character's behalf. Usually this involves food, but depending on the animal and the pack's ability to communicate with it, more complex or abstract arrangements may be made.

Me Heap Good Talker

Animal communication has always been tricky in Werewolf games. Lupus conversation has often been reduced to "Me fear thunderstick — bad!" Not that those reactions are always inappropriate, but understand that something is lost in the translation. Imagine trying to be eloquent in a language you speak imperfectly at best; you'll sound childish or stupid, if you get your point across at all, and the listeners would either patronize or ridicule you regardless.

Instead of using badly-constructed sentences when communicating using a Gift, have the animal "speak" more fluently, but in terms appropriate to its own natural bias. A hawk would describe everything in its visual aspects as opposed to sound; it would also be intimately aware of local weather conditions. Though it has several keen senses, a fox's world revolves around odor, and its natural curiosity (a common trait in mammalian predators) makes it more aware of anything out of the ordinary, human-caused or otherwise. Include concepts within the animal's experience, but make sure anything alien the players throw in confuses it. For instance, the raven is familiar enough with "day", but "Tuesday" won't ring a bell.

Say a Galliard uses the Gift: Beast Speech to ask the local fauna whether some tainted hikers came through the woods recently. If he asks a spider, the response will be something like *Food, Light, Web*. The previously-mentioned hawk may have more details since the hikers sent a rabbit running right into the raptor's talons. The fox knows where they went because he followed their trail a while hoping they would drop some scraps.

Training

It's not unusual for Garou or Kinfolk to keep animals as guardians or companions, and such critters are usually trained in some capacity – except for the deepest of deep wilderness caerns, even lupus Kinfolk need to be taught where they can't go and what they can't eat. As mentioned previously, animals think in terms of "if, then." If making the leaps of understanding that connect "if" to "then" is the basis of learning, then facilitating and encouraging the connection is the key to training. Training a guard critter is far easier when you can speak the language (whether by speaking the wolf tongue or using a Gift); if you doubt it, imagine learning a task by being told versus learning a task by being told… by a mime. If that sort of direct communication isn't possible, then training takes some skill and a lot of patience. Smart animals learn faster, but may also be prone to act up. Remember that animals learn quickest the tricks that mimic natural behaviors. For example, teaching the dog to fetch is relatively easy since toting things in their mouths comes naturally to them. Teaching a rescue dog, drug-sniffer or shepherd involves normal hunting behaviors and narrowing the focus. Teaching a dog to tap dance would probably just frustrate you and annoy the dog.

To sum up: animals are brighter than we often give them credit for, but their perception, intelligence, and subsequent behavior is not like a human's. Putting some thought into your animals (and maybe some basic research) is recommended to make them really come alive (so to speak) in your game. With the proper personality and reaction, critters can be an important and memorable part of any scenario.

Getting into the Spirit

Travel through the Umbra means entering a world of spirits. The dual nature of the Garou — part human or wolf and part spirit — makes the spirit world a second home for Gaia's chosen warriors. Depicting Umbral pathways and landscapes involves detailing an environment that sometimes differs radically from the "real world." The creatures that inhabit the Umbra, likewise, possess qualities that separate them from the beings that dwell in the physical world.

As a Storyteller, you need to make your players realize that whenever they enter the Umbra, they not only enter a different world, they have the potential to interact with the spirits that dwell there. Spirits represent a very important part of Garou life. Garou learn Gifts from spirits, gain help from friendly spirits, battle hostile ones and bind both kinds into fetishes and talens.

What is it like to meet a spirit? To talk to one and to have one talk to you? The following guidelines may help Storytellers bring the residents of the Umbra to vivid, sometimes frightening but always interesting, life.

Seeing Is Believing: Describing the Spirits

Visual descriptions set the stage for the interaction that makes up the meat of any story. As a Storyteller, you are responsible for making the world your players' characters inhabit seem real and vital. Your Garou characters must believe that when they stand in the presence of Owl or one of his avatars, they are face to face with a totem spirit of Wisdom, not a dingy barn owl. What the players (and their characters) see is in your hands.

When you describe a spirit that has a real world counterpart, whether animal, plant or mineral, make certain that the spirit stands out in the minds of your audience. Find some characteristic that best represents the essence of the spirit and bring it to the fore in your description. A few ideas are presented below.

Animal Spirits

The Umbral air around the Garou travelers grows heavy with foreboding. All around them, the forest through which they pass ceases to move. No breeze stirs. No sound disturbs the passage of the uneasy pack. Suddenly, overhead, they hear the almost noiseless rush of wings and a vast darkness covers the sky. Owl has arrived.

Animal spirits have many of the same traits as their physical counterparts, but they are somehow more than the sum of their parts. An owl spirit does not merely resemble an owl. It embodies the essence of "owlhood." Ask yourself what best describes an owl. Glowing eyes? An expression of innocence and wisdom? A predatory nature? Silent wings and the death cry of a small beast? Use these elements in your description to set the tone of the encounter.

In the perpetual twilight of the Umbra, Owl perches knowingly on a branch just above the heads of the Garou seekers. A pair of pale golden eyes blinks once and the massive, ghostly white head turns to examine each individual, as if looking into their very souls. An aura of silence and danger gathers around the enormous night predator.

By focusing on two major elements, the owl's expression and the sense of quiet danger that surrounds it, you communicate some facts to your players. First of all, you let them know that the owl-spirit is not necessarily going to bend over backwards to assist the Garou. Second, you intimate that Owl can sense the truth or falsehood of any words spoken to it. Lastly, you create an element of danger that should place your players on their toes. They can't afford to say the wrong thing or offer Owl any disrespect.

Plant Spirits

A wall of roses towers into the Umbral skies, forming an impermeable barrier thick with dark pointed leaves and spiny thorns. The flowers themselves exude an aroma of seductiveness and deadliness, the odor of sanctity and of decadence. A cascade of brilliant colors, ranging from bloody crimson to pale alabaster, surrounds a single rose, larger than the rest. It rises now from its place in the center of the rose-barrier and turns its petals toward the visitors to its garden.

Plant spirits provide the template for their earthly manifestations. The spirit of a rose represents the essence of what a rose is — beauty, danger, love and passion. Though Garou generally do not spend time with spirits that lack mobility, preferring to seek guidance from and companionship with more volatile spirits that understand their own anger and impatience, the occasion might arise in which a Garou must confront the spirit of a plant. Plant-spirits are generally better inclined toward shapeshifters with low Rage than they are toward high-Rage werebeasts; but you needn't let this tinge of perceived "pacifism" drain color from the encounter. As a Storyteller, you can transform what might otherwise be a lackluster encounter with vegetation into a memorable meeting.

Books on plants or herbal healing and collections of fairy tales and legends abound in historical and mythical footnotes on the properties of plants. These can prove helpful in bringing your plant-spirits out of dormancy into activity and imbuing them with unique and surprising personalities.

Rose radiates a wave of power and desire as she rises upward on her supple stem within the protective threat of her thorny arms. Though she possesses nothing that resembles eyes, her essence gazes into your soul, judging your innermost thoughts and motivations. Her petals unfold, revealing a scarlet slash that opens as she speaks.

Roses symbolize romance and passion, but they also carry a hint of opulence and danger. Sleeping Beauty's thorny prison consisted of rose bushes, and older versions of the story call the dormant princess Briar Rose. The spirit of Rose should offer Garou not only the promise of deep emotions but also a subtle threat and an obvious challenge. Use words in your description of Rose that evoke power, mystery and foreboding. Your Garou will never view mundane roses in the same fashion again.

Abstract Beings and Inanimate Objects

A storm rages in the Umbra. Bolts of black and indigo lightning strike the ground around the young Black Fury and her packmates. The ground shakes with each impact and the

very air that surrounds the Garou surges with hostility. A jagged form solidifies from a shard of lightning. Anger hangs in the air, questioning why you have intruded into his territory.

Though plant and animal spirits may challenge a Storyteller's talent at portraying characters, abstract concepts and inanimate objects pose a different problem. How do you describe an emotion or an abstract idea? How do you bring "life" to a rock? Spend a few moments thinking about what feelings and attitudes you associate with certain words. What symbols or objects do you associate with pain or sorrow or anger? What feelings arise when you think of rocks or sand or thunder? Use these words and ideas to construct a personality for your abstraction or inanimate object.

The Garou draw back from one another, as hostility surrounds them. Past slights and present grudges hover on the edges of consciousness. The spirit of Anger rises to its full height, its voice, hot and searing, scratching its message in the souls of its petitioners.

Ideas and objects do not have the same spectrum of emotions and responses that humans (or even animals) do. Don't be afraid to experiment with substituting sounds and colors for emotions and words. Create a picture your players will remember as long as their characters do.

Mythic Spirits

Unicorn steps into the glade, his hooves striking sparks as they touch the ground. Innocence covers the great beast like a blanket, but there is nothing gentle about the creature's eyes. It bows its head, acknowledging its visitors, but that gesture only serves to emphasize the brutally keen tip of Unicorn's horn. Raising its head, Unicorn holds court, standing in judgment over your pack.

Encounters with magical beings or totem spirits should never be less than epic. When Garou enter the Umbra to meet with a spirit, whether to petition it for aid or to learn a Gift, they leave behind the world of the everyday and enter into a place of myth and archetype. Storytellers need to make it clear to their players (and their characters) that they have not only "stepped sideways" into the world of possibilities and potentials, they have also stepped outside the boundaries of reality and into a whole other place. Unicorns are not sweet, gentle creatures of froth and wide-eyed innocence. They do represent the absence of guilt, but they also symbolize total amorality and feral freedom. Garou encountering Unicorn should wonder if the legendary custom of using virgins to lure them into captivity did not originate in the idea of human sacrifice — and whether the virgin actually survived her encounter.

At first glance, Unicorn appears composed of shining white light. A longer look — and such a gaze brings pain to your eyes — reveals other hues: cerulean blue, royal purple, hazy gray and sparkling silver. Unicorn shakes its head, and from its long, flowing mane thousands of tiny sparks of light stream into the air, crackling with energy and Gnosis as they surround the pack. One small beam touches the pack leader's cheek and burns — a cleansing fire that scours some small pettiness from the Garou's essence.

Try to engage all the senses in your descriptions of spirits. When dealing with fantastic creatures such as wendigo, dragons or chimerae, emphasize not only the sight of the creature but also the aura of power that surrounds it. Use sound and color and feel to heighten the atmosphere of wonder. Even before your spirit has uttered its first word, the characters should be wondering if they haven't made some horrible mistake in coming into the spirit's presence. If you can create this feeling in your players, then you have succeeded in portraying a legendary spirit.

Now that you have some ideas for setting the stage and placing your actor — the spirit — in the spotlight, you need to put words into your spirit's mouth. Here's how to do just that.

Talk This Way

Spirits have a different way of speaking than mortals. They do not have the same concerns that humans or even Garou have. Gaia made spirits as embodiments of certain ideas, so they have limitations that humans and animals do not have. Spirits are both more and less free than humans or Garou or other free-willed supernaturals. They do not have the same political hang-ups or social awareness that mortals have. On the other hand, they exist for a single purpose — and that creates restrictions on what they may say or do. Communication implies more than just the words a spirit uses. It also includes the context (or lack thereof) of the spirit's experiences. A Storyteller can demonstrate all this through language.

Spirit Language

Owl arches its wings and turns its eyes on the pack's leader.

"Speak."

A single word, both greeting and command, echoes in your ears. The young Ahroun begins speaking, but his voice falters. He grows wordy. Owl ruffles its feathers. "Enough. Too many words. Start over." The pack leader takes a deep breath and begins again, choosing his words more carefully this time.

Spirits do not speak as humans do. How they use words and how they put sentences together, what they talk about, how patient or impatient they are all depend on their nature. Animal spirits, such as Owl or Lion or Turtle, speak with the same cadence as their animal selves. Owl's language should use short words, possibly with soft "oo" sounds to mimic the owl's distinctive cry. Lion, on the other hand, uses harsh guttural words that echo the animal's roar or growl. When speaking as Turtle, the Storyteller should keep in mind the creature's reputation for slowness, drawing out words and thoughts to match Turtle's plodding, methodical pace.

From deep with her crimson center, Rose's voice caresses the breeze, carried to your ears on soundwaves drenched in a heady sweetness.

"Touch not the sharpness," Rose cautions. "Linger only long enough to take one perfect petal. Renew your body. Leave softly."

Shyly, the wounded Ragabash reaches out and takes a petal from Rose's outer layer. A healing softness fills the Garou with the scent of well-being. She hesitates for a moment, then catches sight of Rose's thorns and thinks better of overstaying her welcome.

Plant spirits have fewer references than humans or even animals. They possess the ability to communicate with other creatures, so they presumably have the knowledge of vocabulary necessary for communication. They do not often use words that speak of human emotions. Plants know about growth and dormancy. They feel the sun, wind and rain and know the words attached to those forces of nature. They serve as homes and food for insects and herbivores and have some knowledge of these as well. They do not, however, understand words like good and evil. They know the Wyrm, but perhaps think of the Destroyer in their own terms, calling it the Desiccator, the Great Dryness or the Scorching Flame.

Garou may have to puzzle out the meaning behind the sometimes cryptic comments of plant spirits, but this should provide the Storyteller with the opportunity to challenge her players in a way that does not involve combat or one-upmanship. Think about the kind of plant the Garou encounter. An oak tree speaks very differently from a daisy. The tree's words fall heavily on the ears of its listeners, while the daisy's voice should sound as sibilant and mobile as if blowing in a breeze. Choose your words and vocal tone to match.

"Why stand you here?" Anger lashed out, its voice clashing like mismatched cymbals in the roaring wind. "Tell me, or begone!" Its shriek pierced the sensitive ears of the Garou, causing the Galliard to howl a challenge.

"Done!" cried Anger. "Fight and gain your boon or flee and know shame!"

The spirit took shape as a jagged wolf made of darkness and lightning. The challenge for the right to aid from the anger-spirit had begun.

Abstractions have an even more alien mindset than plants. Storytellers should attempt to convey this utter strangeness to the players through more than just language. Tone of voice plays an important role in describing spirits that correspond to emotions. Anger should speak with hostility and vitriol. Sorrow should sob its words, while Desire should attempt verbal seduction through soft speech and a suggestive vocabulary. Don't be afraid to experiment, though you might want to practice your spirit speech before trying it during a game session, just to be safe.

Inanimate objects present a similar challenge to Storytellers. How does a rock "talk?" Think of words that are heavy (pun intended) with concussive sounds. Let your voice boom out, but slow down your speech so that it takes on a ponderous quality. Rocks have no sense of transience. If your players grow impatient, remind them that their characters are probably just as impatient with Rock, but that the consequences of angering that spirit make showing their frustration unwise.

Unicorn walked forward until he stood before the trembling Child of Gaia. "Banish uncertainty from your heart, young one," the great creature said, its voice bypassing the Garou's ears and settling with warmth within her heart. "You have sought wisely and honestly for something to save your dying world. You have not always made the best choices but you have acted in accordance with your heart, and so you have done well. I will grant you the favor you seek."

Mythic creatures should be *mythic*. The beasts from legends usually possess great intelligence and extraordinary wisdom. They come from a time before time, an age that did not know the meaning of slang or contractions or idiomatic speech. Don't sell your mythic spirits short by using popular speech or psychobabble. Read some of the classic fairy tales from various cultures to get an idea of the words to use and the cadence of your speech. Your players will appreciate the time you take to make a meeting between their characters and Unicorn — or Pegasus or Dragon or Griffin — unforgettable.

Thought Patterns

Remember that spirits aren't the same thing as people or animals. The spirit world is full of symbolism, and things are "truer" to their nature than their physical counterparts are. In short, a spirit doesn't think like a person; not even the spirits of wholly human concepts like art or romantic love.

One of the most important aspects of spirit nature is that spirits don't really have free will, at least not to the extent that humans and Garou enjoy. They are bound by their very nature, in ways that a Western person might find alarming. A fire-spirit will never volunteer to go for a swim, no matter how convincingly a Theurge argues that no harm will come to it. An oak-spirit cannot argue for bending in the wind, just as the spirit of a blade of grass cannot decide to stand fast and unbowed. This is a very important aspect of an animistic world; sometimes things are the way they are not because science has yet to contradict them, but simply because that's the way they *are*. It may seem like a simplistic way out, but if you allow a spirit to go against its own nature with nothing short of painful, Herculean struggle, you lose the power of symbolism that makes the spirit world so important in the first place.

Of course, there are always exceptions — sort of. For example, the more powerful the spirit, the more leeway it has to interpret its role and duties. A shark Gaffling cannot resist an offering of bloody meat, but the Incarna of Shark himself might do so long enough to question the person making the offering, or to strike a complicated deal involving the trade of meat for favors. This is partly because Incarnae and Celestines represent a variety of concepts within themselves. Great Fenris is anger, *and* battle lust, *and* a harbinger of Apocalypse, *and* an aspect of Wolf, *and* strength, and so on. Great Pegasus stands for a number of important things, of which the protection of Woman and the defense of the Wyld are but two. With these added aspects comes flexibility, and with an Incarna's wisdom and willpower comes the power to choose its own path — so long as that path serves its ultimate nature, that is. Even the Wyrm cannot choose to build rather than destroy.

Also, it's evident that spirits can change their Triatic affiliation; that's where so many Banes come from, after all. However, this change is usually brought on by outside entities; a spirit becomes a Bane because it's caught and infused with Wyrm-energy, or because its physical counterpart is destroyed or corrupted, and so on. Theoretically, only the greatest spirits can "choose" to change their affiliation — and there's not really any proof of that.

When portraying a spirit, always keep its motivation in mind. Thankfully, the straightforward, symbolic nature of spirit thought makes it fairly easy to figure out just where a spirit's coming from, what it might want from a pack, and how it might propose to achieve its goals. Liven up the spirit with a few quirks as needed, but really, you don't have to worry about making it as complicated a persona as an actual person — in fact, a too-complicated mindset in anything other than a spirit of intrigue or deceit might actually detract from your portrayal. Players expect Bluejay to be chatty and Wolverine to be crass and violent — use this to your advantage. It's less work and more effective at the same time; what could be better?

Unless, of course, you're dealing with ancestor-spirits — but those are something else entirely.

Final Words

While there are no hard and fast rules for roleplaying spirit encounters, the following guidelines should help you bring your Umbral residents to life and make your players take them seriously as the wondrous beings they are.

• **Use Slang Wisely** — When portraying spirits of great age and reverence, use speech that is a little more formal than everyday conversation. Don't use contractions or idioms. Spirits don't usually say "Cool!" or "All good." Exceptions do exist, however. City spirits might very well pad their speech with the latest stylistic fads. The Spirit of the 1960's would pepper her sentences with terms like "far out" and "groovy." Weaver spirits might use techno-speak. A Raccoon Gaffling knocking over suburban trashcans might sound like a suburban teenager himself. Language is symbolic of the spirit's nature, and slang implies modernity — which may or may not suit your purposes. Just remember that most spirits don't say "don't."

• **Use Visual Language** — Words not only communicate ideas, they paint pictures. Use language that creates images in the minds of your players. Plant spirits use words that have to do with forces of nature and with the cycles of dormancy, budding, blossoming and bearing fruit. Animal spirits speak of hunting or fleeing, of mating and challenge. Abstractions use words that conjure the emotions or ideas they represent. Rocks use words that fall to the ground or sit heavily on the tongue.

• **Sit into Your Role** — Bring body language into play by sitting into your role. Turn your head from side to side and try not to blink when portraying Owl. Sway back and forth like a willow tree in the wind when speaking as a plant spirit. Pace grandly about the room when you speak as Unicorn. You can even wear a turtleneck sweater or wrap a scarf loosely around your neck when you take on the role of Turtle so that you can imitate the motion of a turtle withdrawing into its shell in times of stress or between words. Your extra effort draws your players into the mood and increases their suspension of disbelief.

• **Don't Be Afraid to Set the Scene** — Take a few minutes to place your characters in the proper context. Describe the surroundings in which the encounter takes place. Use words that create a landscape appropriate to your spirit. Once you've done that, your players should be ready to listen to what your spirits have to say.

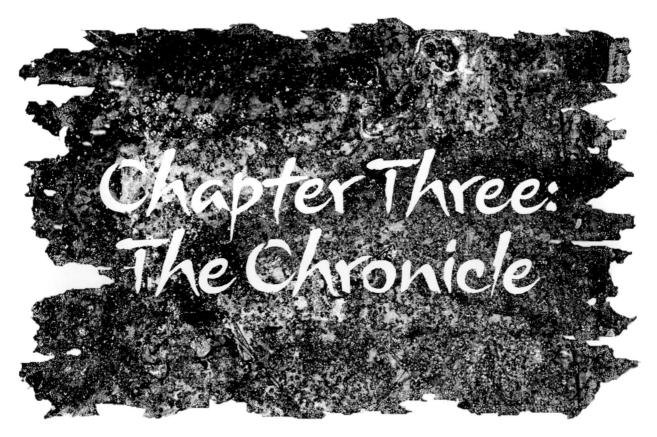

Chapter Three: The Chronicle

"If we ever meet again, Hazel-rah," said Dandelion,
as he took cover in the grass verge, "we ought to have the
makings of the best story ever."
— Richard George Adams, *Watership Down*

Beginning

Werewolf does not have an easy, pre-determined focus. Chronicles — or even stories within chronicles — run the gamut from high-drama, world-altering plotlines to tales about young werewolves coping with their duties as "Gaia's defenders" interfering with their human lives. Tribal politics, the Umbra, the Red Star, the other Changing Breeds — even in the core book alone, the Storyteller is presented with a daunting amount of information. It can be quite a chore to remember how characters regain Gnosis and what form they can soak what kinds of damage in, to say nothing of how each of the tribes arrange leadership and how they all feel about one another.

All this said, **Werewolf**'s strength lies in this diversity. There are so many options available that any troupe should be able to build a chronicle to suit them. High-drama or "realism", bloody combat or spiritual quest, it's just a matter of identifying what you and your players will enjoy most.

But where to begin?

Character Creation

"So, where's this game going to be set?", asks Brian. The other four players — Halle, Ryan, Keith, and Julie — are lounging around the basement, picking through books, getting to know one another.

"Not sure yet, really," answers Matt. "Depends on what you guys want to do. You want this game to be modern-day, or Wild West, or anything like that?" The group confers for a moment and decides that, since Ryan and Julie are new to role-playing in general and since none of the group is familiar with **Werewolf**, *a modern-day chronicle makes the most sense.*

"So, like, do you turn into a wolf on the full moon and eat people?" Julie asks.

Matt grins. "Not necessarily. Let's go through the basics and then you guys can make characters. First, though," he says, pulling out an atlas, "where do we want this game set?"

• • •

All role-playing games begin with the characters. Therefore, character creation should be the first (or one of the first) steps along the way. The best way to arrange character generation (often termed *chargen* by aficionados) is to get all of the players together to create characters at the same time. This is especially true for **Werewolf**, as the pack as a whole should receive the same attention as the individual characters.

Restrictions

If some (or all) of the players are unfamiliar with **Werewolf** cosmology, this is a good time to explain it. You'll want to let the players know where the game is set (or, as in the example above, let them help you decide) and what, if any, restrictions on character creation you

are imposing. For example, if you've decided that your game is going to center around an urban caern in Seattle, controlled primarily by Glass Walkers, you might well wish to restrict Red Talon characters.

Be careful, though, when assigning such restrictions. Sometimes a player will come up with a concept that, while seemingly disrupting things, actually opens some interesting plot possibilities. When you place restrictions on chargen, keep in mind why you're doing it. For instance, in the example above, the Storyteller restricts Red Talons because the caern is urban. Red Talons feel decidedly uncomfortable in urban settings, so the choice seems logical. However, there isn't any plot-driven rea-

Merits and Flaws

Storytelling tool or twink-bait? Useless crutch or valuable resource? Both, really.

Merits and Flaws are meant as optional rules designed to open up possibilities to characters. They provide a way to quantify the little foibles that characters tend to have. After all, if your character is going to be a smoker (for example), which is in many ways debilitating, even for a werewolf, what's wrong with getting an extra freebie point for it?

Well, nothing. The problem comes when players take Flaws like Phobia (sharks) in a landlocked chronicle, or take Obsessions or Compulsions they have no intention of playing. Of particular worry are Flaws like Driving Goal: it's a potential plot-wrecker if roleplayed correctly and it isn't worth the three points you get for it if it's not. Also, some extremely melodramatic players enjoy psychological flaws like Deranged or Vengeance because they wish to eat up time in the spotlight or overact (these are the same sorts of players who enjoy playing Fera because they feel it makes them "special").

And on the other side of the coin, some of the Merits are horribly unbalancing. Immune to Wyrm Emanations? *Silver Tolerance?* The Traits allow Garou to ignore (or at least diminish the horror of) some of their greatest weaknesses! Surely any right-thinking Storyteller, eager to preserve the integrity of the game, would disallow these Merits immediately, and probably just chuck the rest of the Merits and Flaws system for good measure.

The catch, though, is that there really isn't any such thing as "the integrity of the game". There's only *your* game, and you're perfectly welcome to pitch the system if necessary. Merits and Flaws are optional, and that means if the Storytellers says "No" then the players don't get to take them. End of story.

With all of that said, though, there are some good reasons to allow them. These reasons work

under the assumption that a) they will be played as intended, not used as point-dodges, and b) the Storyteller knows what she's getting into.

Merits and Flaws can provide concrete reminders and consequences of a character's history. The character's line was cursed generations ago? Maybe the Pierced Veil Flaw is the lingering reminder. The character entered a berserk frenzy during his First Change and only knows that he came to covered in blood? Perhaps the character is now Hunted… or Haunted. This works with Merits, too. A character known to be preternaturally lucky (via the Charmed Existence or Luck merits) will very likely acquire a reputation — and probably has some little rituals (rubbing a rabbit's foot or something similar) that she feels bolster her fortune. A player who comes up blank on ideas for a character's history might find an entire back-story waiting in one Merit or Flaw.

In much the same vein, the Storyteller can use such Traits as springboards for entire stories. If a character has the Flaw: Enemy, does that enemy reserve her venom for just that character, or for the entire pack? What if the enemy is an acquaintance of one of the other packmates — or one of their mentors? What if the enemy doesn't consider the enmity to be anything more than a long-forgotten tiff, and it's the character that's nursing the grudge?

The astute reader might well point out that any of these ideas would work just fine without imposing point costs or bonuses. This is quite true. But in the end, what do three or four more freebie points really amount to, especially if the trade-off is an original history that the player might not have otherwise considered? Again, as long as the story and not the points (or the "kewl powerz") are the focus, there's really no reason not to allow Merits and Flaws.

son why a player *couldn't* play a Red Talon, so if a player comes up with an evocative reason for the character being at the caern, why not allow it? Maybe the Red Talon was born in a zoo and decided to return to the city after her Rite of Passage. Perhaps the Talon is in disgrace from her tribe and is sent to join an urban pack as punishment (what would *that* do to the pack dynamics?).

The aim here isn't to squelch a good character concept, of course, but simply to keep the game on the level that you want it. If a player really had her heart set on playing a Red Talon, and you decide that Talons, for whatever reason, really aren't welcome at this sept, ask if perhaps the same basic concept wouldn't work for a lupus-breed werewolf of another tribe.

You might choose to place other requirements on the group. For example, you might wish to require that each of the auspices be represented in the pack (which requires at least five players). This is rarely a problem; most players would rather play something different than the others anyway. If you plan for much of the first story to take place in a nearby city, find out if the characters (homids especially) are native to the city. If so, you might choose to give those characters a few free dots of Area Knowledge (or require the players to purchase those dots).

Problem Players

Character creation is when you get to know the players, if you don't already. You'll get a glimpse at what you can expect during the chronicle, for better or worse. Pay attention to people's decisions at this stage — it will help you decide what kind of game these players will enjoy.

Every group has its problems, and chargen is a good time to identify and address them. The story hasn't begun yet, there's no continuity to disrupt, and you can identify behaviors that may prove damaging later. Some of these include:

• **Better late than never:** Punctuality isn't an issue if no one has a curfew and everyone is all right with gaming until the wee hours of the morning. That's rarely the case, however. If you find that a player is late for the character creation session — especially without reason — ask if this is going to be a recurring problem. It may seem nitpicky, but remember that one chronically late person can seriously derail things down the line, forcing the group to either wait or have the Storyteller play the errant player's character.

• **The man without a face:** Some players, be it because they are new to gaming or because they just can't think of a strong concept, let the books think for them. They read the tribe description and come up with concepts like "Ahroun warrior" or "Ragabash trickster." This is all right for a base, but if the character is going to

be more than a caricature, she needs some life and detail. The "Preludes" section, below, gives some ideas on how to coax such things out of recalcitrant players, but watch for dots that seem randomly assigned. If a homid-born character has 3 Brawl, ask why. After all, that's enough to indicate that the character could fight professionally; very few people are that skilled. Calling it into question shouldn't disallow it, of course, just make the player think to justify it.

• **The mathematician:** It happens sometimes that players forget that **Werewolf** is a Storytelling game, not a video game. You've barely finished saying that the chronicle will be set at a caern of healing and how Dove is the caern's totem when you get a sheet handed back to you with ratings of 5 in Brawl, Melee, Firearms, and Kailindo. Some players equate "success" with "kills," and, with that formula in mind, it's perfectly natural to arrange their characters as combat monsters. The trick here is to change the player's focus, not to deride him for being a "twink." Let him know that success is measured by everybody having a good time and by telling a good story. The "good story" part of that requires three-dimensional characters. It's quite all right to play a warrior — the Garou culture is brutal and violent, after all — but a warrior with some depth is a must. Plus, if the character starts out already maxed in offensive capabilities, how will he develop? (If logic doesn't prevail here, you might well be dealing with a true twink, and expulsion via catapult is recommended.)

• **The Unique Freak:** No Garou is "typical." Twelve tribes (thirteen, counting the Stargazers, should your Storyteller allow them), innumerable camps within tribes, five auspices, three breeds — the combinations are endless. But some players feel that the only way to have a truly "special" character is by playing something truly removed from the group. Other Fera are popular choices for this, as are Abominations and members of the Lost Tribes. Playing other Fera in **Werewolf** games is discussed elsewhere (page 187), and has it's possibilities. As for the other foolishness, the best bet is to ask *why* the player wants to play something like that. If the answer is something like "Because it would be cool," then remind the player about the myriad possibilities afforded by the combinations of characteristics listed above. If she's really having trouble finding anything new there, choose her breed, tribe, and auspice randomly and see what the combination suggests.

Totems

One of the first decisions the troupe will make as a group is what totem the pack follows. The Storyteller can handle this decision in a number of ways, depending on the type of chronicle she wants to have.

First, she can allow the players to choose the totem before the game actually starts. The players total their Totem ratings and decide what totem best represents them and their characters, and decide how to spend any Totem points beyond the totem's base cost. The advantage to this method is that it gives the players a good degree of control over their pack's purpose, which in turn gives you, as Storyteller, a clue as to what kind of stories the troupe wishes to tell. On the downside, inexperienced troupes may simply choose whatever totem they feel to be the "best"; i.e., greatest bonuses for easiest Ban, and not worry about what it may mean in the long run to serve Coyote (for example). If you choose this method, make sure the players understand what they're committing to by choosing a particular totem.

Another method is to let the players choose the totem, but during play. This likely involves a spirit quest of some kind; perhaps an Umbral journey (likely with a more experienced Garou as a guide, perhaps the mentor of one of the characters) in which the characters are faced with several possible totems. These totems, all vying for a promising young pack to represent them, present tasks or challenges and decide based on how the pack meets these challenges what spirit best exemplifies the pack (the totems in question, of course, should be those that the pack's collective Totem rating make possible). This method of choosing a totem need not be so involved, however. The pack could simply ask an elder to perform the Rite of the Totem for them, and hope that their chosen totem accepts them. Whether or not it does depends on whether or the Storyteller feels the need to make a story out of the totem choice. If she does, however, the players will hold their pack's totem in much higher regard, for they worked to earn it. Regardless of how much effort the Storyteller requires before the pack finally receives their totem, the "in-play" method is advantageous because it allows the players a good look at the spiritual nature of

Garou society in a (relatively) benign framework. About the only disadvantage of this method of totem choice is that it can be time-consuming. A troupe that meets only once a month might wish to skip this preliminary step and get on to the meat of the chronicle.

Finally, the Storyteller can choose the totem for the pack. Based on how many Totem points the characters have among them, the Storyteller finds what she feels to be the appropriate spirit to act as patron to the pack. The advantage here is clear; it grants the Storyteller the freedom to determine the role of the pack and establish plot hooks based on the totem. This method is frankly more true to the legends and traditions that visionquesting is based on; in a visionquest, the totem chooses *you*, not the other way around. The disadvantage, of course, is that it removes an important decision from the player's hands, which some players will find frustrating.

And what if none of the players purchased the Totem Background? The Storyteller should work with the players to decide why the pack is shunned or ignored by spirits. Perhaps the pack has an ignominious destiny, one that no Incarna wishes its brood to be part of. Perhaps the pack simply needs to prove itself before any spirits will grant favor. Whatever the explanation, the lack of a totem is just as telling about a pack as the choice of totem.

Preludes

Preludes — the one-on-one vignettes between player and Storyteller meant to cover a character's First Change — are discussed to some degree on pages 102-104 of **Werewolf**. This section presents some ideas on how to run preludes for maximum effect, and some alternate ways of running them.

Preludes, as the main rulebook suggests, should be solo time with the Storyteller, possibly even in a separate room. This is the player's time to decide and roleplay the character's "formative moments" of her lycanthropic life, and the less distraction involved, the better. What happens during a werewolf's First Change should shape that character's outlook fairly seriously. For example, a character that changes in response to an attempted mugging or rape is likely to wind up killing her attackers. This may result in the character feeling that she is some sort of avenger, but it just as easily might wrack the character with guilt. However, if the character's First Change is in response to something less violent — simply being out under her auspice's moon and changing to run — the character is likely much less stressed about it. She may still feel that it is something to hide, but may learn to control it (since her shapeshifting does not seem, to her, to be attached to uncontrollable rage) before other Garou find her.

Preludes should also take a character's Backgrounds into consideration. The prelude should give the player a hint as to how difficult it will be to maintain Backgrounds such as Resources and Allies over the course of the chronicle. Perhaps the Curse results in a character losing her job (reflected by that character not having any dots in Resources), or a friend of the character sees her change and loses her mind to the Delirium. At the same time, a character with the Ancestors Background should receive dreams and whispers as her spiritual guides try to assist her (which may have the effect of pushing her to the brink of sanity). A character likely won't have a fetish during the prelude, unless it is some sort of family heirloom that she's also owned. If that's the case, what happens if she sets it off by accident?

Metis and lupus characters require different approaches to their preludes. A lupus werewolf's attitude towards humans is a very important consideration, as the majority of Garou she will meet will be human-born. Did she grow up in captivity, well fed and warm, loved by human keepers? Or did she skulk around a farming community, her territory shrinking every year, living in fear of being shot? The prelude should also serve as a chance to practice roleplaying the lupus mindset. Wolves don't think the same way that humans do, and the way a wolf relates to suddenly being able to think in concepts, rather than images, should be key to roleplaying the character. As the lupus learns about humans, she'll discover that her instincts can be used against her, and she needs to ignore them sometimes. This revelation should be as scary as any that a homid werewolf endures.

Metis Garou have been part of werewolf society since birth, and are arguably better equipped to deal with the sudden transition into "active members" of that society than homid and lupus Garou. However,

the stigma attached to their birth should color every aspect of their upbringing. Imagine being a metis Philodox, and being told that your auspice is responsible for enforcing the Litany — of which you are a walking violation. A metis will likely know the pack's home sept better than any of the other characters (as she very likely grew up there) and should know the other members, at least by name and reputation. The prelude is a good time for the metis to "meet" these characters and discover how they feel about her.

Storytelling the preludes in "mini-sessions" is one (and probably the best) option, but what if the group is pressed for time? The Storyteller may choose to simply give each player a list of questions (email works quite well for this). The questions should be similar to the ones found on page 104 of **Werewolf**, and should be tailored to each character. Ask about Backgrounds — names of Allies and Contacts, where the character got the Fetish, any illustrious Ancestors. If the Storyteller allows Merits and Flaws, those should receive attention here, too (see the sidebar).

Another possibility for preludes is a game called "hot seat." This involves each player taking their turn sitting in the center of the room and letting the other players ask questions, which the player then answers in character (or at least about the character; it's perfectly all right to refer to one's character in third person during this game). The advantage to hot seat is that the players will likely think of some good questions that the Storyteller does not. Also, if one player asks about a character's favorite ice cream flavor (for example), the other players will think about it even if they aren't asked. There are several caveats to hot seat, however. First of all, some people get uncomfortable being "on the spot," and that should be respected. Also, make sure that the player is writing her own answers down. If she doesn't, she will likely forget interesting details that you could use as plot devices later.

Whatever method of prelude the Storyteller chooses, she should pay very close attention to what each individual player focuses on. If two different characters include the deaths of their fathers in their concepts, but one player writes a detailed description of her life with her father, the circumstances of his death, and the day of the funeral, whereas the other player spends more time considering how her character has adjusted to her role as a Garou and other post-First Change events, you have some good clues as to what each player finds important. Perhaps the first player could run across an uncle she barely knew later in the chronicle, a relative who can tell her things about her father that she never got to discover. Maybe the latter character, by throwing herself so completely into her life as werewolf, is trying to escape something from her human life. Even if the players can't tell you straight out what is important to them, the things they choose to detail should give you more than enough material.

Thematic Elements

The players have gone home for the evening, and Matt sits with a pile of character sheets and a stack of **Werewolf** *books, not quite ready to sleep. The players decided on Louisiana as their home, and Matt decides to create a sept in the southern reaches of the state, within spitting distance of the Gulf of Mexico. With that decision made, however, he isn't sure what this chronicle is going to be about.*

Matt reflects that the characters are all, in their ways, outsiders and strangers. The pack is a motley crew, indeed. Different tribes, two metis, all young, all rather ignorant.

As odd a group as they are, Matt reflects that they symbolize the current Garou Nation perfectly — overshadowed by doubt and fear, at odds with each other, and thrown together only by circumstance (Matt decides that the five of them are the only cliaths at the sept). If they can learn to reconcile their differences, they could teach the Garou Nation as a whole, but teach them what? Matt considers, and his eyes fall on his stack of books again. **Nuwisha**, **Corax**, **Mokolé**...*what if this young pack could reconcile with some of the other Breeds?*

Designing a chronicle is such a big task that knowing where to start is difficult. Depending on whether you want the characters to influence the chronicle or vice versa, you might start with character creation (the player's characters, of course, should always take center stage, which is why character creation is presented first in this chapter).

When building the chronicle, you'll want to consider whether it will be driven primarily by the characters or by the plot. Likewise, you'll want to pay attention to themes and moods, and employ symbolism and atmospheric elements to make the chronicle live for the players.

Chronicle Focus — Character vs. Plot

Do you have a plot already forming in your head, only requiring the intrepid pack of Garou to struggle through it? Or would you rather let the pack form whole cloth from the player's imaginations, and see what suggests itself? Either method has merit. If you have strong ideas about where the game will go, the game will feel more structured and probably more epic. If you rely on the players and their characters to build the chronicle one story at a time, you will certainly see those characters develop, and the players will probably care about the events in the chronicle a great deal more.

You can combine these methods, of course. You might choose to start off a chronicle with a story that doesn't involve the characters' histories directly, just to get them working together and establish the setting of the chronicle, and then later design stories more personal to the characters.

An important factor in all of these decisions — probably the most important — is what the players want. You might have a great idea for a post-Apocalyptic **Werewolf** game, but if the players are more interested in playing a modern-day game, you'll do better to listen to them. This doesn't mean that the players should control the chronicle; you're the Storyteller, and you're perfectly within your rights to do as much or as little stage-setting as you feel necessary. Just be aware of your players' thoughts on the matter, and be ready to make some concessions to them if need be.

Theme

Most **Werewolf** books (indeed, most White Wolf books) talk about a theme and mood important to the book's subject matter. The two terms are similar, but fundamentally distinct. In brief, the theme is *what the story is about.*

For example, in the example above, Matt decides that a major *theme* of his chronicle is going to be the young teaching the old. This is a variation of the Marked by Destiny theme mentioned in the **Werewolf** book; the characters, whether they know it or not, are going to show their sept what the Garou should be — *not* what they once were. To further specify this theme, Matt decides to use the other Fera and the War of Rage as focus points — the young pack has a chance to atone for (or exacerbate) the wounds left by the Garou's war on the other Breeds.

But how to make the theme shine through in the chronicle? The Storyteller needs to consider each individual story. As the story begins, he should think of ways to integrate the story's events into the overall theme of the chronicle. If the theme of the chronicle is that the Garou are alone, without teachers, and effectively "reinventing" Garou tradition as they go, then a new story should probably include a new facet of the society that they never learned, and must now try and cope with. In the example above, Matt might introduce a member of a different Breed during each story.

The Storyteller should not be heavy-handed when applying the theme to stories. If the players wish to take the chronicle in a different direction, try to apply the theme to the stories they wish to tell, not yank the plotline back to where you feel it should be. The "Young and Scared" theme mentioned above might take on a quite different twist if the pack decides to quest for another sept of Garou to help them, but that quest would be a fine story. Don't make the theme feel forced — doing so throws the players out of the story.

Mood

The *mood* of a chronicle should "set off" the theme. The mood describes the general feel of the chronicle, and can be expressed by such things as weather, attitudes of Storyteller characters, and the music the Storyteller plays during the game (if any). The mood should enhance the player's understanding and appreciation of the chronicle, so if the players just don't seem to be "getting it," the Storyteller might need to make the mood a bit less subtle.

The mood can and should play a large part in the way the Storyteller structures the game. For example, Matt's chronicle is thematically about the young members of a traditional society schooling the old. This suggests a hidebound, ritualistic backdrop, but the stated setting for the game is southern Louisiana. This simply means that the traditionalist mood needs to come through in other ways. To enforce this mood, Matt might decide to have the sept leader be especially xenophobic — new members and visitors to the sept are rare, and while the moots aren't as formal as some other septs, the same Garou perform them in the same manner every month. This stubborn, "that's-the-way-it's-always-been" ambiance will set the characters (who, as mentioned, are not only new to being Garou but outsiders in many other ways) into their roles as teachers and rebels, whether they mean to be or not. This emphasis on "knowing your place" and "sticking to tradition" helps to create the mood of orthodoxy and hidebound rituals.

The Storyteller can (and should) use visual elements as well; perhaps the sept grounds include the decaying remains of a once-beautiful plantation house. While in past years, the house was magnificent and included slave quarters and several other outbuildings, all that remains now is the main building, covered in moss and vines, cellar flooded with swamp water, snakes sunning themselves on the porch.

Note, however, that just as not every story needs to be tied slavishly to a chronicle's theme, the mood of a story might well vary greatly from the mood of the chronicle. Suppose the characters go on a spirit quest far from their home? The mood will likely be very different, simply because the surroundings are so different. However, the Storyteller may wish to throw little reminders into the story just to keep the overarching mood in the players' minds. While visiting a far-off sept, the characters from Matt's isolationist Sept of the Bayou might run afoul of a cranky, suspicious Master of the Rite, and one of the characters might mutter, "Just like being at home."

Even more than the game's theme, the mood must be maintained. If the Storyteller uses a certain fragrance of incense to set the mood, he should use it for each game. That way, when and if the pack does go traveling and he deliberately doesn't use the scent, the players will notice the change and know that their characters are far from home. Storyteller characters should be played consistently — that way a sudden (or even subtle) change in personality will tip the characters off that something's amiss. The Storyteller might even wish to choose "theme songs" for important places or characters; after a while, the players will associate a given song with its character. This allows him to give players subtle hints (if the players are wondering which sept elder to ask for advice, playing a given elder's song might be helpful without forcing their hands too much).

Game Design

"All right, ladies and gents," says Matt as the players take their seats. "Go ahead and write "To End All Wars" under "Chronicle" on your character sheets. Anybody need anything explained before we start?" He pauses while the players glance over their sheets. They all look fairly confident, so Matt presses play on his stereo and the sounds of wolf howls quietly play in the background. "All eyes are on you as you take your places around the moot fire. This is the first moot you've attended as a pack, and the elders of the sept —"

"Are we gonna order pizza?" pipes Ryan. Matt shoots him a glare and growls a reminder about out-of-character interruptions, but concedes that the idea has merit.

Theme and mood should contribute heavily to the events of the chronicle, but how does the Storyteller decide what those events will be? How does he populate her sept or create enemies for the pack? The theme of the chronicle is a fine concept, and the mood might provide the Storyteller with music ideas, but how do those things translate into game play?

Inspiration from the Players

It would seem a no-brainer, but Storytellers often ignore the characters in designing the game. This is a mistake. If a player states that she and another Garou developed a rivalry that nearly erupted into lethal combat during a Rite of Passage, why couldn't that rival have taken a minor sept position (such as Wyrm Foe) and hold it over the character's head? If a character is obsessed with learning the Silver Record, perhaps the sept is home to an aloof but widely renowned Galliard who knows a large chunk of the Record by heart.

Placing such importance on the character's motivations and goals encourages the players themselves to emphasize these things. When the Storyteller finds herself stuck for ideas, glancing over the pack's character sheets may well yield some plot hooks.

Mythic Cycles

A detailed discussion of the different types of folkloric patterns in literature is beyond the scope of this book (though the Bibliography contains several good suggestions). However, several suggestions on using such patterns in **Werewolf** chronicles are presented here:

• **The Hero's Journey:** You don't need to know a thing about mythology, sociology, or literature to use the Hero's Journey. All you need to do is have a look at *Star Wars*, or *The Matrix*, or any one of hundreds of other films or books. The Hero's Journey actually has twelve stages, which typically happen in a pre-determined order. These steps are:

1) The Ordinary World — The characters in their normal routine.

2) The Call to Adventure — Exactly that; the characters are jarred from their everyday lives and forced into action (or reaction).

3) The Refusal of the Call — The characters save themselves during the Call to Adventure, but for whatever reason, do not pursue the matter further.

4) Meeting with the Mentor — This can be a mentor as dictated by the Background of the same name, or simply an elder interested in the characters. The mentor usually explains the Call to Adventure and impresses on the characters why they should follow it.

5) Crossing the First Threshold — The characters enter the story whole-heartedly. This stage marks the "no turning back" point; they are enmeshed in the adventure for the duration.

6) Tests, Allies, Enemies — The characters gain information about their enemies, make new friends, discover traitors, and endure battles and hardships. Regardless of what happens here, it should relate to the story as a whole.

7) Approach to the Inmost Cave — The characters discover their goal; what they need to do to defeat their enemies. In some cases, this means figuring out who their enemies actually are.

8) The Supreme Ordeal — The characters lose. They lose a battle, lose hope, lose allies — in general, they are defeated. This is the stage where the characters hit rock bottom and must confront their own demons.

9) The Reward — The characters reap the benefits of their tenacity; although they suffered a defeat, they come away with information or another edge that will allow them to best their foes.

10) The Road Back — The characters haven't won. They must now race to implement whatever they gained during the Reward phase. This usually involves being pursued or otherwise dogged by their enemies.

11) The Final Threshold — The characters confront their foes and use what they've learned to win. The victory may indeed by costly — the characters may not all survive it — but in the end, there should be some monumental change.

12) The Return — Renown is handed out, rank challenges ensue, the pack's leadership may change. This is the denouement, where all of the fallout from the Final Threshold is realized. Plotlines left dangling should be tied up somehow. The end of the story should receive at least as much consideration as everything before it.

The Hero's Journey does not need to be structured this way. It can and should be varied, otherwise it will feel formulaic. Take into account where the characters begin — perhaps there really isn't an "Ordinary World" for them. Perhaps they don't refuse the call and wish to pursue the adventure from the get-go. Don't force the players to follow a pre-ordained schedule of events just because Hollywood always seems to.

• **Urban Legends:** Urban legends are folkloric stories presented as real occurrences that usually carry some sort of message. That message can be real and applicable, or it can betray a society's fears and prejudices, but either way both specific urban legends and their general tone can make for good **Werewolf** stories.

For example, stories have circulated for years about giant alligators in New York's sewers and monster catfish living in reservoirs. Nothing says these creatures can't exist and plague — or even aid — the noble Garou. (Examples of such beasts can be found in the **Book of the Wyld**, in fact.) But other, less fantastical legends make for good story fodder, too. How about the story of the kidney thieves, where an unfortunate victim wakes up in a bathtub full of ice after a wild party, only to discover that one (or both) of his kidneys have been removed to be sold on the black market? There's no truth to this story — but doesn't it sound like something that would happen in the World of Darkness? What if such a victim was Kinfolk to one of the characters — or worse, what if the victim was Garou (this would require a drug potent enough to knock the character out, but that only adds to the horror)? Who would do such a thing? Pentex? DNA?

Rather than using urban legends as plot hooks directly, the Storyteller may simply take their style and implement it for a story. Urban legends usually have a poetic or ironic twist, or at the very least, a simple moral. The familiar story about the babysitter who receives phone calls from a madman on an upstairs phone, for example, has a very clear moral — child care demands a great deal of responsibility, and the children *do* need to be checked often, threatening phone calls or no. The "kidney thieves" story usually involves a traveler who meets a stranger at a party or club and wakes up missing organs — this story cautions us to take care when traveling. The Storyteller can work in these simple yet brutal methods of driving home the truths of living in Garou society. Perhaps a member of the sept develops a wasting disease that spreads to the others and misses the pack by sheer chance. The pack investigates and eventually discovers that the first Garou to contract the disease killed and ate a human being, and thereafter became sick. Whether or not the disease is curable, the pack has witnessed a gruesome, firsthand reminder of one of the tenets of the Litany.

• **Brainstorming:** One of the best methods for developing ideas about a chronicle (or simply one story) is to clear one's mind and then think about **Werewolf**. What elements of the game appeal? Why? What associations come to mind? Take a pen and paper and make a list of story elements and ideas, and then choose the ones that flow together nicely, and then see if a story suggests itself.

Example: Matt has ideas for the theme and mood of his chronicle, but doesn't quite know what to do for the first story. (The importance of the first story in a chronicle is discussed below.) He takes up his four-color pen and notebook and starts jotting down thoughts. A few moments later, he has the following list:

- Corax
- Shiny things
- Treasure
- Pirates
- Vampires
- Curse
- Leech-like Banes
- Bane-infested 'gators
- Violins
- Bayou
- Cajun music/zydeco
- Lovecraftian horror beneath Marsh Island
- *The Colour Out of Space*
- Saloon near the beach
- Small bayou towns

After looking over the list, Matt scraps the "tainted alligators" idea for now. He also discards the Lovecraft inspiration; he may come back to these ideas later, but for now he wants to focus on the vampire pirates and their buried — and possibly cursed — treasure.

A major caveat of this method is not to try everything on the list in one story. Pick and choose elements that work nicely together, or create a nice contrast (how about

playing zydeco music as the vampires descend from their ship to find their treasure?). Be willing to postpone or forget entirely elements that seem gratuitous, silly, or over the top.

The First Story

"I think there's something else on Marsh Island," says Brian. The first story is over, the vampire pirates vanquished with the help of the pack's new ally Guards-the-Hunters, a pleasant (if somewhat pedantic) Corax. The players are chatting out of character as Matt decides how much downtime there will be before the next story begins. *"Remember those weird spirits that showed up?"*

"Sound like something your pack will be investigating?" asks Matt casually.

"Depends on if the elders want us to," answers Halle. Her character, the fish-out-of-water Fianna, is the pack alpha, and the other players nod. Brian, however, looks thoughtful. Matt smirks. Dissention in the ranks, *he thinks.*

The first story is a test for everyone involved. The characters are facing their first challenges together as a pack. The players are testing their

characters to see if the concepts they dreamed up will stand against the rigors of roleplaying, and to see if those concepts are appropriate to the chronicle. The Storyteller is testing moods, themes, ideas, his own characters, and his storytelling and gamemastering abilities. The first story needs to have effort poured into it — it is, after all, the measuring stick by which every other story in the chronicle will be judged.

Length and Breadth

The first story probably shouldn't go more than three sessions. There needs to be a distinct end to it, to emphasize that this story is a lead-in to the chronicle, but is not the whole chronicle. The story should be fairly concise — while it can certainly introduce plot hooks that are left dangling, the main challenge of the story should be resolved. This gives the characters a minor victory they can claim (or perhaps a defeat to live down) and gives the players a good jumping-off point.

If the players are not familiar with **Werewolf**, use the first story to lightly incorporate as much of the game as possible. Combat, the Umbra, Gifts, rites, spirits — make the story a light overview of **Werewolf**. Don't focus too much on one aspect (especially not combat) — let the players sample various elements. They will decide (and probably let you know) which parts they like the best.

Tweaking

When the first story is over, you may wish to allow the players to "tweak" their characters slightly. Perhaps a player flippantly referred to her days as a high school athlete, but has no rating in Athletics. You might consider letting her swap dots from another Ability to bring her character in line with this past experience. Just as a play can't really be appreciated unless it's seen in production, a character can't fully be tested except in game play. The first story should still be considered part of the preliminary stages of a chronicle, and that means minor changes to everything, characters, plot, and so on, are acceptable.

You should also nail down any house rules you decide to use by the end of the first story. You might decide that the botch rules presented in **Werewolf** are "too soft" and rule that a roll is botched if more one's are rolled than successes. Tell your players about this change, test it during the first story, and keep it or scrap it before moving on the next story.

Experience and Other Rewards

You are setting a precedent in how much experience you give out at the end of the first story. Reward practices you wish to encourage — a particularly good scene might merit an experience point granted on the spot. Likewise, it is acceptable to dock experience from players who show up late or disrupt game play consistently. Just make sure

you have a system from doling out experience, so that if someone asks why they only received two points this session instead of three, you know how to answer.

Likewise, pay attention to Renown. Do the characters accrue Renown during game play, or is it all granted at a moot when the characters tell the stories of their exploits (which puts a great deal of responsibility on the pack's Galliard)? Chapter One gives more information and advice on Renown and Rank, but again, be consistent.

Decide how difficult it is for characters to learn Gifts and raise other Traits. Don't allow one player to simply spend the experience and learn a new Gift while another must go on a prolonged spirit quest (unless the latter character has some stated handicap when it comes to learning Gifts, of course).

Downtime

After the first story, the Storyteller must decide how much time passes between stories. This is important — if the next story begins only a day later, the characters have barely had time to breathe, much less recuperate (which might be exactly the effect you want). Ask the players to consider what their characters do during the downtime. Do they attempt to learn new Gifts or rites? Do they seek training from other Garou, or do they return to their pre-Garou lives given half a chance? If they wish to follow up on leads and hints discovered during the first story, listen carefully. They are complimenting you on a well-crafted tale by paying attention and caring about the story. Your thanks should take the form of letting their characters follow the paths that the players find intriguing, and using these paths to craft the next story.

Middle

Once the chronicle has begun and a story or two have been told, Storytellers may be tempted to coast. After all, the pack has likely made some friends — and enemies — and the players have discovered what they like and do not like about **Werewolf**. If the players seem to enjoy a rousing combat, why not throw one into every session? If they enjoy questing into the Umbra, why, there are thirteen Realms mentioned in the core book — enough for more than a dozen stories.

The danger here should be obvious. No matter how exciting a plotline was when the players first experienced it, it will not have the same effect the second time. During the body of the chronicle, the Storyteller should keep her eyes on progression, not repetition. That is, where is the chronicle going? This section deals with how to make sure the chronicle goes somewhere, preferably somewhere entertaining.

Chronicle Development

Matt closes the door behind his players and walks back into the living room. He puts away the books and the character sheets, and flips open a notebook to write down the events of the recently concluded story.

The pack is not the same doubtful, tentative bunch of Garou that he began the chronicle with. Halle's character, Vevila, is pregnant. This will entail her making another character, probably at the end of the next story, as Vevila will soon be too far along to shapeshift. Brian's Fenrir warrior has stopped drinking, and has functionally assumed leadership of the pack, even though Vevila is still technically alpha. The Red Talon — Julie's character — has begun accompanying Blood Rain and the other Red Talons of the sept on their "hunts". Like the other Talons, Red Shadow does not know that Blood Rain is a Black Spiral spy. All in all, the characters are coming along nicely. But where to go next?

Pack Development

As the chronicle progresses, the pack must develop as an entity. Each character develops separately, and tracking character progression is simple (at least in game terms) as the players spend experience points. The pack's development, however, is a bit subtler.

Pay attention to what the characters do during downtime. Do they go their separate ways? Do any of them pay homage to their totem? Do they hang out together as friends, or do they consider each other co-workers? A pack has a spiritual bond, and most pack members would fight to the death to protect each other. That doesn't make them friends, however, and that truth can be hard to understand.

If the pack does not spend any time improving itself as a pack, perhaps they find pack tactics harder to use as their mystical connection erodes. Perhaps their totem grows distant or shows favoritism to the pack member(s) that pay attention to it. If the pack starts fragmenting, introduce a Storyteller-controlled pack that makes the characters looks pathetic. The pack is one of the central components of a **Werewolf** game, and it needs as much attention as any of the werewolves that comprise it.

One reason the pack needs so much attention is that each pack in the End Times has a quest to complete. Once that purpose is filled, the pack need no longer remain together. Indeed, it is possible for a Garou to join a pack while still young, stay with that pack until it completes its quest, and then join another pack later (though this is by no means common).

As Storyteller, you should be thinking about the pack's quest from the very first story. The pack's totem should be a guide — a pack that follows Fenris, for example, likely has a different purpose than one that follows Dolphin. Also, consider what tribes the pack

member belong to — a tribe composed mostly (or entirely) of Uktena and Wendigo might be destined to right some great wrong the Wyrmcomers inflicted on the Pure Lands (on the other hand, a pack composed of Wyrmcomers might have the same purpose, but the stories involved would be quite different).

Perhaps most importantly, listen to the players. They will very likely find their own goals for the pack, and although it might pain the Storyteller to set aside her carefully planned storylines, hearing the player's rousing cheers as they destroy their arch-enemy or reopen a lost pathway to a home realm inevitably makes it worthwhile.

As the pack's path becomes clearer, you can start giving them signs and visions of their destiny. Dreams are one possibility, especially if the pack's Theurge has learned the Gift: Sight from Beyond. The way that other beings react to the pack might also foreshadow their fate. If a pack's purpose is to prevent a caern from defilement by the Wyrm's forces, perhaps spirits begin referring to the pack members as "honored guardians" or "noble defenders". The pack will probably assume that the spirits are referring to their duties as Gaia's defenders, at least for a while.

A pack's Renown should also help to gauge their purpose. If the pack has a reputation for prowess in battle, Ahroun will likely acknowledge that when they meet the pack. You can gauge a pack's Renown by averaging the permanent Renown scores of the individual members, or you could keep a loose record of Renown for the pack as a whole. As Galliards begin singing tales of the pack's exploits, the pack might discover that Theurges have seen visions of them performing some great deed. That deed may well become their purpose.

As the pack develops, you might consider a story that stresses (or puts stress upon) the bonds between its members. Play on the differences between the characters' back-stories and attitudes. Perhaps some of them feel that the Wyrm is the greater threat, while others fear the machinations of the Weaver. Put them in a position where they must choose their foe — all things being equal, how does the pack handle that kind of decision? Another way to highlight the importance of the pack is through its totem. Totems are not omnipotent or necessarily benign forces; many of them have agendas, which means they sometimes work at cross-purposes with other spirits. Take a good look at the pack's totem and see what images — and stories — come to mind.

Character Development

Each member of the pack has her own story to complete. As Storyteller, you must be ready to help the players in telling these stories, and there are many ways you can help players to develop their characters.

One of the simplest is to guide experience point expenditure. Buying new Traits should always be a joint effort between player and Storyteller. The Storyteller is the final judge of whether or not a character is ready to buy a new Trait or increase an old one, and because increasing an Ability or Attribute is a twenty percent increase (as each such Trait has a five dot maximum), a substantial amount of study and practice should take place before raising the Trait. Be particularly careful about letting players raise Abilities to four and five dots. Having such a score indicates that the character is among the world's best at the Ability! Also, take into consideration the character's foibles when allowing (or restricting) experience purchases. If a character is uncomfortable in the spirit realms and prefers talking to material beings to trying to deal with spirits, it doesn't make sense for the character to buy a new Gift every session. In fact, you may well rule that the sept's Theurge needs proof that the character can handle learning a Gift before he summons a spirit to teach it. Likewise, if a character wishes to learn a new language, make sure that she is devoting the necessary time to it. If you plan on taking a great deal of downtime between stories, the player can simply say "My character devotes three hours a day to studying," but if the character needs to learn the language while a story is actually going on, her player needs to find the time for the character to hit the books.

Before experience is spent, of course, it has to be earned. Another way to guide character development is by the Learning Curve point award (see page 180 of **Werewolf**). If the character learned anything during a session, the lesson grants an experience point. However, the Storyteller should make sure that what the character learned isn't going to be forgotten by the next chapter, especially if the character gained some interesting insight into the pack, the Garou, or herself. If a character comes to the conclusion that the elders in the sept are just posturing and aren't really as great and wise as they're made out to be, write that down so that you can refer to it in later games. Perhaps the Wyrm's minions might use the character's rebellious thoughts against her. And what if she voices her attitudes and the elders find out? That might make for difficult rank challenges later on.

Each character has (or should have) a history, a story that began long before the character joined the pack. The more detail the players provide about their characters' pasts, the more attention you can give to their futures. Likewise, if a player leaves large segments of his character's past empty (which the Storyteller should discourage during the Prelude, but even then, sometimes there are holes that don't get filled) the Storyteller is within her rights to make some history up herself (within reason and with player approval, of course — the player should retain control of her character!). After a few stories have passed,

look at each character's history and background and see if there are elements that are as yet unresolved that could be worked into upcoming stories. Likewise, look for any new developments. New enemies, new friends, lovers, major battles (and possibly battle scars) — all of these things can change a character's outlook. So what if a character had a girlfriend before becoming a Garou and hasn't seen her since he left to join the pack? Now, after venturing through Wyrm-infested cesspits and Umbral reaches, she comes to visit and asks why he hasn't written lately. How does he view her? Is she a safe haven from the horror that his life has become? Or is she a stifling reminder of the banality of human life? Lupus and metis characters may have similar experiences. What if a lupus werewolf desires to visit her old territory and finds much of it paved? What if a metis has always wanted to find his real parents? Any of these can become stories for the entire pack, and because they involve the characters (or at least one of them) so directly, the stakes are much higher in such stories. Also, they encourage pack development, as the entire pack lends its efforts to the needs or desires of one of its members.

Renown and reputation contribute to character development in much the same way that they do to pack development. Perhaps a character enters Garou society without a deed name, and gains one during a story. The story of how the character gained her name will likely be told at a moot, bolstering the character's Renown and cementing her place in the sept. As characters gain reputations, other Garou — even elders — might seek them out for advice and aid in certain endeavors. Such reputations are usually specific; in a society full of warriors, it is unlikely that a character will ever be known simply as "a good fighter." Instead, the character's penchant for tearing out opponent's throats might become a subject of conversation — even among her enemies. As characters gain Renown, and eventually rank, they should find themselves shouldering new responsibilities. Ahroun may be required to train new Guardians. Galliards, Philodox, and Theurges are all expected to learn rites of various kinds. Of course, no one really knows what to expect from the no-moons....

Story Development

As the pack progresses towards whatever goals it may have set, keep in mind the direction of the story. While the players may take control and develop their own agendas, and while these agendas may take entire stories to realize, the Storyteller must always be ready to throw the characters headlong into another plot twist. Some Storytellers, after a few stories (or even just a few chapters), run dry and find themselves floundering for ideas.

Inspiration for new stories is all around us. Read the news — there's always some crisis occurring somewhere, and perhaps the latest one would make for a good **Werewolf** story. Likewise, books, film, television, and even music can suggest a story.

However, in the middle of a chronicle, the best source of inspiration might well be what has gone before. Are there any dangling plot hooks that could suddenly become crucial? Does the pack have enemies that could show up to make trouble? Avoid gratuitous use of "bad guys" here; if they're going to show up to challenge the pack, their plan shouldn't be "throw ourselves at the pack until they kill us." Ask yourself what the antagonists want that would bring them into conflict with the characters.

If nothing from the chronicle to this point inspires you (or if the chronicle is still young enough that the characters' exploits haven't had far-reaching consequences), throw the pack a curve ball. Perhaps a venerated elder dies, apparently of natural causes. One such death can easily fuel a story. Someone, after all, must perform the Gathering for the Departed. Perhaps the elder left instructions with another Garou regarding the treatment of his body — or his fetishes. And what if the elder didn't really die of natural causes at all?

Another possibility is to ask the players what they would like to see (which the Storyteller should do periodically anyway). One method that works well is to ask each player to write down three ideas or suggestions for the chronicle, and see if any of the suggestions match up. The players will likely remember events and characters that the Storyteller thought insignificant at the time. If the players think the blond-haired man they chatted with in a diner during the very first session was important in some way, make him so. Create a persona and history for him, and bring him into the chronicle again, this time with motivation and agenda. You can also let the players subtly shape who he is — "Remember how thin the guy is? And how he picked at his food? I'll bet he's a Corax!" When you hear things like this, put on your best poker face and let the players enjoy saying "I knew it!" when the blond man grows feathers.

Storyteller Character Development

The elders of the sept, the characters' lovers and friends, even the pack's worst enemy — these characters are as deserving of development and growth as any

---

The Dreaded Metaplot

"Fuck you, I won't do what you tell me!"
— Rage Against the Machine, "Killing in the Name"

Some Storytellers follow White Wolf "canon" religiously. If a caern falls in **Rage Across Ohio**, then it falls in the chronicle. A major villain dies? Too bad that he's been terrorizing the character's sept and the pack was looking forward to meeting him in battle.

Other Storytellers, of course, couldn't care less. After all, the Golden Rule — supposedly the only inviolate rule of the game — says that the game belongs to the players, right? So who cares if Tah-Kcalb, the Scion of the Wyrm, dies in some sourcebook? Not in *your* World of Darkness, he didn't!

Frankly, either of these attitudes is fine. The metaplot isn't there to dictate how you run your games. It's there to make the world of **Werewolf** a bit more dynamic. If something happens in a sourcebook that you feel would never have happened in your chronicle, ignore it (or better yet, have your players' pack become the stars of the show). We don't mind. You know the needs of your chronicle better than we ever could.

All well and good, but what about when a player scoops up a new sourcebook, reads about a "canonical" event, and wants to base a major facet of his character around it? Do you veto the idea, simply because it would rely too much on metaplot? Of course not. Read the sourcebook in question and decide, first of all, if the idea has good story potential. If so, work with the player, change whatever is necessary, and go forward with the idea.

On a related note, if you're planning on making a major change to established canon, or changing the basic rules of the game in any way, tell the players *before* play begins. It's perfectly all right to decide that the Garou have already won the war in the Amazon, or have made peace with the Ananasi, or even to rule that the bite of a werewolf is infectious to humans (see Chapter Five for tips on variant **Werewolf** games, in fact). But the players deserve to know about it, so that they may take such changes into account when creating their characters. Plus, you might want to run your ideas by the players first. You might detest the whole idea that werewolves learn "Gifts" from spirits, but your players may feel differently, and might well resent such a fundamental aspect of the game being yanked out from under them.

In general, just remember that published sourcebooks are resources for **Werewolf**, not instruction manuals. They should provide ideas and plot hooks, not force you to give up playing a certain tribe because a book says they all disappeared one fine day. With all that in mind, don't let the metaplot make you angry, either. If every event in every book came with a little disclaimer saying "Only use this idea in your games if you really want to," the books would contain about 10 pages of real content. There's a lot of good material in these books, so let it *inspire* your stories, not *influence* them.

that the players control. These characters learn from their mistakes and experiences just as the players' characters do, and their motivations and goals — especially with regards to the pack — can and should evolve. If the Storyteller characters are not well-rounded and interesting, they're little more than the healers and vendors of computer "role-playing games." The more detail the Storyteller puts into her characters, the more the pack will feel that the story is a living, ongoing drama.

This doesn't mean, however that the supporting cast has all the answers. Sometimes they lie. Sometimes they don't know what they're talking about — or just misunderstand what they're asked. If you have a good grasp of a character's background and knowledge (sometimes it's a good idea to make a "what she knows" list on the back of a Storyteller character's sheet or in a notebook), you run a much-reduced risk of portraying the character inconsistently — and the more consistent a character is, the easier it is for the players to notice when something does change….

Friends: The pack's allies and friends can be difficult to play well. It is tempting, for both the Storyteller and the players, to regards characters represented by Backgrounds (Allies, Contacts, Kinfolk and Mentor) as resources for the character to call upon. Consider these Backgrounds to represent not the actual people involved, but the character's relationship with them. By taking dots in the Mentor background, the player isn't creating a higher-ranked Garou, he's creating a relationship between that Garou and his character. This in mind, these relationships need to be maintained, and the cost of that maintenance is largely up to the Storyteller. Mentors may demand help with complicated rites, or may send young Garou on missions to fetch herbs or spirits. One character's Mentor may be the rival of another character's Mentor, and the two doting elders may begin a sort of "pissing contest" as each one encourages his charge to outdo the other's.

Allies are the character's friends, and that means that the Storyteller needs to know not only what the Garou gets out of the relationship, but what the Ally gets out of it. It's great that the character bowls with the county sheriff, and since they're friends, the character can nudge the sheriff to look into environmental crimes, but what does the Garou do for the sheriff (other than increase their bowling team's average)? The Storyteller should occasionally have Allies contact the character and ask for whatever favors the character would seem to be able to grant. If a character goes for a long period of time without contacting his Allies, consider whether or not the Ally will take offense. An old college buddy with whom the character exchanges Christmas cards, but has

little contact with otherwise, will probably not be annoyed at not hearing from the character in months, but the bowling buddy will be justifiably miffed if the character misses league night three weeks in a row.

Maintaining Contacts is much simpler. Since a personal relationship is not assumed, as it is with Allies, Contacts can usually be called upon with impunity. However, the Storyteller can still use these characters to further the story. Suppose the character has a Contact who happens to be a secretary for an executive at King Breweries. What happens if she gets promoted to management? The character now has to worry whether or not her new position will taint her — and what that might mean to the Garou. Likewise, since Contacts often don't have any particular loyalty to the characters, the pack's enemies, either to gain information or set up ambushes may lean them on. And if the police ever have a reason to investigate a character, they will look up any known associates. A Contact with a good memory and a reason to talk can often give out damaging information on a character.

Kinfolk, even more than Allies, require a character's attention. They are family, and that means that they can relate to Garou in ways that no one else (including other Garou) can. The temptation to use Kinfolk as bait — having them kidnapped by Black Spiral Dancers or possessed by Banes — can be great, and this is certainly a way to motivate characters. However, beware of turning Kinfolk into weak, helpless mortals who exist only to be rescued. Kinfolk are most Garou's greatest link to the human world. The Curse prevents many werewolves from taking active roles in society, but they can often work through Kinfolk. This requires treating them well, of course, and some Garou don't. As Storyteller, pay attention to how a character treats his Kinfolk. Does he visit them often, or does he shy away for fear of leading enemies to his family? Does he include them in Garou society, or does he keep them protected as much as possible? **Kinfolk: Unsung Heroes** provides an in-depth look at Garou-Kinfolk relations, and gives some good ideas on how to best use Kinfolk in a **Werewolf** chronicle.

Foes: Chapter Four goes into detail about various kinds of antagonists that may show up in a **Werewolf** chronicle and how to use them well. However, something to keep in mind, no matter what sort of supernatural powers a foe exhibits, is that antagonists should develop and grow from their contact with the pack.

If the pack fights a pack of Black Spiral Dancers and kills one, the survivors will probably remember the "Gaian scum" that murdered their packmate and will return to even the score eventually. But those Dancers don't have to simply show up slavering and foaming, spoiling for do-or-die combat. Perhaps they watch the characters closely for months, learning their strategies and weaknesses. Perhaps they set up ambushes or learn Gifts to compensate for their own shortcomings.

But even beyond the level of strategy, if a rivalry or enmity is to be kept hot between the pack and their foes, what's keeping it hot? Is the pack gaining a reputation as the "Constant Foes of the Screaming Sludge Pack?" Is one side perpetuating the feud simply because it garners them renown to have such powerful foes? If so, then what happens when one side wins? Or perhaps the fight is more personal — if there is history between the pack and their enemies, detail it (if it didn't happen during the actual chronicle). How did the first skirmish end? Has the pack witnessed their foes' awful deeds, or only heard about them?

And enemies need not be Wyrm (or Weaver) servitors, anyway. Police, hunters, even a character's own family can fall into adversarial roles, and as they learn more about the pack, their tactics and attitudes should change. Perhaps a cop is chasing a character on suspecting terrorism charges and discovers that the "terrorist" is actually a werewolf. That cop isn't necessarily going to immediately go home and start loading shotgun shells with silver. He might ask around on the force to see if they've seen anything similar, which may attract attention from other agencies, which then might investigate the characters. Even if the characters manage to stave off an assault or shake a shadower, the question remains: How did they find out about us in the first place? When developing antagonists, keep in mind how much they know about the pack and who might be able to get hold of that information.

Storyteller characters should never remain static. Between each story, the Storyteller should make a list of the major characters in the chronicle and perhaps some notes about what they've done during downtime and whether any major changes have befallen them. Their lives should not be steady and uneventful; no one's life is. Perhaps a character's Ally gets divorced and takes some time off work, effectively making that Ally useless for a time. Perhaps a Kinfolk gets into a car accident and is in intensive care. A character could use Mother's Touch and heal her easily — but not without breaking the Veil. While the pack should retain the starring roles, other characters should be vital and dynamic as well, otherwise they become two-dimensional, and ultimately not much more than information-dispensers for the players.

Player Issues

Matt opens the door and finds Halle standing there with a guy he hasn't met. "Hey, Matt," she says, "can my boyfriend play tonight?"

"Hi, Halle's boyfriend," says Matt, not a little annoyed. He invites them in, however. It turns out that Halle's beau has a character ready, a Bone Gnawer who is almost completely ignorant about Garou culture and was never given a proper Rite of Passage. Matt opens his notes and rearranges some events, and decides that he can work the new character in. He does warn his new player that he isn't going to force the pack to take him in or even accept him.

The game begins, and Matt runs a scene with the pack, while on guard duty, discovering the new character skulking around the caern. He introduces himself as Bacon Bits. Matt shakes his head as the other players laugh. Lost, hopeless, and ignorant — Bacon Bits actually fits right in, thinks Matt. OK, he can stay.

Gaining and Losing Players

A troupe that stays constant long enough to make up a chronicle is, sadly, a rarity. More often, one member will drop out for one reason or another, or one of the players wants to bring a new boyfriend or girlfriend along to play. How should the Storyteller handle it?

Gaining new players in the middle of a chronicle can be difficult to handle gracefully, particularly if you have no need of another character. This can be especially difficult in **Werewolf**, where the characters are bonded by a totem and adding new members to the pack requires ceremony and challenges.

The first consideration should simply be whether or not there is room in the chronicle for another player. If the chronicle is drawing to a close, the addition of another character might just bog things down and sidetrack the story. Plus, the new character wouldn't receive the amount of attention and time she deserves. Also, some Storytellers are not comfortable with more than a given number of players, and going from five to six people to keep track of is too much to handle. The Storyteller is perfectly within her rights to refuse a new player if she feels that either the chronicle or the troupe can't support a new face. However, she might consider running a side story or a one-shot game including the new player, especially if that player wishes to try role-playing for the first time.

If the Storyteller decides that she does wish to allow a new player, what then? The Storyteller and the new player should, if at all possible, meet and play through a solo game or two, getting a feel for where the character is coming from and why he'll be in the area in which the chronicle is set. If the new player doesn't have a character concept, the Storyteller might well be able to suggest one that would fit into the story well. If the story is set in a caern of Visions, perhaps another sept sends an emissary to ask permission to use the caern's oracular powers. If the pack has made a name for itself finding lost cubs, maybe the new player could play a young werewolf in the throes of his First Change.

Gaining players is normally a bonus to a chronicle. A new character can take the chronicle in new directions, spice up pack dynamics, and, if necessary, shake a game out of a rut. Losing a player can do this as well, but rarely does it go as smoothly.

Players can drop out of games for any number of reasons. Family or job concerns can force people to reexamine their priorities, and hobbies often have to take a back burner to more important obligations. Sometimes a player will quit a game she finds boring — this is why it is so important to maintain communication between Storyteller and players. A player that feels she can talk to the Storyteller if she starts losing interest in the game is much less likely to simply quit.

If a player must leave a game, ask why. If she truly isn't enjoying herself, the troupe is better off without her. If, however, the problem is something correctable, work to fix it. If she has a problem with scheduling, see if the troupe could meet on a different night. If the problem is something temporary — final exams, perhaps — offer to temporarily sideline her character and run a solo game when her schedule calms down. Most problems can be worked around, if the player really wants to remain in the group.

If the problem is with the group, however, the situation becomes somewhat less flexible. A troupe that includes a couple may be in trouble if the couple breaks up. In such a situation, try not to take sides. Simply tell the affected parties that if they cannot resolve differences and play together that one or both of them will need to stop playing. If they cannot resolve this themselves, it may fall to the Storyteller to excuse one of the players from the group. This can also happen if a player is causing problems and offending other players (see Maturity, below).

A Caveat for Storytellers:

Ask the new player — *not* the player attempting to bring her in — if she really wants to be a part of the game. It happens, sadly frequently, that a player wishes his significant other to be part of the hobby (which is only natural) and the significant other in question goes along with it without a clear idea of how the game works. Make sure the player has some enthusiasm, or at least curiosity, about **Werewolf**. If you are unsure, ask if perhaps the potential player would care to sit in on a game and observe for a session before actually playing. Take time to answer any questions she has about the game and the characters, and gauge how well you think she would take to the game. You don't want a new player who is only playing to humor her boyfriend — it's nearly always detrimental to your games.

Asking someone to leave is never easy. The most mature way to handle it is to calmly explain to the player what the problem is, and tell him that the other players would be more comfortable playing without him. If the player offers to make an apology and try to curb whatever the problem behavior is, let him, but don't make any promises. This is obviously not an enjoyable part of being a Storyteller, but the point of the game is to have a good time, and if one player disrupts that good time for everyone else, the Storyteller needs to make the proper adjustments.

Character Death

Having a player leave the game is, of course, very different than losing a character. A character might disappear from the action for any number of reasons. She might die in battle, or become wounded or sickened to point that she can no longer travel with the pack. She might even become tainted and wind up in Erebus.

If a character becomes inactive because the player wishes to retire her and play a new character, all a Storyteller can do is try to finagle the events so that they don't disrupt the story too much. Try to set up the event during the course of a story so that it doesn't feel gratuitous, and focus on the character, giving her the send-off (even temporarily) that she deserves. (Of course, this may result in the player deciding she really likes her character after all, but that's just part of the fun of being a Storyteller.) If possible, try to introduce the player's new character during the story as well.

If, however, a character dies in battle, the Storyteller has two options. She can let the chips (and dice) fall where they may. Battle is, after all, a dangerous pastime, and a sudden casualty may serve to remind the pack (and the players) that even the mighty Garou are not indestructible.

On the other hand, it is a game. If the player would obviously feel cheated by losing her character to a random throw of the dice, let the character off with a Battle Scar. It's up to you as Storyteller to judge whether or not the drama offered by a character's death is worth the trouble of introducing a new character. If you let the character "off the hook," stress how close she came to death. Have one of the elders perform a Rite of Wounding and have a Galliard sing her praises, but at the same time, perhaps her Kinfolk lover is suddenly standoffish and aloof, trying to cope with almost losing his beloved. Make the threat of death real and scary, and even if death doesn't actually touch the pack, it can have an impact.

If you do decide to lower the proverbial boom, however, play the moment up for maximum drama. Run the character's Gathering for the Departed, making sure the rest of the pack gets a moment to say a few words. Show the reactions of any Storyteller characters close to the deceased, particularly Kinfolk and close friends. And what if the character has friends who don't know about the Garou? It falls to her packmates to make up some kind of story to tell her friends. A packmate's death may very well fuel a story on its own. *Never* cheapen the moment by glossing it over, simply bringing in a new character at the end of the session. That's disrespectful to the character, the player, and the story.

Maturity

Talking about maturity when discussing a fantasy game in which the "mature" people involved pretend to be werewolves might seem a bit incongruous. However, maturity really is key to playing **Werewolf** well, and it has little or nothing to do with the game specifically. When we speak of maturity within the confines of a role-playing game, we actually refer to treating other players with maturity and sensitivity. Certain issues, while they exist in the real world and certainly exist in the World of Darkness, elicit bad reactions from players. These include rape, molestation, sex, drug use, and family member death. This doesn't mean that these things can't be used as game elements, but a good Storyteller will ask before a chronicle begins if there are any topics best left avoided. If a player feels uncomfortable during a game, that player isn't having fun, which is, of course, the point of the whole thing. As Storyteller, make sure the players know that they can voice concerns over such issues and expect to have those concerns heard. You can encourage this kind of behavior by example and by keeping communication lines between you and the players open. If one of the players is being offensive, it falls to you to smooth things out (see Problem Players, on page 113).

End

Stories were not meant to go on forever. Sooner or later, a chronicle has to end. Hopefully, the ending comes at the right time — the Storyteller does not have to end the game prematurely and has not tried to drag it out beyond its logical conclusion. This section offers some advice on how — and when — to end a **Werewolf** chronicle.

Preparing for the End

When is it appropriate to end a game? When the characters reach a certain rank, or dispose of their greatest foe? Or when the players simply get tired of playing **Werewolf**?

Knowing when it is time to end a chronicle is difficult. This is one reason to start thinking about the pack's quest early on in the chronicle (see Pack Development, above). If you have ideas for what the pack's spiritual quest will be, the chronicle should end with them completing it (or perhaps failing to do so).

Premature Ends

Ending a chronicle before its time is always an unhappy possibility. If players — or the Storyteller — suddenly discover that they must withdraw from the chronicle, it is often better to end it than to struggle to keep the story going. Make the last story something really special. Ask the players if there are any characters they would like to see again (if only for the purpose of wreaking revenge). Bring the powerful antagonists out for a fight to the death (see Final Battles, below). But beyond all of the violence and pyrotechnics, try to weave the threads of the story together. See if it would make sense to combine several dangling plot points, if only to give some closure. If the characters have consistently run afoul of a circle of human mages, and occasionally found themselves beset by crab-like Banes, reveal in the final chapter that the mages were summoning the Banes from the darkest reaches of the Umbra. So what if that conclusion goes entirely against what you were leading up to? The players won't know it, and as long as you present it convincingly, the story won't suffer from a last-minute behind the scenes change.

If there are pack members that have skeletons in their closets, try to flush them out during the last story. Such things really should be resolved before the chronicle's conclusion, so that the heroes can confront their nemeses with clear consciences, but if the chronicle must end suddenly, that isn't always possible. Have the nemesis in question throw the character's darkest deeds in her face. Test pack loyalty at every turn. In desperate situations, when the stakes are highest, will the pack turn on itself?

Planned Conclusions

If you have time to build up to a conclusion, however, take the time to wrap up any loose ends that don't have any bearing on the final story. If you've planted seeds that never came to fruition, however, scrap them. Even if you had a great idea for a story in Pangaea, if the characters never picked up the bait and ventured there, you shouldn't force them into it now. Again, keep communication open with the players and find out what's really important to them in the chronicle, which characters they'd like to see again, what places they'd like to visit (or revisit) before the end.

Decide on what is going to happen during the last story. What event is going to mark the climax of the chronicle? **Werewolf** is about savage horror, and therefore should end with a bang, not a whimper. Is there going to be a horrible battle? Are the characters going to lead an invasion of a Black Spiral Hive? Attempt to hold a Grand

Moot? Open a new caern? Or perhaps the stakes are somewhat smaller — perhaps the chronicle ends with the once-inexperienced pack holding sept positions and running a moot at their home sept for the first time.

The final chapter need not be traumatic, either. A wedding or birth can hold all the drama and excitement of a battle to the death (ask any married person). Perhaps the final chapter is a celebratory moot. Much could go wrong, true, but the atmosphere will be very different. Use the final chapter to play up the theme and mood of your chronicle, and make it a logical conclusion.

Final Battles

Halle throws her dice again. "Three more successes," she says. "This is gonna be close." The other players look tense. If Vevila — Halle's character — cannot open the caern before sunrise, her life may well be forfeit.

Matt turns to Julie. "You smell something strange, rolling in off the water. It doesn't smell like seaside decay, more like oil…."

"Oh, shit," says Julie. "Red Shadow's going to howl the Warning of the Wyrm's Approach. And I'll add 'Thurifuge' to the howl."

Final battles do not have to mean battles for the fate of Gaia, though they certainly can. The last battle in a chronicle should be bloody, brutal, and epic, whether the characters are fighting a Pentex First Team or the Duke of Malfeas.

Enemies of the Pack

During a long chronicle, a pack of Garou can make enemies in high places fairly easily. Powerful Wyrm-beasts, elder Black Spirals, even other Garou can regard the pack as mortal foes. And when the chronicle ends, those enemies should come looking for the characters (or vice versa).

A final battle with longtime foes may seem Hollywood, but actually the notion is much older than that. Consider Ragnarok, for example. In the final battle between the Norse gods, many of the combatants sought out and slew their greatest foes — often at the cost of their own lives. That notion should give the characters pause — certainly, they may hate their enemies, but are they willing to die to take those enemies with them?

That question applies to the enemies as well, of course. If the enemies are indeed willing to sacrifice themselves to slay the pack, how are they going to ensure victory? Silver weapons? Explosives? Bane allies? And if they don't wish to die, but wish to win, do they have an escape route? If so, give the characters hints about it, and perhaps a chance to stop their foes from fleeing. This is the final battle, after all, so a clever escape plan is a bit out of place.

If ever there was a place for cinematic combat, this is it. Dramatic speeches are the order of the day, and the Storyteller should not cut off a character during an accusation or a final curse. However, during a final battle, all bets are off, and the Storyteller should have little compunction about allowing the death of a character.

Running the Apocalypse

While a final battle on such a grand scale is hardly necessary to have an exciting conclusion, it is admittedly hard to imagine the stakes any higher. What do you do if the characters decide to invade Malfeas and cut out the heart of the Wyrm? Or, what if you wish to bring the Final Battle raining down on their heads?

One important consideration is to give the characters a clear goal. **Werewolf** is not a war game, it's a storytelling game, and that means that large-scale battles involving miniatures aren't really this game's style. If the Apocalypse has begun consider what the characters can do about it. Is there one target they should attempt to destroy? Or perhaps Gaia charges them with surviving the Apocalypse to make sure that the Garou don't die out. Maybe they can even stop the Wyrm from eating the world (or the Weaver from calcifying it) if they can retrieve a mighty fetish from the Umbral reaches. In that case, the final battle becomes a race against time, and a battle against any Wyrm or Weaver minions who might want to stop the characters.

If the Battle actually takes place, read up on "final battle" mythology and take notes. Ragnarok has already been mentioned, but what about the Book of Revelations (you might want to consider finding a copy of the Living Bible, as it's much easier to understand than the flowery prose of the King James Version)? Most religions have a myth about the end of the world, and most of the time the gods themselves come down from Asgard (or wherever) to settle old scores, crush their enemies, and generally make trouble. The World of Darkness should be no different. Perhaps ancient vampires rise from their graves to consume whole cities. Maybe the giant statue at the Sept of the Awakening in Washington D.C. rips itself from the ground and goes on a rampage. The Veil should be the least of the Garou's worries during the Apocalypse; the humans are about to find out the truth anyway.

Another major issue you must consider before running an Apocalyptic story is: Can it be stopped? Either way, there are advantages and disadvantages.

If the Final Battle cannot be stopped, the whole tone of the game changes. Unless you have been running the entire chronicle up to this point with the Final Battle in mind, everything that happened heretofore is for naught, and that can be very frustrating for the players. *Do not* run the Apocalypse simply because you think it would be an exciting ending to the chronicle. If the Battle is unstoppable, find some way to give the characters hope. Give them something to fight for, even if it's only that they might destroy some powerful Wyrm creatures before dying themselves.

If you give the characters a way to prevent the Battle before total chaos ensues, beware of the "two-seconds-

on-the-timer" effect. Innumerable action movies end with a race against the clock, only to see the hero disarm the bomb/become the One/blow up the alien mother ship two seconds before the "explosion." It can be done well, but even when it is, it's cliché. Instead, perhaps the preventative measure simply evens the odds a bit for the Garou. Perhaps it gives them a clear way to win the battle. For example, maybe the pack stumbles on a way to free the Wyrm from the Weaver's clutches. The Wyrm might still wreck the world in the process, but then there might be something left over.

Aftermath

When all is said and done, the last Black Spiral vanquished, the fallen characters buried, what happens then? Where does the troupe go from there?

As Storyteller, answer any questions the players have about the game. Chances are there are plot points they didn't understand that they would like clarified. Spill the beans to them. Now that the story is over, there's no harm in letting them "behind the curtain," so to speak.

You should have some questions for the players, as well, notably, "How did I do?" Get feedback from them, find out what they loved about the chronicle and, more importantly, what they think you need to work on. Don't take offense; if the players have stayed with you long enough to finish a chronicle, they probably had a great time overall.

You may wish to take a break from Storytelling for a while. One of the other players might like a turn in the director's chair, anyway, perhaps with a different game. Take the opportunity to participate in a chronicle, probably with some new appreciation for what both the players and the Storyteller must do.

Gods from a Machine

No matter what kind of ending you choose for your chronicle, or even for a story, avoid *deus ex machina* at all costs. *Deus ex machina* occurs when a Storyteller-controlled character arrives to save the characters' lives. The problems here should be obvious: this plot device robs the characters of their dignity, makes a Storyteller-character the star of the show, and takes control of the story so far away from the players that they don't even have a hope of influencing it.

The players and their characters are the heart, soul, blood, and guts of the chronicle. It does not matter how cool a character the Storyteller has created or how well she can describe him. Never use powerful characters to steal the pack's thunder. They are the stars of the show, and they deserve better than that.

Note: Of course, if they call up an ally and *ask* him to come save their necks, that's different. But then that ally can lord it over them later, and they can't complain.

Chapter Four: The Adversaries

Though the hero may win the day, it is his terrifying opponent who gives vitality to these tales. Monsters and dragons come in all shapes — and can, of course shift shapes at will… Evil may enter the world in the guise of a single creature, but its family multiplies quickly, and there is never an end to the trials of a true hero.

— Richard Erdoes and Alfonso Ortiz (editors),
American Indian Myths and Legends

The Triat

Along with "Gaia," "the spirit world," and "people who turn into wolves," the Triat is one of the basic elements that makes **Werewolf** the game it is. Without the Triat, there'd be no impending Apocalypse, no threat to Gaia — really, there'd be much less for a werewolf pack to do, and the spirit world would be profoundly less interesting besides. Two out of three of the Triat are forces that spawn legions of antagonists for the average pack of Garou, and the third isn't even their ally.

For all that, the Triat isn't easy to pigeonhole; **Werewolf** isn't a game about clearly identifiable Good and Evil. The Wyld is no true friend to the Garou Nation; it's just in such dire straits that the Garou find themselves defending it out of necessity. There are spirits allied to Wyrm and Weaver both that are more ally than enemy. Although the Changing Breeds like to simplify the relationship between the various members of the Triat,

the truth of the matter is that the cosmic dance between Wyrm, Weaver and Wyld is a complicated one, particularly as it plays out on Earth. The Triat is a source of countless antagonists and story lines, but it's a great disservice to these three pillars of Creation itself to boil their influence down to "It's of the Wyrm; kill it!"

If there's a way to win the Apocalypse at all, it will be thanks to a clever understanding of the Triat: what they should be doing, where they've gone wrong, and how to get them back on track. In chronicles where there's some hope of winning the Apocalypse, it's key to show your players in-game things that promote that understanding. And in chronicles where there is no hope, only the possibility of racking up an impressive resume of deeds before your glorious end, it's still important to show your players the real face of their enemy, so at least they know why they're fighting.

Expanding Horizons

The ugly truth is that the Triat lend themselves to some fairly unimaginative stories, if not handled carefully. It's painfully easy to let a chronicle devolve into a repetition of "Look! That object/person/place smells of the Weaver/Wyrm/Wyld! We should destroy/kill/protect it!" After all, it doesn't take much work, and the players seem to enjoy it. But if you're interested in presenting the Triat as something more than a duo of antagonist-spawning entities and a quest object, it doesn't take *that* much extra effort — only a little attention to detail. By stressing the Triat's multiplicity and their less than all-encompassing earthly influence, you can help your players see the Triat in the light they deserve.

Multiplicity

One of the most fundamental concepts behind the Triat is that they operate on a cosmic scale; according to some legends, the three of them essentially ran the Universe itself. And because of that scale, each of the three is too large to be summed up by a simple word like "Stasis" or "Creation." Just as Gaia is both desert and forest, both glacier and swamp, each member of the Triat has a multitude of facets that express the whole.

Be very careful of making absolute statements about the Triat; those can easily limit your game's spiritual aspect in unhealthy ways rather than providing helpful guidelines. A statement like "The Wyld is Creation, so therefore it cannot destroy" is not only inaccurate (the Wyld is more than Creation), it limits your ability to do interesting things with the Wyld. A spontaneous outbreak of flesh-eating bacteria can be seen as *very* Wyld in aspect, as might a natural disaster — do you really want to rule out the possibility of either just because of an off-handed absolute statement of "fact"?

The multiplicity of the Triat is your friend. A spirit of Balance can detect as just as much "of the Wyrm" as a spirit spawned by a Maeljin Incarna; a spirit of technological innovation might be "of the Weaver," and it might be "of the Wyld." By showing your players the different aspects of each Triatic force, you encourage them to think more about what it really *means* to be aspected to one of the Triat. And when your players start to appreciate these different facets, they'll begin using that knowledge to their advantage — helping Banes revert to the Wyrm-spirits they *should* be rather than the Wyrm-spirits they are, discerning the mad elements of the Weaver from those that are necessary and worthy of preservation, and so on. As noted before, this is some of the most useful work they can be doing if they actually want to win the Apocalypse, not just die gloriously.

Earthly Influence

It's easy to fall into a certain mindset when working around the struggles of the Triat: namely, the assumption that everything of any significance is "of" one of the Triat, bolstering its cosmological patron's power to no end with every minor goal it achieves on earth. Now admittedly, assigning a Triatic affinity or allegiance (whether or not the person or entity in question is aware of it or not) is kind of fun, but when you start taking questions like "So are the Imbued of the Balance Wyrm, or what?" more seriously than idle chit-chat, you *can* run into problems.

Remember, in a perfectly functioning universe, most everything in the physical world would likely be equal parts Wyrm, Weaver and Wyld. A healthy person would have a set form (granted by the Weaver), the capacity for growth and procreation (granted by the Wyld), and the ultimate fate of death so that the cycle could continue (granted by the Wyrm). Now, since the Wyrm lost its ability to properly function as Balance (or so the story goes), this perfect universe is now impossible, but the imbalance that the Garou fight against isn't as omnipresent as it might seem. An ordinary person, an animal, a philosophical ideal — all of these can be "of" neither Wyrm, Wyld nor Weaver.

This is, by the by, the main reason that werewolves tend to be so nervous or trigger-happy when they sense the "taint" of one of the Triat on a person, supernatural being or section of the world. In a perfect world, one that had no need of Garou, such beings or places would be few and far between. The presence of Triatic taint implies a problem, the sort of problem that the Changing Breeds were allegedly created to resolve. The wise Garou, when confronted with such a "tainted" entity or locale, first asks himself why the taint is present, and then asks himself what he can do to resolve the trouble (if indeed the spiritual scent indicates a problem). Not all shapeshifters are this wise, of course, but it would be doing the Changing Breeds a disservice to assume that even the wisest elders don't act with at least a little forethought.

The Wyrm

The Wyrm is the leading candidate for "most misunderstood member of the Triat," simply because it is, and has been, so many different things to so many different shapeshifters. It has been the Balance Wyrm, a personification of careful destruction in the interest of a smoothly running universe. It has become Corruption, the embodiment of Destruction gone wrong. Some have called it Entropy or Death; others associate it with Madness, Hatred or even Evil. The Wyrm is all of these things, and not truly any one of them.

Originally the Balance Wyrm, the force keeping Wyld and Weaver alike in check, the Wyrm has now become the Corrupter Wyrm, a force of spiritual as well as physical decay. According to Garou cosmology, the Wyrm's consciousness has been lost to madness, trapped within the web of the Weaver. Its effort to escape has given its darkest drives and aspects lives of their own, splitting them into new heads of the hydra — the Triatic Wyrms, and the Urge Wyrms.

As a result, the Wyrm is stricken with something akin to multiple personality disorder — but because of the scale of the entity, each one of its separate "personalities" is able to act on its own, recruiting its own servants and further dividing itself into lesser aspects. Most scholars of Wyrm lore use the name "Hydra" to distinguish the Wyrm-as-it-is-now, divided and mad, from the Wyrm-as-it-was, the great serpent of balance. For those Garou who know anything about the Wyrm's true nature, the task at hand is not "killing the Wyrm" — it's severing the twisted heads that have sprung from its body.

The Heads of the Hydra

As noted in the **Werewolf** rulebook, the three Triatic Wyrms are the primary "children" of the Wyrm, the three great heads that grow from its body. The first, Beast-of-War, is the "Calamity Wyrm" of unrestrained wrath, violence and destruction. It is the least subtle of the Triatic Wyrms, and it has little need for subtlety; every war, every act of mindless violence, every kill made for reasons other than survival feeds Beast-of-War, strengthening it for the day it can break free and smash Creation into dust. Many Black Spiral Dancers revere Beast-of-War above all other aspects of the Wyrm, hailing it as the Father of the Apocalypse and the spiritual patron of their mad crusade.

The second Triatic Wyrm is Eater-of-Souls, the "Consuming Wyrm." It is the aspect of unwholesome hunger, of the desire to draw everything into itself and thus make all the universe into the Wyrm. Greed, gluttony, lust and desire of all sorts fuel its power. Unlike its brethren, Eater-of-Souls once managed to manifest itself physically on Earth, where it surely would have devoured the entire planet if not banished by the sacrifice of the entire Croatan tribe. Although this act weakened Eater-of-Souls severely, the rapacious crimes committed on Earth in the name of greed continue to strengthen it so that it may someday return. The naked greed of Pentex and its corporations is one of the strongest allies Eater-of-Souls has.

The final Triatic Wyrm is in many ways the most dangerous, for it is both the most subtle and the most self-aware. The Defiler Wyrm is the expression of ultimate corruption, of degradation and misery and all spiritual ills. It is notably active in the schemes of its followers, who are in many ways the worst of the Wyrm's servants. The Defiler Wyrm hates innocence, virtue and spiritual strength, and works to tarnish and corrupt them into viler emotions that serve its own purpose. The Defiler Wyrm has its adherents among all the followers of the Wyrm, although various human cults, loathsome Black Spiral Dancer factions and packs of fomori-creating Banes are among its favorites.

Below the Triatic Wyrms are the Urge Wyrms, manifestations of each of the Wyrm's darkest desires. As the Wyrm sought to escape the Weaver's web, its base emotions splintered off into separate "heads" of their own like dough being forced through a steel mesh. Each Urge Wyrm and its servants do indeed strive to work for the ultimate freedom of the Wyrm, but their own agendas come first; after all, how can a manifestation of corrupt Desire itself set aside its own urge to promote corrupt desires in others? The Urge Wyrms work to make themselves stronger by fostering their own ideals in others. Some Garou scholars fervently hope that the Wyrm manifested as yet undiscovered Urges of somewhat more altruistic nature, potential keys to healing the Wyrm itself, but the evidence for such benevolent Urge Wyrms is sorely lacking. The recognized Urge Wyrms are as follows:

- Foebok, the Urge of Fear
- Vorus, the Urge of Greed
- Mahsstrac, the Urge of Power
- Karnala, the Urge of Desire
- Abhorra, the Urge of Hatred
- Angu, the Urge of Cruelty
- Ba'akshai, the Urge of Violence
- Khaaloobh, the Urge of Consumption
- Pseulak, the Urge of Lies
- Sykora, the Urge of Paranoia
- Gree, the Urge of Despair
- Lethargg, the Urge of Apathy

The final four greater aspects of the Wyrm are those that were born when the Wyrm's corruptive force contacted the four elemental forces of air, earth, fire and water — Hoga, the essence of Smog; H'rugg, the essence of Sludge; Furmas, the essence of Balefire; and Wakshaa, the essence of Toxin. These four elemental forces, and the corrupt elemental spirits that serve them, are the aspects of the Wyrm that have the most to gain from pollution of the natural world, and are therefore most interested in such activities. Rumor has it that there are two more essences relevant to the Asian spirit world, corrupted versions of metal and wood, although the Garou Nation has yet to formally recognize these.

"The Wyrm Did It!"

One of the most common misconceptions about the Wyrm is a matter of taking the Garou too literally. Werewolves, and indeed many other Changing Breeds, tend to lay the poor state of the world at the Wyrm's feet, or blame the Wyrm itself for the actions of its offspring and devotees. Although technically true, this can lead the impression that the Wyrm pays much more attention to the details of the world than it actually does.

Consider the plight of the drug-addicted prostitute slowly becoming a fomor. Although most werewolves would easily admit the Wyrm is to blame, they don't usually mean that they think the Wyrm itself looked down and commanded a Bane to tempt this miserable woman into power — and thereby, possession. More likely, the Bane attempting to possess her did so of its own accord, given its ingrained need to foster the spiritual vice or toxin it stands for. It's possible that the Bane may have been directed to this woman by a higher power, but said higher power is likely a personal servant of Karnala at best; probably not the Defiler Wyrm itself, and certainly not the Wyrm in all its might!

Use this hierarchy to your advantage. The greater the head of the Hydra, the less plausible it is that it's involved in petty acts of corruption. Convey scale by starting small, then gradually showing your players more and more of the hierarchy of corruption that is the Hydra. Save the direct intervention of an Urge Wyrm, the Maeljin Incarna that serve it, or the Defiler Wyrm itself for the climax of a story or even a chronicle. Not only will the effects be more powerful, but the players will also gain a greater understanding of just how much the Wyrm is and isn't directly responsible for. They can continue to use simple terms like "The Wyrm's forces" and "This serves the Wyrm" for ease's sake, but without assuming that the phrases have no meaning beyond the most literal.

And when your players realize that so much spiritual corruption occurs *without the Wyrm actually thinking about it* — then, with any luck, you'll be rewarded with a most satisfying shudder.

When to Use the Wyrm (and When Not To)

The big advantage of the Wyrm (and all its forces) is that it's a fine motivator. Not only can it threaten outright violence, but it can threaten far worse. Compare the threat of a Black Spiral caern raid to that of a captured Dancer leering at a character and complimenting him on his "pretty sister" — and then noting that some of the others at the Hive have noticed, too. A burgeoning Wyrm threat is a great way to get your players' attention and launch into an evening of savage action and horror. Fomori and monsters are optimal "blood and guts" opponents, should you want a dirty, bloody, Wyrm-as-Destroyer game.

However, you should also use the Wyrm subtly, not only for contrast, but also to reinforce that the fangs, balefire and ichor are only a portion of the Wyrm's arsenal. Banes are particularly effective for stories that emphasize the quiet, seductive aspects of Wyrm as Corrupter, but clever Black Spiral Dancers and fomori work well, too — as do humans or supernatural beings who have no idea what the Wyrm is, much less that their deeds are directly strengthening it. And certainly prepare stories where the Wyrm is best "fought" not through direct combat, but through combating its spiritual influence — helping out at a clinic for abused women, feeding the hungry and homeless, even helping clean up a neighborhood. Werewolf is a game about spirituality, and elevating the human spirit is as worthy a goal as tearing the throat out of a corrupt land developer (if not more so).

By all means, avoid the temptation of having the Wyrm's forces directly at work in every encounter with the spiritually corrupt. Vampires are an excellent example of antagonists that are in many ways "of the Wyrm," but who know nothing of the Apocalypse. Dealing with a vampire slaver who buys and sells adolescents as blood-toys for other Leeches fits wonderfully with the themes of Wyrmish corruption and defilement, but if the story is run without even a glimpse of a Bane or fomor, all the better. Humans are equally wonderful antagonists for stories of this nature, save for the fact that when the Garou finally track them down, they put up considerably less of a fight. Stories such as this help emphasize that the fight against the Wyrm is fought on all levels, not merely on the most literal — they emphasize that the Wyrm, like all spirits, is not just its manifestations, but also what it *stands for*.

And the Balance Wyrm?

Considering the once-noble purpose of the Wyrm, it may be tempting to bring in some agents that still serve the Balance Wyrm as it was, to showcase that the Wyrm's corruption is not inborn. Old Wyrm-spirits that have resisted corruption are the primary tool of choice, but these should be few and far between. It's no easy thing avoiding your now-corrupt brethren for millennia on end. Such spirits are best used as the objects of great quests, potential sources of information and power that might be the Garou's last hope for healing the Wyrm. (And, of course, they'd register to Sense Wyrm, which would be yet another way to reinforce to your players that sensing "Wyrm-taint" is *not* the same thing as detecting evil intent.)

But as far as mortal agents — well, here's a little secret.

In a way, the Garou — indeed, almost all the Changing Breeds — are the closest thing to an active force upholding the ideals of the Balance Wyrm today. They defend the Wyld — not because they believe it's their friend, but because it is the weakest of the Triat. They fight the Wyrm and the Weaver, trying to cut them back to size. Most hope to cure the Wyrm rather than destroying it, so that Balance might be restored.

It just goes to show you that being "of the Wyrm" is sometimes a good thing.

The Weaver

Although the Weaver is a much less multifaceted entity than the Wyrm, it still suffers from the same basic problem — it is not what it should be. The Weaver's original purpose of giving structure to the unformed, building the laws and certainties of the universe, has been perverted. In its purest state, the Weaver represents reason, science, law and order — all concepts with the potential for good as well as ill. But with the Weaver's madness comes a perversion of these ideals. The Weaver is now the force of reason that strangles out possibility, of science that directly opposes mysticism, of law and order pursued for their own sake above all other ideals.

This does *not*, of course, mean that science and technology are considered "evil" in the World of Darkness, even in Werewolf's cosmology. A werewolf can hail a cab, fire a pistol or use an ATM without having sinned against Gaia. This is a point of contention among more extreme elders, particularly those of the more Wyld-aspected tribes, but it's generally held that technology and science are not innately corrupt or to blame. It's the proliferation of these things, and the way in which they skew out of control, that concerns the Garou.

As an example, take the pursuit of medicine and science meant to delay aging and eradicate disease. Certainly healing the sick and easing the pain of the old is a worthy cause. But in the World of Darkness, the Weaver's mad influence encourages humanity to develop such advancements heedless of whether or not humans are morally capable of handling such a respon-

sibility. If the humans preserve their own lives without reducing their own birthrates, thus causing more of a population problem, that's no concern of the Weaver's. If anti-aging science or even "immortality treatments" wind up in the hands of the richest and most powerful, keeping them in power indefinitely while strangling later generations' chances of determining their own destiny, what does the Weaver care? As a result, science born of the best intentions is misused and abused, contributing to the poor state of the world. The Weaver's idea of progress throws off all natural cycles, placing the power to destroy the world in the hands of those who aren't sufficiently prepared to use it responsibly.

The Garou see this trouble unfolding, and that is why they consider the Weaver as she is now an enemy. Most werewolves suffer Renown penalties for relying too much on "Weaverish" gear rather than their own abilities; it's considered unwise to place yourself in the enemy's power. Cities expand but don't contract; urban sprawl devours new land all the time, while the areas at the heart of the city corrode and become the Wyrm's playground. The Weaver's influence is a very real concern, and not for the stereotypical (and inaccurate) "science bad, forest good" reasons popularly cited.

When to Use the Weaver (and When Not To)

The Weaver and its minions are perhaps the most versatile group of supporting cast in **Werewolf**. They can be the worst of enemies, or the best of friends (although admittedly the latter is likely only for Glass Walkers). Whereas Garou can easily feel a moral obligation to oppose the Triatic or Urge Wyrms, opposing the Weaver is less a matter of morals and more a matter of ethics and practicality. This allows for some juicy moral dilemmas, if you care to address them. Does a man of science deserve to die, if his work threatens the balance between human and nature even further? The answer isn't always clear, despite the werewolves' willingness to make that judgement call.

For most werewolves, the Weaver represents the alien — human ideals taken to their spiritual extreme, denying the natural cycle. Weaver-focused stories are optimal for stressing this sense of alienation and oppression. The Weaver can also be used to challenge a few of your players' perceptions — are all laborsaving devices necessarily a good thing? Do we really all need cars and highways? Or, if your players are more Luddite in outlook, you can challenge their assumptions just as easily; is all progress really bad? What if a particularly perceptive human who could make real progress in the fight for Gaia was born with an ailment that would be fatal without Weaver-medicine? It seems strange to classify the Weaver as flexible, but the role she serves in the average Werewolf chronicle is just that.

Remember that the Weaver can be as subtle or as unsubtle as the story demands. To set your players on edge, you can easily describe a very faint but persistent droning in their characters' ears while they're in the Penumbra of an urban area. Although certainly no threat, this sound neatly conveys the unrelenting, pervasive nature of the Weaver. On the other hand, you can certainly get the players' attention by setting a massive chrome-and-glass spider-spirit the size of an eighteen-wheeler on their heels. But even though such a threat is more immediate, don't forget to make the pursuer just as relentless, in order to properly convey the Weaver's unyielding, mad obsession.

Also, not everything scientific, technological or even human should be "of the Weaver." Although most man-made structures appear as webs in the Penumbra, if they appear at all, spiritual "Weaver-taint" should be present only when appropriate. A log cabin in the deep woods shouldn't evoke the Weaver, even if there's a rifle inside. However, if the cabin contained a computer with Internet access, a touch of the Weaver's webs would be appropriate.

And finally, remember that the Weaver represents Progress just as much as she represents Sterility. Scientific innovation is the finest proof that the Weaver is more than just unyielding form — it is the Weaver's finest tool for Naming, for locking down unlimited potential into limited form. Each scientific advancement may add more knowledge to the world, and seemingly more possibilities — although once a thing is proved to be true, a number of "untruths" are removed as possibilities forever. In a way, the Weaver represents evolution and even change — the question is whether or not her idea of evolution is truly what's best for the universe.

As always, remember that the Weaver is a thing of spirit first and foremost — intentions mean as much as actual implementation. When asking yourself if something should be "of the Weaver" or not, think not in terms of the letter of the law, but in the spirit.

The Wyld

At first glance, the Wyld seems to be the junior member of the Triat in more ways than one. It's not a proper antagonist such as the Wyrm or Weaver; it doesn't have nearly as many spirit minions, and those it does have are nowhere near as organized as the broods of Banes and Weaver-spirits. The Wyld is still strong in places, but across most of the world (at least, the portions of the world that your chronicle is likely to explore), the primeval force of creation and flux is badly on the ropes. Most Garou consider it their responsibility to protect and nurture the Wyld places, in the interests of balance if nothing else. Some tribes, such as the Black Furies, take this duty even more seriously.

And in the course of defending the Wyld against the depredations of its stronger, more rapacious siblings, some Garou — and some players, of course — get the impression that the Wyld is their ally. After all, it represents (among other things) fairly benign concepts such as life, birth and growth. It isn't listed among the antagonists in the rulebook. Some even reason that the Wyld is more "of Gaia" than its siblings are, that it, like Gaia, is the born ally of werewolves everywhere.

This preconception is, like many others, not very accurate.

Like the other members of the Triat, the Wyld itself does not have the interests of the Garou — or of any other sentient race on Gaia's face — in mind at all. The Wyld simply *is* — it does its best to fulfill the role ordained for it at the beginning of creation, and all else be damned. If a pack of werewolves, or their caern, would be adversely affected by a sudden burst of Wyld energy in the area, the Wyld isn't going to scale back its efforts to grow and thrive there any more than a tornado would change course to avoid the caern. In fact, getting the tornado to change course would probably be easier for the Garou; weather-spirits have Gaia's best interests at heart, but Wyld-spirits do not. The Wyld answers to its own inner mandate and nothing else.

Needless to say, this tendency can make life very difficult for werewolves. A werewolf sworn to defend the Wyld is bound to protect something that might turn on him at any moment, for no understandable reason whatsoever. The Wyld itself is just as alien as the other Triat members, a Celestine so vast that its most powerful Jagglings are little more than the "thoughts" racing along what might be described as its nervous system. Wyld-spirits can be negotiated with, of course; they operate more closely to the Garou's own level, and "think" in a more understandable fashion. But they are inevitably reflections of the Wyld itself, and share in its chaotic nature.

In all the world, few things are more sobering than the Garou theory that the world is what it is today because two of the fundamental forces of the universe were driven mad millennia ago — and the third has been as near to mad as makes no difference all along.

Antagonist or Ally?

Like the other members of the Triat, the Wyld is amoral. It acts on what can best be described as instinct, pursuing its original purpose — to create raw potential and act as an agent of change — to the exclusion of all other goals. Whatever overall consciousness guides the Wyld, it's likely that it is no more aware of the Garou's efforts than an elephant is aware of the antibodies that defend it from disease.

Yes, the Garou defend the Wyld from the depredations of its siblings. Yes, some strike pacts with Wyld-spirits and call these spirits "friend" — after a fashion. However, the Wyld *itself* does not respond with gratitude. The difference between a pact with a Wyld-spirit and an allegiance with the Wyld is roughly equal to the difference between one's relationship with one's pet dog and one's relationship with Nature itself.

As Storyteller, you have the remarkable freedom to paint the Wyld as beneficial, allied force in some chronicles and as an uncaring hostile force in others. The Wyld is in the mudslide that levels a village of innocents just as much as it is in the spark of life that thrives at the heart of a wasteland. You can keep your players guessing as much as you like. Eventually, they're likely to come to the same conclusion that the majority of the Garou Nation has made — that there's little gratitude to be had in defending the Wyld, but it must be done anyway. The alternative — a world without the creation of new things or the force of change — is too horrible.

The Wyld Is Not Gaia

It bears repeating. It's fairly easy to confuse "the Wyld" with "the wild" — to assume that the Wyld is also the force of the wilderness itself, the spiritual reflection of the portions of the world as yet unshaped by humans. From the strictest **Werewolf** viewpoint, this isn't the case.

Werewolves tend to look at it in these terms: The Wyld represents the *potential* for life, the Weaver represents the *laws* by which such life must abide, the Wyrm reflects the *end* of life and the turning of the cycle — but Gaia *is* life. Gaia is the soul of the universe, the higher portion of the cosmos' being that gives birth to forces such as love and beauty (although some cite her as the original author of cruelty and other negative emotions as well). Werewolves also more often paint Gaia as capable of emotions herself, particularly the emotions of a mother devoted to her creation, than they consider the Triat capable of such higher ideals.

In the default interpretation of the cosmology, the Wyld is strong in untouched natural places not because it is the soul of those places, but because the Weaver is correspondingly weak there. Gaia is also strong in these places, partly for the same reasons, but also because these sites are where the natural world runs at its "purest" — the ecosystems functioning as they have, more or less, since the world began. The two share a similar interest — but this doesn't make them the same.

When to Use the Wyld (and When Not To)

The Wyld is actually one of the more important motifs in **Werewolf**—and yet it isn't always appropriate to have Wyld energies or spirits making a personal appearance in your chronicles. One of the fundamental problems in the state of the world is that the Wyld is beleaguered, the weak member of the Triat that runs the risk of being annihilated or overrun entirely. It's difficult to convey this desperate state of affairs if you have Wyld-spirits popping up as supporting cast every session.

For that matter, the Wyld will be a more effective tool in your Storytelling repertoire if you use it not only sparingly, but also evocatively. The Wyld should set the players on edge, at least a little bit — its motivation is alien, its methods unpredictable and its power often startlingly dangerous. Consider the frightening spontaneity of a tornado, the random nature of an outbreak of disease, the uncaring nature of a flash flood. While not all manifestations of the Wyld are dangerous to those in the immediate area, they *could* be — the chance is always there. The players (and their characters) should feel the risk inherent in any Wyld manifestation; it's the double-edged nature of the Wyld that makes it so interesting.

The Wyld is obviously well suited to stories that involve strange patches of land, sudden natural disasters, irrational outbreaks of chaos and other such motifs. Its alien nature complements the unfamiliar settings where it's likely to thrive, a trait you can use to your advantage. The farther the characters get from the civilized areas their players are comfortable with, the more the players will themselves feel slightly out of their element — an emotional state that, while rarely powerful, will work to your advantage when introducing the Wyld elements of your story. The wilder (or Wylder) the land, the less "safe" the players might feel, which is all for the best.

But as noted in Chapter Two, the Wyld also has its place in urban chronicles—no city is strong in the Wyld, and surely the Weaver and Wyrm threaten to crush their weaker sibling's influence there, but the Wyld is part of urban life nonetheless. It appears in the random accidents, good and bad, that befall a city's inhabitants. It thrives wherever the Weaver's laws of conformity falter, such as the disused and abandoned areas of an inner city. Feel free to use the Wyld in an urban environment just as you'd use it elsewhere — to create tension, but also hope.

Which Is Bigger, Gaia or the Triat?

The answer to this question has been left deliberately vague. Some Storytellers prefer to interpret the cosmology such that the Triat is universal, whereas Gaia is limited to the immediate vicinity of Earth (both physical and spiritual). Others prefer the idea that Gaia *is* the Universe, and that the Triat are her wayward children — albeit children with the power to slay their mother, should it come to that.

The Changing Breeds themselves don't know the answer to this question, although they have their own ideas, and often blatantly disagree. Therefore, don't worry about any "book-legal" right or wrong answer to the question — your answer is the one that matters.

Pentex

Trust him not with your secrets, who, when left alone in your room, turns over your papers.

— Johann Kaspar Lavater

It always starts small.

In the course of their duties of protecting and cleaning up the lands around their caern, a pack of werewolves begins, among other things, to start picking out the humans who are doing the most ecological damage to the land. In some cases, a little Kinfolk activism or influence is all that's required; in other cases, stealth and misdirection can turn the offenders around. In more extreme cases, a little sabotage or eco-terrorism is the order of the day; it may not be the most efficient way of doing things, but it appeals to the Garou desire to see their enemies founder and fail.

And as the pack continues these various actions, they start to notice a few familiar names. When they travel farther from their caern or exchange news with Galliards of other septs, they start noticing that a few corporations seem to be more reliably callous toward the environment, more brutally conscious of efficiency and the bottom line. A few names start working into the pack's vocabulary: Endron. Magadon. O'Tolley's. Rainbow.

But as the investigation continues, the pack finds… worse things. They find that these corporations follow the aggressive "make people need our products" tactic a bit more seriously than other companies do. They discover that some of these corporations have fomori guards at their manufacturing plants, fomori that couldn't quite feasibly pass for human during a job interview. They discover signs that someone in upper management must know a few things about summoning Banes to act as guard dogs.

And then they start to find hints that there's something *bigger* behind these corporations. Something larger and more powerful than these billion-dollar multinationals; an entity that's able to give these corporate giants' CEOs orders with impunity. They start crossing paths with elite black-ops teams of killers, assassins targeting them as "potential problems" — and some of these elite teams have more than one supernaturally potent member among them.

And once the pack is finally aware of the tremendous scale of the threat facing them, of the sheer financial and political power this entity can bring to bear against the Garou and their lands, they finally have a name for this most insidious of enemies:

Pentex.

Running Pentex

The above description may not be the default way that Pentex enters the average chronicle, but for most werewolves, that's exactly how they found out about **Werewolf**'s corporate behemoth of an antagonistic organization. It wasn't because a giant van with the Pentex logo rolled up to the caern and started disgorging wave after wave of heavily armed fomori in snappy corporate uniforms, that's for sure.

Pentex is an all-but-invisible megacorporation. Pentex itself makes no products that you see on the shelves; it owns subsidiaries that produce many of the household name products of the World of Darkness, but Pentex itself is a largely administrative body. Most people go their entire lives without ever seeing the Pentex logo. And that's exactly the point.

Where the Black Spiral Dancers are the dark counterpoint to the Garou, and the Banes are the embodiment of spiritual corruption, Pentex serves the role of the mostly mundane, horribly subtle threat that operates quietly in the human world. Much of Pentex's evil is the same sort of devotion to the "bottom line" that you see in companies in our own world; simple, easy-to-understand selfishness. At the lower levels, Pentex and its subsidiaries could be any disreputable corporation in our own world — but the key difference is that the higher you go, the more Pentex becomes like a twisted conspiracy movie. The managers start becoming more and more intelligent, but no less malicious — their various sins against the environment and humanity can no longer be attributed to short-sightedness. As the characters uncover more and more of the nasty little secrets hidden at all levels of the organization, the players may pine for the good-natured conspiracy theories like oil companies suppressing cars that run on water. The truth — at least in the World of Darkness — is considerably nastier.

Before we get to the nuts and bolts of who works for Pentex, what they do and why, let's consider effective ways to use this holding company and its subsidiaries in a **Werewolf** game. This is the big picture; the details can wait a few minutes.

Cardinal Rules for Using Pentex:

• Pentex, thematically, is the stuff of conspiracy movies and books. Greedy entrepreneurs doing everything within their power to leverage their financial and political power, callous corporate decisions, secret cabals of People in Power — that's the stuff of the Pentex story. Pentex and its people have plots within plots within (you guessed it) more plots. Everyone seems to work together, but there are always secret dissenters and plans afoot. Player characters may get drawn into some of these plots and think they've got a handle on what's *really* going on behind the scenes, but chances are, they're only going to scratch the surface.

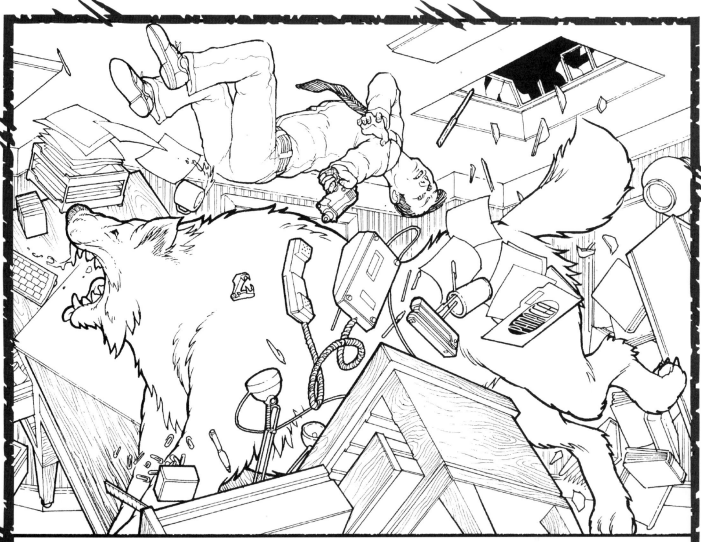

• Seldom, if ever, is this monolithic megacorp going to let its name be used in the field. Even people who work directly for Pentex itself, like their First Teams or other agents, don't run around in jackets sporting the Pentex logo. Any werewolf (or other being, for that matter) who finds out that an entity called Pentex actually owns the chemical company Magadon is either lucky or nosy. Either option spells a lot of trouble for the snoop in question. The powers that be at Pentex won't sit still should they learn someone is digging around in their garbage.

• There are fates more brutal than death. If Pentex can corrupt, maim or coerce an opponent, that's usually more effective (and enjoyable) than simple murder. Consider the delightful arts of blackmail and intimidation should a character find out too much about Pentex or a subsidiary. Poisoning a valuable family member, then rationing the antidote, can force even a rowdy werewolf to be on good behavior… or thirst for revenge. If a player is willing and interested (because this action will probably mean the death or retirement of his character), ponder having a "ringer" within the pack, who will ultimately betray them, for reasons good or ill.

• Deniability is a key word in Pentex. They'll always have a rational explanation for any mishap or mayhem, plus a hapless scapegoat to take all the blame. Be warned, though, that if you overuse Pentex and *always* deny the players the chance to get some revenge, they're going to get bored and frustrated. Consider doling out tidbits on what the company is doing as your game progresses, and then one day, if you think it's appropriate, do let the players blow the lid off things. This should probably be a major turning point in your chronicle. With Pentex, paranoia is fully justified; there really *is* something to worry about!

• Not everyone at Pentex or its subsidiaries is a bad person. Some are simply hapless workers slaving away the best they can so they don't get downsized in the next "corporate restructuring." Plenty are awful examples of humanity, to be sure; the job environment rewards those callous enough to put their welfare (or the company's) over any pesky ethical considerations like environmental issues or proper assignation of credit. There are those that are worse — fomori, willing servants of the Wyrm, or people who manage to be evil without any outside influence whatsoever. But the worst thing that can be said about a great deal of Pentex employees is that they've learned too well to keep their head down and not make trouble. To paraphrase the old saying, evil prospers when good people stand by and do nothing.

• Pentex, like any good company, diversifies. Not everything they do has the stamp of the Wyrm upon it. Some of the antagonists in a Pentex story might be pawns of the Weaver (Pentex supports many advances in high technology and homogeneity), while others might be a third party (such as a vampire's catspaws). Many more might have no supernatural ties at all — they're simply doing things that endanger Gaia, or whatever other werewolf agenda might be at stake.

• Tension is a good thing! You want the players to have butterflies in their stomachs each time they oppose a Pentex agent or foes from one of the subsidiaries. They should be concerned and worried about the outcome; it shouldn't be a walk in the park. What the mortals from Pentex don't have in terms of brute strength, they do have in the form of information and certain dangerous pieces of technology on their side. They do a lot of research and can cook up foul toxins or weapons that really can hurt werewolves. Play up this creepy factor as much as possible.

• Make it personal. A figurehead of one of the Pentex subsidiaries would make an ideal adversary; players will always be much more interested in your conspiratorial plots if these affect the characters in some direct way. Maybe this Storyteller character screws up a pack's plans to protect a certain wilderness area or group of Kinfolk. Whatever the reason, this character is a thorn in the pack's side. Draw it out and let their anger reach a nice boiling point before having a big showdown.

• Throw out plenty of red herrings, but don't forget to actually let the characters discover some truths about Pentex and its subsidiaries along the way. If you don't let the werewolves feel they occasionally accomplish something, the players will get jaded and discouraged. You should probably have some sort of resolution in your mind, even if it won't appear for a long while. Not much is worse than a conspiracy plotline that doesn't periodically have some closure to all the loose ends.

• Believability… or not. Pentex is large and diverse enough for you as the Storyteller to decide just how you want to use them in your game. Do you want them to be the ultimate in shadowy, gritty realism, or are their plots going to seem more like the most heinous tabloid headlines? That, of course, is up to you; consider your mix of players and characters when tailoring Pentex to fit your individual chronicle.

Sources and Resources

Movies and television shows focusing on conspiracy themes, cover-ups and supernatural mysteries have always been popular. Just a few of the classics and sleepers you should consider watching for inspiration on running Pentex:

The Insider (frankly, a must-see, not just for tactics, but also as proof that people don't need any motivation other than avarice to be "evil"); *A Civil Action*; *Conspiracy Theory* (Patrick Stewart as the villain is an extra bonus); *Enemy of the State*; *La Femme Nikita* (both television show and movie, which are very different); *The X-Files* and *The Lone Gunmen*; *Millennium*; *Murder at 1600*; *Erin Brockovich* (topical environmental destruction); *The Game* ; *No Way Out*; *Ninth Gate*; *The Manchurian Candidate*; *Three Days of the Condor*; *All the President's Men*; *Citizen X*; *Grosse Point Blank* and *True Lies* (campy, but fun) and if you still have the stomach for it, anything having to do with that whole Roswell/Area 51 business.

Pentex Goals

So what exactly is it that Pentex and its subsidiaries hope to accomplish? What's their bottom-line agenda?

Well, the first thing to establish is that "what Pentex wants" is kind of a misnomer. Most of its various agendas can be traced back to "what the Board of Directors want", which is a very different thing entirely. Each person on the Board of Directors has his or her own motivations, ambitions and personal image for "changing the world", to say nothing of those below them. Generally, though, the two main factors determining Pentex policy and action are those employees who know about and serve the Wyrm, and those who don't.

Those "in the know" are the vast minority at Pentex. It's entirely possible that there are people even on the Board who don't know what the Wyrm is, and would be terrified at the thought of being played as its puppets. Further, those Pentex figures who *do* know of the Wyrm (and who, in most cases, worship it) have their own variety of motivations. Some are slavishly loyal to the face of the Wyrm they know best (most often a Maeljin Incarna or other high-ranking Wyrm-spirit); others naively think they're the ones playing the Wyrm's forces for fools. The agendas of these "enlightened" executives vary greatly, but generally fall into a similar pattern — the desire to break the human spirit, making all of humanity an ideal market of consumers. When the world has nothing to offer that's more attractive than what Pentex can provide, Pentex will own the ultimate monopoly. When the "enlightened" order another environmentally destructive measure, it's often as much to destroy something else that might distract people from their ideal "world of consumers" — and if those damned pesky Garou suffer from the measure, too, that's all the better.

The second group, and by far the more numerous, are those Pentex employees who don't know about (or, with few exceptions, believe in) the supernatural. The vast majority of Pentex managers worship not the All-Consuming Wyrm, but the Almighty Dollar. These people just don't *care* about anything more than increasing their own profit margin, even if they phrase it in terms like "now I can buy that sports car I always dreamed of" or "now I can send my kids to a really prestigious college." Such characters should need little elaboration; there are plenty of colorful models in our own world to provide inspiration. The most salient point is, of course, that these people help empower and encourage Pentex's most avaricious and unethical projects, simply because it'll help increase their own share of the pie. (Those managers that are more interested in their personal ethics than an increased paycheck don't last long at any of Pentex's subsidiaries.)

To accommodate their goals, Pentex and its subsidiaries do their best to keep competitive in the Information Age. Currently, Pentex pursues intelligence chiefly in communications (television, telephone and radio), imagery (photographs and surveillance) and electronic mediums (computer data and the Internet). They use these arenas to determine their enemies' capabilities and intentions, analyze the resources of opposing companies, protect their own secrets and negate counter-espionage. The current corporate climate frowns on less subtle acts of environmental terrorism or blatant binding-Banes-into-products; incompetent regional managers who blatantly attract too much werewolf attention without achieving actual results are easily replaced.

Profits are up, and slowly but surely, the top managers' information about werewolves is increasing. Not much could be worse for the player characters than to face an enemy with both real-world power and supernatural connections.

Pentex Bureaucracy

Pentex is a warren of divisions and subdivisions; each pursues its own projects and agendas more or less independently, though all are accountable to the subdivision and division directors, and ultimately to the executive director. The main structure includes the following divisions, with subdivisions noted in parentheses. For many more details, see Book of the Wyrm, Second Edition.

Each head of a division and subdivision sits on the board of directors, actually making Pentex a little different from its subsidiaries, where the lead investors are the folks who end up as the board members (and most are ignorant of the various companies' true aims). Not unlike real-world companies, virtually no outsiders can discover who sits on either the Pentex or subsidiary boards. However, for the subsidiaries, the officers' identities are usually a matter of public record, which of course serves Pentex's needs perfectly; should a subsidiary screw up, the chief officer and her flunkies are perfect fall guys.

The Executive Office:

The Executive division, comprised of the executive director and his personal staff, oversees all other branches of Pentex. The director monitors how well the other divisions' goals are being met, holds veto power over all company policies and oversees board meetings.

Project Coordination (Public Relations and Finance):

As the name implies, personnel in this division oversee the many ventures of Pentex and its subsidiaries. Project coordinators plan endeavors that will bring in profit to the companies; they also monitor public perception of subsidiaries and make sure there is minimal duplication of efforts among personnel. This is the largest division of Pentex, and its director and subdirectors hold considerable power.

Acquisitions (Information Collection Systems):

The Acquisitions division is self-explanatory; here, the aim is to acquire, by whatever means necessary, companies that will benefit Pentex and its goals. The division uses corporate espionage and blackmail on a regular basis (like so many other megacorporations), and to this end, the Acquisitions operatives collect information and data on potential acquisitions (or anything deemed useful) for use as future ammo. This division also keeps an eye on the behavior of all Pentex employees, setting up "disappearances" if necessary, and arranging contacts among certain other… unusual parties (the occasional Black Spiral Dancer or vampire has found its way into Pentex corporate culture).

Operations (Human Resources):

The Operations division oversees the day-to-day affairs of Pentex, including monitoring subsidiaries on a regional basis. Management of workers also falls under this division, although indoctrination is probably a better word than training to describe treatment of employees, even those at the higher echelons. Upper-level management in Operations also works directly with subsidiary directors at Pentex's various underling companies.

Special Projects (Project Iliad and Project Odyssey):

The Special Projects division is the smallest entity within Pentex, but also the most potentially dangerous. It oversees various experiments and research projects, including mind control, genetics and the development of biotech. Iliad focuses on creating fomori while Odyssey concentrates on the development of psychic abilities.

Other Units

Pentex also has a number of "floating" projects that can be most troublesome for the characters. These are among the more maverick schemes of Pentex and its subsidiaries, so Storytellers should feel free to plan and develop these projects (or new ones) as they see fit.

Project Aeneid:

Once a hopeful crossover endeavor between Projects Odyssey and Iliad, the aim of Project Aeneid was to create a reproducible Bane called a Mind Feeder and insert it into the brains of psychics. The end result would be a telepathic fomor, a useful agent by any standard, although test subjects demonstrated an inconvenient, insatiable appetite for human brain matter. Recently, though, the project has been scrapped, although not from any ethical objections; the head of Special Projects, Harold Zettler, deemed that the psychics in Project Odyssey were too valuable to sacrifice. This act received strong agreement from Kiro Yamazaki, overseer of Odyssey, but extreme dissent from the head of Iliad, Francesco. Iliad's top man is extremely anxious to get revenge on both his rival Yamazaki and his boss, Zettler, for scrapping his pet project. Francesco, a Black Spiral Dancer Philodox, is a singularly distasteful creature, but he may be willing to sell out to wreak havoc on his enemies within Pentex. The enterprising Storyteller could parlay this into a moral quandary for the werewolf characters — cooperating with Francesco long enough to get some inside dirt on Pentex, or not.

Pentex First Teams:

First Teams are cadres of highly trained agents who usually work in small units. Their usual objectives range from occasional all-out attacks on organized resistance — septs or packs — to the more common tasks of infiltration and top secret wetwork. They are generally a last resort, sent in when lesser methods just aren't getting the job done. Combat-oriented First Teams have half a dozen agents or more in each cadre; espionage teams typically include only two or three. In theory, a director can assemble squads with whatever specialties are needed for a particular mission, but in practice, pairs or trios of agents generally get used to working with each other and tend to stick together when possible. Specialties include computer hacking, organized infiltration and similar types of skills. If at all possible, a team will include a psychic from Project Odyssey. More martial-oriented teams add powerful fomori as part of the strike force. One change that Mollett has implemented is giving the teams better equipment and training; she has made a good case for not treating the teams as entirely expendable. Thus, in

certain circumstances, teams will have access to drug enhancement and the latest high-tech gadgets, in addition to silver bullets, big guns and heavy transports.

Team Prime:

This group represents the crème de la crème of agents culled from First Teams, Project Iliad and Project Odyssey. They report directly to the Executive Director, and no one among the other Pentex bigwigs knows of their existence. The Exec uses them for all his most dirty work, from assassination and larceny to torture and blackmail. Recruits have all received cosmetic surgery and new identities to become extraordinarily average, so they're virtually anonymous (and certainly unknown to any former friends in the company).

The Omega Plan:

The Omega Plan is in many ways like that "great novel" everyone plans to write someday; it sounds pretty good in theory, but is hard to put into practice. Basically, this is the big blueprint for taking over the world. Step one involves draining the human spirit and the planet's resources to the point of near-global annihilation; this is where the company and its subsidiaries stand currently. In step two, Pentex comes in as the planet's white knight, saving humanity from extinction. Then, by step three, they'll be totally in charge of everything. Needless to say, this stuff isn't written down anywhere, but it's something that every director and subdirector knows about — or thinks they do. Some of the older board members think the plan is perfectly viable; some of the newer members have their doubts but are cautious enough not to quibble over the plan, at least openly.

Project Ice:

With the collapse of Project Aeneid, Project Ice is the new hot item at Pentex. For some time, several of the directors have pointed out that Antarctica is basically an untapped resource. Weird stories and legends abound concerning lost civilizations, prehuman creatures and buried treasures on the icy continent. So, Pentex has finally sent a specially equipped First Team to check out some of the rumors. The team has just established a small base and hopes to start their investigations during the next spring and summer.

Pentex Tactics

Pentex, along with its subsidiaries, has some basic, broad-spectrum strategies to accomplish its goals. The following are some general guidelines for ways to best use Pentex as an adversary in your chronicle.

Think Globally, Act Locally

Even though Pentex is active worldwide, many of its plots focus on causing problems at local levels. It can't create an apathetic public without getting out in the field, after all. What it can do is create a lot of misery in

As Pentex has become more and more involved in corporate espionage, both the Board and First Team operatives have begun using certain code-words of their own for the obstacles and tactics peculiar to their work — especially of a supernatural nature. Following are the more common terms agents may toss around; most espionage agents are "in the know" at least as far as werewolves are concerned (and often chemically immune to the Delirium), although they might not know details about some of the more esoteric resources at Pentex's disposal, such as Banes.

Angel: Unseen backup, such as a Bane.

Asset: An agent.

Community Service: Striking at a target through his friends and family.

DOS: Dead On Sight. A termination order.

Dust and Sweep: One agent smokescreens or stalls a target while another agent searches the target's home or office.

Evaluator: A psychologist who preps agents for fieldwork. Kathryn Mollett is one example.

Family Jewels: The companies' most important secrets and agents.

Filing: Entering an office to steal something, or leave a bug or false evidence.

Honeytrap: A sexual situation designed to stall or compromise a target.

In the Cold: Agent operating without supervision from the corporation; agent operating without Control.

In the Pocket: An agent on an undercover mission.

K9: Werewolves friendly to Pentex (usually Black Spiral Dancers).

Litter: A local infestation of werewolves.

NSUs: Fomori agents. From "nutritional supplement users"; most agents, even the fomori themselves, believe a fomor agent's powers and mutations to be chemically induced.

Quarters: Silver ammunition.

Ride Home: A suicide device such as a cyanide tooth. Many agents are given a "ride home" along with a briefing that emphasizes they're better off dead than caught by werewolves.

Roll of Quarters: A clip of silver bullets.

Sloppy Joe: A killing meant to intimidate, usually through mutilating the target almost wholly beyond recognition.

Stray: A werewolf. Very rarely used to identify other shapeshifters ("stray cat," "stray bird," etc.); most Pentex agents don't even know other shapeshifters exist.

Tells: Specific marks that can aid in identifying an undercover agent.

TFAA: Tragic fiery automobile accident. An assassination that looks like an accident.

Watering Hole: Safehouse with a substantial store of weapons.

typical towns and communities, in a variety of regions and locales. How does this work? Let's look at one medium-sized town that just happens to host a subsidiary factory. First of all, the employees at the factory are probably exposed to faint taints each and every day they go to work. These may create health problems over the long haul, so that products or services from Magadon or Autumn Health Care are needed. The taints might also influence the employees' personalities to make them more susceptible to certain types of advertising, which in turn prods them to use more subsidiary products with more unpleasant side effects. The results for Pentex? Profit, public apathy and greed. It's a perfect scenario that could be ongoing in the characters' own backyards.

Keep Friends Close and Enemies Closer

Pentex doesn't mind cultivating distasteful allies among certain other supernatural factions; while cautious, they'd like to kindle more relationships with warlocks, vampires and the like. Getting into bed with these types is important, but not quite as vital as getting good dirt on the local shapeshifters. Pentex is actively trying to infiltrate a sept, not to destroy the packs (yet) but to find out just exactly how Garou society works. There's time enough for killing later on; what they want now is information. To this end, certain First Team operatives are seeking out that rare werewolf who may be willing to sell out. As horrible as this may seem, Pentex is confident it will happen; all they need is patience.

Misinformation is Key

Not even the members of the Pentex board have all the pieces to the myriad plots within the company proper and its subsidiaries. Moreover, ascendancy to key positions virtually requires the ability to misinform and mislead both superiors and subordinates alike. So for outsiders, finding out real dirt on Pentex and its subsidiaries should be difficult. For every three grains of information, two will be shaky at best; the third may be correct, but it won't be the whole story.

Use Enemies Against Themselves

Pentex may not be experts on the werewolves, but they have discovered that there's some natural friction between local "litters." They'd love to encourage these disagreements into a full-blown war. Moreover, seeing that there are distinct differences between werewolves of the western world and the Asian shapeshifters, Pentex has several agents investigating whether or not there's potential for a cross-cultural dispute. Anything to get the werewolves to divert their energies away from Pentex and towards each other is worth pursuing.

Pentex Companies

If Pentex is the faceless puppetmaster, then its subsidiaries are the down-in-the-trenches enemies most werewolves encounter. For more detailed descriptions of several of these companies, see **Subsidiaries: A Guide to Pentex**.

In addition to the top subsidiaries (see below), there are a number of up-and-coming Pentex-supported companies that are doing quite well, despite the downturn in the economy. These include:

• **Bradford Incorporated:** Taking advantage of the public hue and cry at the sorry state of education, Bradford is one of the many corporations stepping in to run public schools just like small, independent businesses. The "products" are children who can mindlessly show an increase in standardized test scores. The problem with Bradford is that they don't allow for much individuality, much less creativity. Children at these schools make the grades, but at the price of turning into tedious automatons.

Sample First Team Agent

This individual is a typical, well-trained normal operative for Pentex. Storytellers might wish to individualize agents to give them particular specialties, such as demolitions, infiltration or hand-to-hand combat. Don't forget that many agents will carry certain drugs that can temporarily increase stats (although the crash from using these drugs is exceptionally unfun).

Attributes: Strength 3, Dexterity 3, Stamina 4, Charisma 2, Manipulation 2, Appearance 2, Perception 4, Intelligence 2, Wits 4

Abilities: Alertness 3, Athletics 3, Brawl 3, Computer 2, Drive 1, Dodge 3, Firearms 4, Investigation 1, Melee 3, Medicine 1, Stealth 2, Streetwise 1, Subterfuge 2, Survival 2

Willpower: 6

Who's Who in Pentex

Your players might never meet these people, but as the Storyteller, you should know just who's pulling strings behind the curtains, and why.

Peter Culliford, Executive Director: Culliford is a master of deceit and is hell-bent on creating a world full of helplessness and despair.

Benjamin Rushing, Division Director of Project Coordination: Rushing is ambitious and far-sighted. He is dedicated to increasing Pentex's power at any cost.

Adrian Newberry, Division Director of Operations: Newberry is the administrative genius behind Pentex and its subsidiaries. Nothing happens without his knowing about it.

Harold Zettler, Division Director of Special Projects: Depraved and volatile, Zettler nonetheless has a lot of vision, particularly when it comes to his pet projects.

Danforth Stern, Division Director of Acquisitions: Stern is a total basketcase who believes aliens are coming to earth any day now. Much of his power and control has slipped to Lamont.

James Kiker, Subdivision Director of Public Relations: A whiz at advertising, Kiker hasn't kept up with modern trends and technology as successfully as he should have.

Kiro Yamazaki, Subdivision Director of Project Odyssey: Yamazaki is clever and shrewd. While an underdog in Pentex politics, he's not someone to piss off.

Chase Lamont, Subdivision Director of Information Collection Systems: Pentex's newest (and nastiest) golden boy, Lamont is being groomed by Rushing for great things in the future.

Kathryn Mollett, Subdivision Director of Human Resources: The only female on the Pentex board, Mollett skillfully manipulates both her underlings and her peers with shrewd psychology.

Francesco, Subdivision Director of Project Iliad: Despite a rise to prominence in Pentex, Francesco (a Black Spiral Dancer) is not entirely pleased with the way things have gone. He's keeping options open.

Franklin Rubin, Subdivision Director of Finance: Rubin is a total wild card. Despite his tremendous financial acumen, no one at Pentex can find out anything about his background.

• **Meyers, Feinstein and Hargrett:** With multinational interests, Pentex's board of directors saw the need to have a subsidiary law firm with offices around the world. Meyers, Feinstein and Hargrett have practices set up in major US cities and international offices in London, Bangkok and Johannesburg. The firm can have a young, eager and utterly unscrupulous attorney at the elbow of a needy subsidiary employee within a matter of hours, no matter where the crime or problem occurs.

Plots Within Plots

In the past couple of years, several of the Pentex board members have bought and nurtured their own private companies to reap some solo profit and pursue their own interests. Chase Lamont and Benjamin Rushing in particular enjoy the challenge of these secret pursuits. Whether Culliford and others within Pentex know (or care) about these activities is unclear. Storytellers might use these small connections to Pentex as tools to get player characters involved in deeper plots through the back door, as it were.

Southeastern Tech Management (STM)

Ostensibly a technical consulting firm, STM is the brainchild of Chase Lamont. They sell and install high-end computer equipment to corporations all over the southeast; customers include power companies, local governments and various human resource agencies. STM provides firewall services to their customers; however, what they don't explain is that they alone control passwords and access to the firewalls. In short, anyone at STM who wishes to know more about their customers or even their customers' customers (citizens across the southeast) can bypass the security with ease. Thus, Chase Lamont can gather data on millions of people; such information is his bread and butter for blackmail.

Credicorps

Rushing, taking inspiration from his protégé, has purchased his own company through a number of smokescreens. Credicorps is a typical credit management firm; they run checks for various credit card companies and banks. Rushing uses this information to get dirt not only on people who may prove useful to his project endeavors, but also on most of the subsidiary employees and their families. Money talks, and Rushing knows that people will do about anything to preserve their financial well being, should such tactics become necessary for him to get what he wants.

Top Pentex Subsidiaries

Pentex ranks its top companies on two concepts, profitability and usefulness. The following subsidiaries are either prime sources of income or so valuable in reaching Pentex's goals, they've been pegged as major players. Storytellers should note that these are not the only Pentex subsidiaries; if you have ideas for other companies, by all means develop them and sic them on your players.

• **Ardus Enterprises:** Ardus is a waste management firm that collects (and often re-uses) all manner of waste products, from radioactive pollutants to biological refuse. They aren't too picky over how such products are disposed, either.

• **Autumn Health Management Systems:** This firm purchases and manages hospitals and nursing homes, maintaining bare minimum standards of care while reaping exorbitant profits.

• **Avalon Incorporated:** Seemingly an innocent toy company, Avalon's products subtly turn youngsters into greedy, destructive brats. Recently, they've capitalized on the lucrative adult toy market as well.

• **Black Dog Games:** A leader in the roleplaying industry, games from Black Dog encourage players to indulge in whiny selfishness and tragic hipness by playing violent antihero characters. Tellus Enterprises, another subsidiary, produce accompanying software.

• **Circinus Brands:** Circinus produces and sells tobacco products, targeting their ads specifically at young people. They promote smoking as a must for being cool, hip and trendy. Also, against FCC regulations, they use occasional subliminal advertising to attract buyers.

A Certain Scent in the Air?

Many products from Pentex subsidiaries contain spiritual contaminants called taints. Taints are not generally detectable; however, they tend to cause subtle effects in persons that use or consume the products. Such side effects can include addiction, apathy, illness or even personality disorders. Taints don't usually fade over time, so a bottle of King Distilleries wine will be dangerous even for years to come. Many tainted products have a time-release effect as well; hence the user may not connect her extreme fatigue with the Magadon cosmetics she used a few weeks ago.

Certain werewolf Gifts can detect the presence of taints. Otherwise, it's next to impossible to discover the corruption innocently lurking on the grocery story shelf.

• **Consolidex Worldwide:** Despite low returns, this investment firm, which sells no-load mutual funds, continues to attract young, naïve investors even in the slowing market. Consolidex in turn reinvests this money, skims off the top and spreads the funds to other Pentex subsidiaries.

• **Endron International:** Endron is the oldest company under the Pentex umbrella and one of the more destructive. They specialize in the production of petroleum products; if it weren't for some careful bribes on the part of Pentex's PR, OSHA would have shut down Endron long ago. Their factories have no safety standards, and the products produce dangerous levels of emissions. Maybe Endron is old-fashioned in its methods, but the company is still a major bastion in the Pentex family.

• **Good House International:** With one of the widest markets, Good House is a leading Pentex subsidiary. The company produces a diverse array of paper products; like Endron, they actively engage in deforestation and harm to the environment on a regular basis.

• **Hallahan Fishing Corporation:** Not only does Hallahan engage in illegal fishing practices, killing dolphins in nets and slaughtering whales, they also falsely represent their products, selling fake crab and other items as the real thing. O'Tolleys also uses Hallahan's products in their fast food.

• **Harold and Harold Mining, Incorporated:** Recent expansions into South Africa have not only assured this subsidiary's continued existence, they've also increased profit margins. Harold and Harold prefer strip mining to obtain valuable commodities such as zinc, coal and lead.

• **Herculean Firearms, Incorporated:** Herculean produces extremely cheap weapons and ammo, turning a hunk of profits into funding for gun lobbies and political action committees. Their influence on issues of gun control, rather than profitability, makes them worth keeping in the Pentex family.

• **Herrick's:** In the era of superstore chains, Herrick's is near the top of the pack. They provide the perfect means for selling other subsidiaries' products, such as Circinus cigarettes, Avalon toys and King beers. Since there's no "middleman" distributor, profit margins increase for everyone.

• **King Breweries and Distilleries:** By secretly altering alcohol contents and launching an aggressive and successful ad campaign, King snares devoted new

customers each successive generation. Even though the company publicly denounces underage drinking, most ads don't feature anyone over 22 years of age.

• **Magadon, Incorporated:** After acquiring two other Pentex subsidiaries, Magadon is second only to Endron in size and profits. A giant in the pharmaceutical industry, Magadon has also expanded into cosmetics and medical supplies. Magadon's sales tactics are aimed at young women in particular; products include diet pills, breast implants and so-called "permanent makeup" chemicals.

• **Nastrum Enterprises:** A small but profitable venture, Nastrum designs and builds weapons of mass destruction as well as delivery systems and aircraft. Most sales take place illegally to third world countries or to independent terrorists.

• **Omni Television:** This production company has made a real mark in the past few years through capitalizing on the enormous reality television market. Growing from now trite real-life cop shows to gruesome emergency room dramas, they've finally hit the big leagues with *Tooth and Claw*, a show that puts amateurs on safari in exotic locations around the world.

• **O'Tolley's:** Utilizing many products from other subsidiaries, O'Tolley's is a world leader in fast food. It's greasy, unhealthy and utterly irresistible to most consumers. Moreover, the food is cheap. With an O'Tolley's on every corner, families can chow down on tainted burgers any time they want.

• **Rainbow Incorporated:** This subsidiary manufactures and markets a variety of plastic and rubber items, from tires to IV tubing. Rainbow has recently sunk more funds into big ad campaigns on the feasibility of using plastic.

• **Tellus Enterprises:** Tellus has grown from a small video games company into a world leader in the software and hardware market. They still produce lots of games, which promote mindless violence, and reap a huge profit from their sleek, futuristic CPUs, which are priced a good deal lower than competitors' products.

• **Vesuvius Incorporated:** Vesuvius controls a wide array of publishing interests, from magazine and books, to comics and newspapers. This gives them the perfect opportunity to promote other subsidiaries through ads, as well influence public opinion for Pentex's benefit on various pertinent issues, such as gun control and youth violence.

• **Young and Smith, Incorporated:** The third largest subsidiary, Young and Smith manufacture a wide variety of foodstuffs and personal care products. Convenience foods are their biggest moneymaker; all edibles are full of preservatives and incredibly unhealthy.

Storytelling Tools and Techniques

Until now, we've been discussing creating a certain mindset for Pentex based more or less on an espionage and conspiracy model. But the question for Storytellers is how to best *show* players the way Pentex operates, without giving away all the secrets. With that in mind, here are some Storytelling tools and tips you can use to better convey the mood of conspiracy, with the enemies working from the shadows.

Secret Transcripts and Tapes —

Eventually, the characters are going to figure out a way to wiretap or bug one of the subsidiaries (Glass Walkers could be useful here). Instead of telling the players what the characters find out, take the time to prepare a *real* transcript, tape or bit of email. These info samples don't have to be long, but they should show a conversation that will help the players either get some good dirt on their enemies for future use or discover some useful tidbits that will help with infiltration. If you're technologically savvy, you could use props such as digitized audiofiles and image clips; perhaps the characters have successfully bugged some of their enemies' computers and now have access to even some encrypted files.

Informants —

What espionage story doesn't have some variation of Deep Throat? As much as Pentex and its subsidiaries are loathe to admit it, not everyone is a happy camper in the big corporate family. And not everyone is stupid enough to keep his or her feelings private, either. With a little luck and shrewd observation, the characters can probably discover an insider willing to work with them to inflict serious damage.

Details, Details, It's All in the Details —

One essential element for conspiracies is the level of detail. As Storyteller, you're going to need to have things a little more fleshed out than you would for a more physical session; this includes tasks like constructing interesting personalities for the Storyteller characters as well as having it clear in your own head just what everyone's plots and agendas are. Also, make sure the players keep careful records of your labyrinthine plots (the ones they discover, that is). Consider awarding an extra experience point on occasion to the player that makes good notes to share with the group. Likewise, if a lot of time must lapse between sessions, try to keep everyone up to date and in the loop on what's going on. Email or chatrooms can be most effective to remind everyone of what's transpired, who's been involved and what the pack's next plans are; they also provide a ready written record. This is a lot more convenient than trying to rehash every nitpicky detail at the beginning of each new game session.

Rumors —

Sometimes, it's a little more difficult to get characters involved in the big corporate plot; after all, if it were all such a big secret, why in the world would the werewolves know about it? This is where rumors come in. Rumors can get to the characters in a variety of ways: a security glitch at a subsidiary, an employee that talks too much or just plain dumb luck. In any case, a rumor should straddle the fence between being specific enough to catch the werewolves' attention and vague enough to leave them wanting to know more.

Get in the Mood and Write it Out —

The format's not important; you could use a journal, vignette or complete short story. The important thing is that you, the Storyteller, construct some fiction to get you (and possibly the players, if it's appropriate to share the material) in the right frame of mind. Perhaps you want to get into the head of the nebbish corporate peon who's going to screw up and fall into some pretty young werewolf's honeytrap. By writing an entry in his diary, you can get into his head and thus use this Storyteller character more effectively than if he was nothing more than a bunch of stats on paper.

Pentex Toys

Pentex, its agents and its subsidiaries have a wide array of useful devices at their fingertips. Distribution of these items depends on two things: the nature of a mission and the value of the agents involved. Grunts on guard duty won't have access to fancier gear and stimulants! But the well-trained computer tech infiltrator probably will — enough time and money has gone into his training to make his preservation worth the goods (for a while).

Drugs

In addition to most normal pharmaceuticals, certain Pentex employees have access to three potent types of drugs. The first are anti-Delirium drugs; as the name implies, usage can temporarily negate the effects of Delirium when the agent confronts a werewolf. The good news is that these are in fast-acting autoinjector form; the bad news is that they don't last very long, perhaps 15 minutes or so depending on individual metabolism. Their best use is as a "get away" tool; the drug allows the agent to clear her head enough to escape an angry werewolf (in theory, anyway). Magadon is currently working on a variation that has longer duration.

The second category of drugs are the anagathics, or anti-aging drugs. They're difficult to produce and probably the most controlled substances in the Pentex family. For the present, only the Board (and a few of their selected flunkies) has access to these drugs. Side effects are subtle but insidious, including addiction, panic attacks and bouts of extreme paranoia.

Finally, there are the stimulants (colloquially known as stims or boosters). Taken before combat, they can temporarily raise Physical stats by a random d10 points, adjusted as the Storyteller sees fit to embellish Strength, Dexterity or Stamina. After the drugs were off, in about an hour's time, the user becomes useless; he's exhausted and needs about 24 hours to recover completely.

Devices

Agents taking part in large-scale assaults have access to an arsenal of weapons that would rival any nation's military surplus. One of the latest fads is using depleted uranium ammo; not only does it blow up things real good, it leaves behind traces of radiation for some years to come. Even in these small doses, the radiation can cause sickness and possibly trigger worse conditions for the victim.

Pentex also uses the latest in computer espionage technology. Spiders are tiny devices that can suck out and then reconstruct bits of data when retrieved. Data shredders, on the other hand, utterly destroy target data; not even first aid programs can reconstruct material after the shredder finishes its job.

Finally, for use in some of its more local and low-key operations, Pentex has had some subsidiaries manufacture seemingly innocent items that can have long-term effects on a local target population. One of their favorites is the Little League Plaque. This device looks like a simple thank-you plaque; it's given to a local restaurant or business to show appreciation for their support of a kid's sports team. However, anyone who frequents the business or restaurant is slowly affected by a given taint; no family would ever connect its increased fatigue and grouchiness to the local O'Tolley's, would they?

Story Seeds

To give you some ideas for using Pentex and its subsidiaries, here are a few examples of the types of schemes they might cook up. You'll have to tailor fit these, of course, to suit your chronicle and mix of players and characters.

Employee of the Week

A Pentex subsidiary hires a Kinfolk or other important friend of one of the characters. Things seem to go quite well for the new employee at first; he's not asked to do anything out of the ordinary, and the work is pleasant enough. However, as time passes, perhaps he has to stand on shaky ground, ethically speaking. Perhaps, if they are in the know about his connections to the werewolves, upper management begins asking nosy questions. And by this time, the powers that be have enough clout to coerce the employee into committing acts or telling secrets he'd rather keep to himself. He'll go to his friends or relatives for help. How will they respond?

After the Fall

Unfortunately for Pentex, an unlucky First Team miscalculates. On a mission, they make enough mistakes to compromise their position and also litter the area with bodies. Perhaps a routine test of a new subsidiary product backfires, or there is some kind of information leak that allows media to make an unexpected appearance. In any case, the characters stumble on the scene of this mess before a cleaner arrives. They'll have some time to try and work out exactly what happened, and probably gather some useful information and evidence, but eventually a cleanup team will turn up, ready to snuff out any onlookers. The werewolves will have to not only mop up the mess, but also potentially deal with *two* squads of highly-trained soldiers (and the cleaner crew will definitely be more adept than the previous batch), to say nothing of protecting any innocent bystanders.

Piercelings

Magadon officials, looking to get a solid hold on the counterculture as a market base, has perfected a series of special tattoo inks and body piercing rings (they can be used in navels, ears or whatever location the customer chooses), which it releases to a carefully chosen test market, in a town not too far from the werewolves' home base. The inks and metal in the rings all carry a subtle taint that has a twofold effect. First of all, the recipient wants to get more and more of the body art, which of course increases the power of the taint. Second, the taint augments whatever attributes of apathy, self-centeredness and lethargy already exist in the victim. Instead of enjoying the tattoos or piercings as a form of self-expression or art, the customer becomes totally obsessed with her own sense of importance. Characters can get involved in several ways, maybe by noticing a jump in the number of indolent youths hanging around the town, or perhaps by visiting the local tattoo and piercing parlor themselves and feeling strange afterwards. However they get involved, there should be some means of tracing the inks back to Magadon. This could lead to further investigation and using the company as a long-term enemy for the pack.

Black Spiral Dancers

There is no enemy more ferocious or more horrific than the intimate enemy.

The Black Spiral Dancers are unlike all of the antagonists that the Garou face because they are *so much like* the Garou themselves. Have no illusions, no matter how malformed or how monstrously twisted they may appear from time to time; the Black Spiral Dancers *are* werewolves. Being such makes them quite possibly the most formidable foe the Garou Nation can possibly face.

Millennia ago, the White Howlers battled the legions of Hadrian in the Scottish moors of northern Britannia along the Caledonian border. The Wyld was strong here in their age, and the savagery of the White Howlers coupled with their determination to rid their homelands of the minions of the Weaver and Wyrm not only gave pause to the armies of Rome, but bred an obsession within the Pictish tribe that would, eventually, become the key to their demise. The White Howlers took their war and their rage to the very doorstep of the Wyrm, their pride blinding them into delusions of decisive victory against the great annihilator. Instead, the Wyrm swallowed the tribe whole and then vomited them back onto Gaia's face as the Black Spiral Dancers.

The Black Spiral Dancers are as much a spiritual and moral foe to the Garou as they are a mortal one. Every encounter that a player character has with a member of the Tribe of the Fallen should leave the player's character with a distinct sense, not only of mortality, but a fairly solid recognition of just how far a werewolf can fall. The Black Spiral Dancers should not simply represent a target for the sake of combat, nor should they serve as a simplistic form for the enemy. The Black Spiral Dancers represent what the Garou should consider an *omen of death*, plain and simple. Not just death of the body, but the death of the mind and the soul. They are the death of purity and of hope. They are the death of the dreams cherished by the Garou Nation and the horror and uncertainty of death staring back from the faces of any of their long lost brothers or sisters. No Garou should feel comfortable staring down a Black Spiral Dancer. To look into the eyes of one of the Fallen Tribe is to experience what waits should the war against the coming Apocalypse be lost. In many ways, the Black Spiral Dancers represent everything that the Gaian Garou fights to stave off every single day of her life.

Newton's Law says that for each action that occurs there is also an equal or opposite reaction. This is one of the truisms of the universe, to be certain. Where the Garou fight to save Gaia and to preserve that which remains and has not been lost already, the converse agenda of the Black Spiral Dancers is both equal and opposite.

The Great Corrosion

It is very easy to write the Black Spiral Dancer tribe off as a swollen cult of mad traitors, deformed and degenerate criminals, eaters of flesh and gibbering priests of gods long dead or damned and nothing more. Many among the tribes of Gaia have subscribed to this mindset throughout history, and it can be assumed that many do so to this very day. Classifying the entirety of your enemy with the stereotypes inherent to the *weakest* among your enemy's number is convenient. It is an easy thing to do. It is certainly easier to summon courage against an enemy when the enemy is vastly inferior.

This mindset is a grievous error in regards to the fallen tribe, and it has become a weapon that the Black Spiral Dancers exploit at every opportunity available to them.

While the fallen do indeed count the hopelessly insane and monstrously malformed among their number, these individuals within the tribe hardly comprise the majority of the tribe's membership. While somewhere around half of the entirety of the Black Spiral Dancer Tribe are metis, there are a vast number of Dancers who have fallen from Gaia's grace and hence, from the tribes of their births. Many werewolves are inducted into the Tribe of the Fallen by experience and enlightenment to the cruel miracles of the Wyrm rather than through birth. The pride of the Garou is a breeding ground for resentment, covetousness, lust for power, rank, status and knowledge. All Garou are proud creatures, but some are consumed by their hubris and, therefore, their desires. The Wyrm, like a mosquito, gorges itself from within the prison of the Pattern Web on beings whose souls harbor desire and dominion at their cores. In exchange for what it takes, it expels the excrement of corruption into the hearts, minds and souls of those who let their baser desires control and direct them.

Thus the subtlety of the Wyrm is perennial. Gaian Garou that fall to the Thrall of the Wyrm do so more often than not without even realizing what has happened. By the time they have danced the Spiral it is far too late. Rising from the mire and muck of a Hive's pit, the misbegotten prodigals of Gaia's Fangs embrace the whole of the Tellurian with new vision and enlightenment through the oily membrane that the Wyrm has slathered upon their souls. In some cases, entire packs fall to their own rage or pride, or in some cases, a combination of both. The fate of the White Howlers was a fate forged in subtlety, manipulation, pride and deceit. Corruption from within rather than from without is a formula that works for the Wyrm, and it is a weapon that the Black Spiral Dancers employ at every opportunity.

It is important to convey the horror of such a weapon when using the Black Spiral Dancers in a **Werewolf** chronicle. Planting the idea in the players' minds that any werewolf, any pack, represents a potential for service to the Wyrm is vital to the horror represented by the fallen tribe. A character with the Allies Background, for example, might find that when she calls on a former pack mate that they are not at all what they once were and that they are, in fact, something much, much more. A character with the Nightmares Flaw may have recurring night-

mares centered on her involvement in the complete massacre of the men of a colonial New England hamlet and the unnatural violation of the girls and women of the town as she laughs and watches. It may be revealed later to the character that one of her early American ancestors fell to the corruption of the Wyrm and betrayed the Kinfolk he was sworn to protect.

Bringing the Black Spiral Dancers to your characters and chronicles in a subtle manner helps to avoid the overwhelming familiarity your players might develop for the Tribe of the Fallen with too much direct, in-your-face exposure to them. As the White Howlers fell, through the internal corruption and corrosion of the Wyrm, so too shall fall those among the Garou Nation who do not heed the warning that the fallen tribe represents. Black Spiral Dancers are not always made from kicking and screaming werewolf captives that are hurled into Malfeas to face the Wyrm on their own. A lot of times, the Wyrm comes walking right in through the front door as an invited guest.

Robes of Silicone and Rust

If the Black Spiral Dancers were not doing *something* right, they would have been pulverized by the combined might of the Western Concordiat centuries ago. Subtlety, as was stated before, has a lot to do with the success of the Tribe of the Fallen. Their solidarity and organization, however, add insult to the injury of their existence. The Black Spiral Dancers may not agree with one another and they may not all like each other, but they all acknowledge one truth that unifies them as a single body; they all serve the same master. Up until the 20th Century, the Black Spiral Dancers were viewed by many within the Garou Nation as an embarrassing collection of traitorous and hopelessly corrupted riff-raff. For every Black Spiral Dancer pack that struck a blow against Gaia, there were half a dozen packs of her champions to avenge her. This underestimation of the Tribe of the Fallen has cost the Garou Nation in modern nights, as the Black Spiral Dancers now boast the largest single organized tribe of werewolves in the world, easily one tenth of the entire werewolf population.

Unity has more than a little to do with the recent success of the Black Spiral Dancers. While the Gaian Garou bicker and whine among one another in regards to rank, station, leadership, the crimes of their fathers, their birthrights, territory and the correct and righteous way to do battle against the Weaver and Wyrm, the Black Spiral Dancers have only one mission; the Weaver must be destroyed. The Wyrm must be unleashed and nothing else matters. While the ways and means of accomplishing this mission may differ from Hive to Hive, the mission itself is one that each and every Black Spiral Dancer is charged to champion and,

if necessary, die for. Of course, Black Spiral Dancers are still individuals, and have individual motivations that often set them at odds with one another. Theurges within the tribe may debate their omens while Philodox argue over materials and resource allotment and allocation; struggles for power and dominance may turn excessively bloody. But in the end, the Black Spiral Dancers are all on the same side in their war against Gaia. Even their dark litany states that each and every member of the Tribe of the Fallen is obligated to serve the Wyrm in all of its forms and to assist the children of the Wyrm, wherever and whenever encountered, in achieving victory in their struggle against that which the Wyrm seeks to consume and devour.

"So if the Black Spiral Dancers aren't all foaming jaws, matted, rotting fur, putrescence and bad breath, then what are they?"

The Wyrm's imprisonment within the Pattern Web of the Weaver has served to motivate it to empower and armor its shock-troops with the camouflage of that which surrounds them. While there are most certainly more than a few hideously monstrous Dancers that resemble anything but a werewolf in appearance due to the sheer level of their personal corruption, there are also generals in the Wyrm's army who appear totally and completely normal in every possible way. Vanity is a six-shooter on the hip of the great annihilator, and the Black Spiral Dancers, what they fight for and the source of their power can, at times, appear as wolves in sheep's clothing.

The Black Spiral Dancers once hid in the shadows and the dark, labyrinthine tunnels of their Hives from their Gaian cousins and from the eyes of men. In modern nights, the Tribe of the Fallen is quite literally everywhere. The stain of the Wyrm spreads like crude on lace across the Pattern Web. There is no city on the face of the planet that is without some trace of the Wyrm's kiss. Where the Wyrm is present, so too are the Black Spiral Dancers to protect its interests. The adaptation of the tribe to the urban sprawl of man and the price it carries with it rivals that of the Bone Gnawer and Glass Walker tribes. In fact, no other organized tribe of werewolves is better suited to thrive and sustain itself within the filthy pockets of human ingenuity than the Tribe of the Fallen. While they may not be obvious and may seek to remain in the shadows of the skyscrapers and depths of the sewers, the Black Spiral Dancers crawl through the cities of men like termites through a rotten log. This being the case, it is no easy task to simply identify a Dancer among a crowd without the use of Gifts. Permeating every possible level of society as is necessary for their cause, the Black Spiral Dancers occupy a place in virtually every level of the pyramid of human society from the most respected CEO to the lowliest welfare case. This saturation of society assists the Tribe of the Fallen in their efforts to remain invisible shadow players behind the veil of human folly. While they may not directly take part in the affairs and actions of *Corporation X* or the *Brotherhood of Z*, they will most certainly do everything within their power to make sure that any and all obstacles that might stand in the way of *Corporation X* or the *Brotherhood of Z* are removed in the event that their agendas match those of the Wyrm.

The paranoia of being constantly surrounded by the enemy on all sides and in all things is vital to the theme and mood of **Werewolf** and the coming War of Apocalypse. The players should feel that every plot that they encounter, every conflict that comes their way is like an apple. Once they take a bite from it, and only then, they realize the infestation that is corroding and devouring it from within. None are closer to the Wyrm than the Black Spiral Dancers, and therefore the Tribe of the Fallen should be the treated as the *egg-layer* of the pestilence that rots the world from the inside out. The following are a few examples of how the *more normal* Black Spiral Dancers might appear and operate in the World of Darkness:

• **Corporate Benefactors** — A group of businessmen fund the initial expenses for the creation of a landfill just outside the suburbs of a city. Within the plans for the landfill are schematics for a public park built on top of the sodded and landscaped mountain of waste that will result. Beneath the landfill, however, the group of businessmen, a Black Spiral Dancer pack, will dedicate a pit and subsequently, a Hive.

• **The Forsaken** — A pack of Black Spiral Dancers infiltrate the homeless and dispossessed of a city, protecting vagrants, dealers, pimps and whores from the frequent attacks they suffer at the hands of those who seek to oppress them, including the city's Bone Gnawers.

• **The Shadies** — Control of a city's waste management unions would not only prove a profitable endeavor for a Hive, but also give them enormous influence and power throughout the city's infrastructure and organized, criminal hierarchy.

• **The Allies** — Although it is not common, it is also not unheard of for Black Spiral Dancers to forge alliances with the sect of vampires known as the Sabbat. In Sabbat "controlled" cities throughout North and South America, Black Spiral Dancers might be afforded both space and leave to serve their master in practically any way they see fit in exchange for the protection that they offer the vampires in daylight hours.

However they may appear, in what ever guises they choose be they subtle and hidden or full Crinos and in your face, the Black Spiral Dancers are all one

thing if nothing else; the personification of destruction and the ultimate tool of the Wyrm's appetite. Evil is a trite term, especially when applied to creatures like the Dancers. The Black Spiral Dancers surpass the common, accepted definition of evil in that they are completely devoid of any semblance of the concept of good. They have no delusions of morality of any kind. Their consciences, if they ever possessed them, vanished along their dance of the Black Spiral. Even the homids among the ranks of the Tribe of the Fallen are something far less than human on the inside. The Black Spiral Dancers cannot be redeemed, and in fact none of them wish to be. In order to seek redemption, one must first accept that they have transgressed the boundaries of decency. To the Black Spiral Dancers, decency is a catch phrase in a children's book that they have neither the time nor the ability to employ. As James Moore once said when dealing with the Black Spiral Dancers; "In the end, there is no salvation. There is only the illusion of salvation."

The Black Spiral Dancers do not apologize for what they are, nor do they maintain the capacity for angst in regards to what they have, as a tribe, become. The White Howlers are dead. There are no more. Only the Black Spiral Dancers remain to remind the universe that they ever existed at all. While you might make the decision as the storyteller to downplay the sinister depravity that the Black Spiral Dancers represent, it is vitally important that you never lose sight of the fact that they are the complete and total antithesis of everything that the Garou Nation stands for. The Black Spiral Dancers serve the Wyrm and call the Wyrm master. Their adoration for their dark lord is as strong and as devout as any Garou's love and spiritual devotion to Gaia. The Wyrm represents nothing but destruction, consumption and defilement and the Tribe of the Fallen are its champions. While this was not always the case where the Wyrm or the Black Spiral Dancers are concerned, it is now. It is important that you convey to your players that should they forget this or disregard the gravity of what they face where the Black Spiral Dancers are concerned, it will hasten their undoing.

It is important that the Black Spiral Dancers make sense. The template of the gibbering, giggling and drooling Black Spiral Dancer with the tentacles where its ears should be, gazelle horns jutting from its nose, who pisses nitroglycerine on demand works fine for the gross-out effect. It may even have its place within Werewolf (depending on how serious you want to be), but so too does the "Black Knight" that competently champions the forces of darkness and despair. Without foes that test every last bit of the mettle of the player characters, you lose something that is important to

Werewolf; *heroism*. Every great champion from Beowulf to Luke Skywalker is a great champion because he bested a superior foe through his wits, courage, convictions and abilities. Make your players' characters into heroes by making their foils worthy and fearsome adversaries. Bring out their werewolves' rage by confronting them with an enemy that defies the rules and uses the characters' weaknesses against them. Steer your players towards overcoming their character s' flaws and innate weaknesses through the necessity of survival and through the courage of doing what they know in their hearts to be the righteous thing to do, regardless of their apprehension or fear and regardless of the odds against them. No other antagonist in **Werewolf** is as useful a vehicle in achieving this in a chronicle than the Black Spiral Dancers.

Use them wisely.

Wrestling the Devil

Conflict is unavoidable in **Werewolf**. Conflict is inherent to the game and what the Garou are. There will be combat and there will be confrontation, but the Storyteller should handle confrontation with the Black Spiral Dancers with special care. No pack should walk away from combat with the Dancers unscathed.

While the "shoot first, ask questions later" attitude of many players in some cases is effective, where the Black Spiral Dancers are concerned, this should generally be conveyed as a grievous mistake. While the Black Spiral Dancers may be nothing more than dark, hollow reflections of Garou in the eyes of the werewolf player characters that encounter them, they are most certainly their brothers' keepers. Having the immediate advantage in numbers is bad enough, but also having the same strategic expertise as their Gaian enemies where pack tactics are concerned, the Black Spiral Dancers are not a physical threat to be taken with a grain lightly. Unlike most vampires or hunters the Black Spiral Dancers can meet the Garou on any level they have to, including toe-to-toe. The Dancers can (and should) do pretty much anything that the player characters can do. They have Gifts, just like the players. They call upon their totems, just like the players. They can Reach into the Umbra, just like the players and they are every bit as strong, every bit as cunning and every bit as ferocious as the player characters themselves. One thing that should be kept in mind when running combat between players and Black Spiral Dancers is the complete and total abandon that the Dancers can give into regarding their Rage. The Dancers are children of the Wyrm and their Rage is a gift from the Beast-of-War. The further they journey towards the snarling, frenzied beast that Gaian Garou subconsciously fear and consciously seek to suppress, the more powerful and formidable they become in a combat scenario.

Black Spiral Dancers do not hesitate to employ silver weaponry against their enemies. While it is always preferable to convert the enemy to their cause, the Dancers do not agonize over captives whose will and devotion to the "Bitch Mother" overrides any and all attempts at conversion. If the enemy cannot be converted, then the enemy is destroyed outright with not so much as a backwards glance. While the Black Spiral Dancers do in fact take prisoners and are somewhat legendary for their propensity to do so, escape from their clutches is virtually unheard of. Every battle that a pack of player characters fight against the Black Spiral Dancers, it should be emphasized, is to the death. There is no gray area. The players should understand that it is they or the pack of Dancers they face and that they would all rather be slain in combat against them than lose and face what comes next.

Different but the Same

Unity does not necessarily mean similarity where the Black Spiral Dancers are concerned. While the overwhelming agenda of the tribe as a whole is that which benefits the Wyrm, just like the werewolves of the Garou Nation, the Tribe of the Fallen has various and sundry subdivisions within their tribe to get things done. Different prongs on the same pitchfork, if you will. While the Hive of the First Corrosion may strive to undermine the Garou Nation itself through open and direct conflict in a series of well planned, highly technological surgical strikes from caern to caern. The Powder Burn Sept may seek subtler, less violent means of achieving the same goals as their tribal allies by using the weapon of political lobbying to weaken legislation regarding gun control and the availability of firearms and firearm safety requirements. The Hive of the First Corrosion may score one victory after another under the cover of night in their high-tech blitzkriegs across the sparsely populated Canadian wilderness. The Powder Burn Sept is content to sit back and listen to news reports of yet another high-school massacre in the Midwest as they stare blissfully across the Washington D.C. mall and smile. Such diversity not only makes logical sense, it's good stuff for keeping your players guessing.

Devil's Advocate: Philosophies of the Fallen

Of course, it always helps to have some ammunition up your sleeves when your players ask questions like "How can the Black Spiral Dancers want to destroy Gaia?" The following examples of possible Black Spiral Dancer philosophies are presented from the in-character point of view of the Tribe of the Fallen to better assist in debates of belief that might occur between player characters and Dancer antagonists. Note that they are but a few of the possible approaches toward a philosophy of ultimate corruption or destruction; expand upon them, alter them, or supplant them as you see fit.

Nihilism

ni·hil·ism *noun* — total rejection of social mores: the general rejection of established social conventions and beliefs, especially of morality and religion; belief that nothing is worthwhile: a belief that life is pointless and human values are worthless

The world is dying around you, and I know you can feel it. I do. If I can feel it, and you can feel it, then how could you possibly deny that this is not the case? How can you see hope in any of this? People have been talking about the change in the weather patterns and the frequency of earthquakes and the hole in the ozone layer for decades now, but there's nothing that anyone can do about any of it. Maybe this planet wants to be dead. Did you ever think of that? Did you ever think that the loss of balance, for which mankind is more than a little to blame, is something that just can't be fixed no matter how hard you try or no matter how much blood drips from your claws?

There is only one way to fix what's broken; tear it all down and rebuild it from the foundation up. What you call the rape and destruction of Gaia, I call a mercy killing in an effort to recreate that that has been lost. When a house is condemned because of its filth and disrepair, it is leveled. When a racehorse breaks its leg, it is shot to avoid the prolonging of the animal's suffering. How is Gaia any different? How can you call yourself a champion of the Mother when she's a filthy, unkempt mockery of what she was in the days before the Sundering? You should rejoice in that which we offer and strive to achieve. You should praise the passing of sickness and the renewal of the universe through the purification of the cold fire of oblivion. Instead, you waste your time fighting against the terminal, creeping cancer that has no cure, prolonging the inevitable.

The Wyrm is doing what it has always done; it is attempting to maintain balance through any means necessary. The trappings of men and the strength of the Weaver have hindered it in regards to its function in the universe, but they have done little to stop it altogether. The only way to cure this affliction — the disease of imbalance — is to cauterize it completely. All we seek to do is light the pyres that will purify the universe into renewal. How is that wrong? Balance through destruction is still balance, is it not?

Fratricide

frat·ri·cide (*plural* frat·ri·cides) *noun* — killing a brother: the crime in which somebody kills his or her own brother; killer of brother: somebody who kills his or her own brother

Gaia's Fangs are an affront to creation and must be destroyed. For thousands of years the Garou hunted and mauled all that they labeled enemy with indiscriminate ferocity. We are nothing more than the karma that has returned three-fold to punish them for their centuries of hypocrisy and waste. Humanity stands as the dominant master of the savanna of the world; an organism as complex as can be found within the whole of creation while at its core, as simple as a virus. Mankind is a superior creation and a triumph of the potential of balance between order and chaos. The Garou, fearing for the loss of their station within the food chain, hunted and herded humans like cattle, eliminating those that posed a threat to them while preserving the weak as breeding stock. When the Impergium finally ended, the Garou turned on their cousins, the Fera, for the same, self-serving goal of asserting their dominance and protecting their position within the worlds of flesh as well as spirit.

As agents of the Wyrm, we are charged with the maintenance of universal balance. The Wyrm once served as the goalkeeper between the Wyld and Weaver, eliminating the creations or classifications of each which threatened the balance of creation. Now, the Wyrm lies trapped within the Weaver's intricately insane Pattern Web. We serve its purpose and act as the champions of its will while it is imprisoned. Rather than serve as the lapdogs of the Bitch Mother's will, we serve as the heralds of the Devourer; scions of its rage and fury against those who would seek to subdue it and, by doing so, destroy the fragile balance necessary for the proliferation of the universe. The Garou have disturbed, if not destroyed the last semblance of balance that remained on earth through their prejudice and stupidity. Their pride and their simplistic natures make them incapable of reason or compromise, and therefore, we have been created to destroy them. Only when the last of the Gaians coughs the last of his life's blood at our feet will we have achieved the plateau where balance can truly be restored to the whole of creation.

Dominion

do·min·ion (*plural* do·min·ions) *noun* —1. ruling control: ruling power, authority, or control; sphere of influence: somebody's area of influence or control

The Darwinism represented by the Garou Nation is virtually inconceivable to any outside of their ranks. They claim to be the Fangs of Gaia and the ultimate predators. In reality, we are what the Gaians wish they were. We are werewolves, but we are werewolves who have been stripped of our pettiness and our weakness. We serve none but the Wyrm, who demands we do nothing but fight for dominance above all that are lesser than we. We allow mankind to poison itself by immersion in its own filth and waste, and this makes us insane? The concepts of sanity and insanity are legalist terms developed by men for the judication of men through the vehicle of man's law. We are not men, and therefore we are not subject to their laws. We are not children of their gods, and therefore have nothing to fear from their heathen blasphemies. The litters of the Bitch

Mother cannot decide what they are; they walk a delicate line between the world of what they truly are and the world of men, careful or fearful to never fall to far to either side. They believe that this is balance. It is weakness.

The weakness of Gaia's werewolves is the strength of the Black Spiral Dancers. We have been stripped of all of our confusion. We have been bled of all of our imperfection. The Wyrm has baptized us in its rage and shown us what we truly are and what must be achieved; the Wyrm must be free. Through the might of the freed Wyrm we will witness both humanity and the Garou bow down before us in the final nights of Apocalypse. This world is rightfully ours. Who are you to question what we do or do not do with it and how it is or is not done? Service to the Wyrm is reward in and of itself and this world, every bit of it that surrounds you, every bit of air that you breathe, every bit of bathwater you throw out of your window, every drop of grease that drips down your fat ape face as you chew what you've raised for slaughter belongs to us. Enjoy it while you can.

DNA: Developmental Neogenetics Amalgamated

We must never make experiments to confirm our ideas, but simply to control them.

— Claude Bernard

DNA is a dark weft in the Weaver's web. They're perhaps the worst kind of enemy because the misguided scientists at Developmental Neogenetics Amalgamated truly believe they are doing valuable, lifesaving work. To all outward appearances, they are the heroes rescuing humanity from a terrible threat. Deep in the hearts of their laboratories, though, the suffering of werewolves and Kin has been unspeakable. DNA's aims may have been pure at one time, but now these scientists are twisted and blinded to their own hubris. No longer do these men and women follow basic research ethics and practice humane care with their patients. All that matters to them at present is their objective to wipe out the "lycanthropic disease" that supposedly threatens humanity's survival. At best, the scientists view their test subjects as interesting anomalies for study and treatment. At worst, they want werewolves and any humans or wolves related to them eliminated, before they contaminate the world's gene pool. All the scientists at DNA are, of course, totally oblivious to their own conceit and narrow-mindedness.

Using DNA in a Chronicle

Why use DNA at all? There are plenty of reasons. First of all is the moral ambiguity. Most of the scientists that work for the institute are terribly callous as far as the rights of werewolves go, but their motives are generally

much nobler than the outright profiteering of Pentex or the cruelty of Banes. If you're interested in promoting a few moral dilemmas for your players — and who isn't? — DNA may prove fertile soil for such story seeds.

Further, DNA is as effective a way to create stories with a feel of conspiracy-related paranoia as Pentex, but with a much more impersonal and sterile flavor. In particular, it serves as a model example of just why werewolves work to preserve the Veil — there's no better proof that humans are dangerous and probably shouldn't know that werewolves exist. DNA can threaten Kinfolk in a more subtle, creepy way than marauding fomori or Black Spiral Dancers; the violations of well-meaning but merciless scientists are just as frightening in their own way as the ungentle talons of the Wyrm's forces. And, of course, DNA powerfully stresses the Weaver as enemy, and makes for a refreshing change of pace from the constant diet of fighting the Wyrm.

DNA is quite different from Pentex, even though they share some of the same methods in their madness. First of all, DNA doesn't have any supernatural resources. No employee, even at the highest echelon, directly "worships" or "swears allegiance" to the Weaver. None of the highest-ranking DNA executives would even believe in the Weaver if they were told of the concept. Instead, DNA's ties are more subtle and circumstantial than deliberate; their philosophies and actions power the Weaver without the necessity of devotion to the Weaver as a concept. The company's employees, while often well educated, are no more powerful than the neighbors down the street are. The danger of DNA comes from the amount of accurate information and data they've obtained on werewolves over the past decade or so. They still have much to learn, but what they *do* know is pretty staggering… and within their environment, knowledge is power. Moreover, being scientist types, they have plenty of unpleasant technology to back up their schemes. It's true that no lab-coated DNA scientist is going to survive a claw to beaker battle with a werewolf, barring some weird twist of fate. However, even in death, DNA can be deadly. Consider the effects of the recording devices stationed all around a lab; even if half the staff gets killed, DNA will still have an extremely accurate record of what happened. Any and all kinds of data will be put to good use.

So the best use for DNA is behind the scenes. They're active all around North America, in clinics, schools and their own private labs, watching and listening. Any rumor is well worth checking out, so they're particularly interested in "wild dog attacks" or people who end up with bloody clawed wounds yet can't remember what happened. When the Delirium strikes, and mortals are witness, there's a reasonable chance DNA might also make an appearance… all in the interest of eradicating a terrible epidemic, of course.

Why DNA Exists

DNA represents the madness of the Weaver in its desire to enforce stagnation, inertia and rigidity. They want to eliminate deviations from standard patterns in the gene pool, regardless of the consequences. In the process, the DNA scientists have developed their own view of how biological life should progress, and the werewolf "disease" is simply not part of that process.

They believe shapechangers are victims of an unfortunate genetic anomaly, and that by whatever means necessary, that disease must be cured or eradicated. Even if they were to hear supernatural explanations, DNA scientists would completely disbelieve them, postulating instead that historical cases of werewolf legends are rather examples of mutant strains of GLS running rampant in small, inbreeding populations. In other words, everything has a rational explanation with a firm grounding in science.

Historical Background

DNA began around 20 years ago as a joint venture between two scientists, Dr. Mitchell Howak and Dr. Alan Kenchlow (see Project Twilight). Desperate to find a cure for Kenchlow's ALS (commonly known as Lou Gehrig's Disease), the two parlayed their considerable fortunes and expertise into developing a genetic research institute second to none. Branches opened across the United States and Canada. Though Kenchlow eventually departed, on good terms at first, the company continued to thrive and do meritorious work.

But in 1992, everything changed. A werewolf broke into one of the DNA facilities and against the odds, was badly wounded and captured. Howak became a madman when he saw the werewolf and began studying it. He tossed aside research ethics, disregarded the advice of his horrified former partner Kenchlow and vowed to discover a cure for what to his eyes was a terrible new disease. Howak and his staff kept the werewolf alive for many months, performing countless experiments on the specimen and gathering data on the Delirium, the effects of silver and even the use of mirrors to step sideways. The original test subject was eventually euthanized, but other werewolf and Kinfolk captures followed. Not only geneticists, but also psychologists, anthropologists and wildlife experts joined the staff. DNA gave a name to the disease: genetic lycanthropic syndrome, or GLS, and their volume of information swelled.

Howak disappeared under strange circumstances in 1997, but DNA continued their work under the expert direction of geneticist Dr. Ruben Sendlar. He has moved the company's research agenda along quickly, making plans to hopefully test curative gene therapy for GLS as early as 2010.

DNA Goals and Plans

First and foremost, DNA staff members are interested in the genetic heritage of GLS victims. Any concerns for ethics come second to this goal because they believe the threat from the disease is too great to wait for approval from any regulatory agencies. They accomplish their research aims in two key ways: by direct field observation and by exhaustive testing in the lab.

Field observation is a trickier and riskier business than lab work, as unexpected encounters with werewolves are always possible, but fieldwork also reveals some unique and valuable information. DNA starts the process by looking at statistically probable geographic locations for GLS outbreaks. Canada, Appalachia, tribal reservations and certain cultural enclaves within large cities fit the bill nicely (and strangely enough, past evidence has indeed turned up both victims and carriers of GLS in these locations). Mexico and India are other trouble spots waiting to be investigated. Occasionally, local legends, media and the rumor mill also lead DNA to locations of GLS outbreaks.

Once a probable area is targeted, field researchers head out. They establish themselves among locals (and it's especially helpful when a researcher is from the area or has contacts there). Then, the researchers patiently and painstakingly begin interviews, observations and ongoing analysis of data. If they find reasonable evidence of GLS victims (werewolves, in other words), they may requisition a capture team skilled in working with dangerous animals. After capture or completion of the observation, the field researchers return to the labs, compile their findings and share it with others at DNA.

Labwork with captured subjects of course has its own set of risks. Usually, the staff heavily drugs and restrains a werewolf so that they can collect all types of specimens. The scientists analyze these samples, comparing them to those of previous test subjects and field samples. Behavioral scientists also study the effects of prolonged imprisonment on the psyche of the victim. Eventually, all captured test subjects are euthanized.

Thus, with the data and knowledge they have collected, Sendlar and his associates have made the following strategic plans and goals for the future:

Eliminate GLS

This is job one at DNA, receiving about half of all company funds and resources. Much of the money goes toward hiring the most qualified staff, purchasing the best equipment and funding field and lab work. DNA burns through quite a bit of money, most of which is derived from various research grants expertly obtained by the directors' remarkable lobbying skills, but a good portion of which stems from philanthropic backers. It's uncertain where Sendlar found people with so much money to spend on an obscure project that isn't easily explained to the public, and whatever the answer, it would likely be bad news to the werewolf that found out.

Complete GLS Genome Mapping Project

About a fifth of DNA resources fund the mapping of the genetic patterns of GLS victims. This is a long-term project, but one that is vital to finding a cure.

Experiment with Curative Gene Therapy

Although just starting to come of age, gene therapy holds great promise. This is how DNA eventually hopes to cure GLS; currently, about a tenth of their funds go towards this aim.

Perfect Methyldelerian

The Delirium causes great difficulty in studying GLS victims. To forestall this difficulty, DNA has developed a synthetic drug called Methyldelerian. It's still risky and unpredictable to use, so DNA devotes a tenth of its funds to perfecting this substance for use by lab personnel and field researchers.

Project Reaper

Even though DNA hopes to cure and eliminate GLS in the near future, they've also got a contingency plan called Project Reaper. If too many humans and wolves become infected, the company will release a carefully designed virus that will presumably kill any being that carries the genetic code for GLS. The effect would of course be catastrophic for the Garou nation, as it would destroy werewolves and Kinfolk alike.

What DNA Thinks They Know

Despite their fancy equipment and alphabet-soup degrees, most of the scientists have lost a lot of their creativity; they can make observations and record data, but in the process, they've sacrificed their leaps of intuition. So, while DNA has uncovered a lot of information about werewolves, they're also missing out on some important conclusions. What they have learned includes the following:

The breeds:

DNA has concluded that, against all scientific odds, GLS affects humans and wolves in similar ways. They've also pinpointed that the most afflicted victims of the disease, metis, result from "inbreeding" between GLS victims (two humans or two wolves who are also sick). It's a puzzle to them why, knowing the results of such breeding, that infected wolves and humans breed at all.

Werewolf forms:

After seeing GLS victims in the field and the lab, the scientists have identified five "body contortion patterns," the five forms of werewolves in other words. They haven't yet discovered that metis are born in Crinos, though, nor have they postulated an explanation for the variation in mass from form to form.

The tribes:

While they've noted that GLS occurs more prominently among certain cultural and ethnic groups (namely Celtic, Native American and Germanic peoples), DNA has no clue about the differences among the tribes, or even that tribes exist.

Kinfolk:

One enduring puzzle for DNA is why carriers of GLS seem to consciously cluster around GLS victims, even to the point of marriage and breeding. Unfortunately, they have managed to find a few uninformed Kinfolk, and these carriers have unwittingly given DNA a fair bit of information.

The Delirium:

The Delirium was one of the first secrets DNA discovered; its effects were pretty obvious during the first capture of a werewolf. The scientists have long sought a means to counter the Delirium effects and came up with Methyldelerian, a synthetic drug, that can forestall the hysteria for short periods of time. It's now standard equipment at all DNA labs.

Mirrors:

They may not understand it, but DNA knows letting captured werewolves near any reflective surface affords their victims a chance to escape. The scientists have a lot of wild theories about how this works. Admittedly, the scientists don't know that werewolves don't *need* reflective surfaces to escape, but the Gauntlet around the average DNA lab is so dangerous that trying to step sideways without one is a perilous, perilous proposition.

Silver:

Using silver was one leap of intuition DNA managed to capitalize on. If, postulated the behavioral scientists, the GLS victims think they're werewolves, then perhaps silver would do them grave injury. Imagine the reaction of the more traditional scientists when this theory proved true. Silver bullets are now standard equipment at all labs.

Where DNA Hasn't a Clue:

For now, DNA knows nothing about the traditions and cosmology of the Garou, nor would they particularly care. They also have no clue about the existence of other shapeshifters or hengeyokai. They haven't made the connection that metis are sterile, either.

People and Places in DNA

At present, DNA has research facilities in numerous cities in the US and Canada, including Rochester, Minnesota; the Research Triangle; Toronto; Atlanta; Baltimore; Vancouver; Boulder; Palo Alto, California; Stovington, Vermont; Miami; Boston; and Dallas. They're in the final stages of completing their first labs in Great Britain, in Oxford and Bangor, Wales. Storytellers should of course feel free to put new DNA labs wherever most benefits their chronicles.

All DNA labs have four key divisions: Management and Finance (MF), Research and Development (RD), Cyberbiotechnology (CBT) and Security and Investigation (SI). An executive director (ED) oversees all labs, though each one has its own site-based management and more or less operates independently. The present ED is a savvy geneticist named Ruben Sendlar, who's had a successful tenure at the helm of DNA since the disappearance of Howak. For more details on the personnel of DNA, check out Book of the Weaver.

What does a typical DNA lab look like? It's actually going to seem pretty innocuous, a multi-storied building in some ubiquitous office park. In reality, though, it's a different picture. First of all, security will be top notch, both inside and out. Invaders will see the obvious mounted cameras; chances are they'll miss the ones carefully hidden inside walls and fixtures. Most administrative and low-contamination labs are above ground, with the real work taking place in extremely secure bunkers underground. Armed security guards patrol the grounds and building at all times, and emergency stashes of silver bullets and Methyldelerian are behind glass access panels in several locations on every floor. Would-be attackers will face a tough battle getting into any of these facilities.

Another characteristic of the labs is their state-of-the-art networked computers. Scientists share findings and also socialize occasionally with their comrades in other labs. Still, encoding is required for everything, and ignorance isn't tolerated as an excuse for a security breach.

Standard Equipment

DNA has a dazzling assortment of mostly legal drugs, weapons and electronic recording equipment available to scientists and field agents alike. As long as the proper personnel make the approvals, these items are free for the taking.

Drugs

With the proper requisition orders, DNA field agents can obtain several useful drugs. The first is, naturally,

---

Methyldelerian, which can forestall the effects of the Delirium if taken in time; oral and injectable forms are available. For capturing werewolves, agents can use either Penacothrane, an odorless, invisible gas that can easily affect a large group of people, or Verinal, a liquid mixture ideally delivered by a dart. Neither drug completely knocks out a werewolf, but both make the Garou lose muscular control and mental awareness. The victim takes a cumulative -1 to dice pools involving Wits and Dexterity for four turns. To fully resist the effects, a Willpower point must be expended each turn. The two drugs are intended to make the target so befuddled, he won't know where to run or even that he needs to get away.

Combat Gear

Combat agents regularly carry field kits that contain Methyldelerian, Verinal and Penacothrane. These kits also contain measuring tape, pens and pencils, data sheets, spare doses of drugs, syringes, tweezers, specimen bottles, scalpels, lip tattooing punches and a basic DNA manual. Additionally, agents carry dart guns and a personal firearm. For all the good they do, Kevlar vests are available, as are a limited number of CBT suits (see information following). Some teams carry a small cryo kit to preserve tissue samples and subdermal microtransmitters for use in tracking victims that escape.

Basic Field Kit

Social scientists whose intentions are observation and interviews rather than capture carry personal firearms (though these sometimes get left in gloveboxes), but other than an autoinjector of Methyldelerian, their kits are pretty mundane. Standard equipment includes audio and visual recorders, a camera, notepaper, a cell phone, binoculars with night illumination and computer programs that assist in the qualitative and quantitative analysis of data.

Recent Advances

In recent years, Sendlar and his staff have become more convinced than ever that elimination of GLS depends on early detection. To this end, they've greatly increased what they call "outreach efforts," to pinpoint children and adolescents who show early symptoms of the disease. DNA has been lucky to find a handful of children who have tested positive as carriers, and just a couple of adolescents who seem to be on the verge of developing GLS — lucky because for whatever reasons, the werewolves had lost track of these very few cubs and Kinfolk. DNA was thus able to bring them in for study without much of a hassle. Still, if they keep looking, they'll eventually run into more knowledgeable families that won't let their kids become lab rats. And then, the scientists will face a lot of pissed-off werewolves out for blood.

Sample DNA Personnel

These are suggested Traits for two types of field agents, one trained in social science techniques and one prepared to combat and capture dangerous animals. A template for a lab scientist is also included. Storytellers should feel free to make changes for more specialized characters.

Social Scientist

Attributes: Strength 2, Dexterity 2, Stamina 3, Charisma 2, Manipulation 3, Appearance 2, Perception 4, Intelligence 3, Wits 2

Abilities: Alertness 1, Animal Ken 1, Computer 2, Drive 1, Empathy 2, Enigmas 1, Etiquette 1, Expression 1, Firearms 1, Investigation 1, Medicine 1, Melee 1, Occult 1, Science 4 (choose from Psychology, Sociology or Anthropology), Streetwise 2, Subterfuge 2, Survival 1

Willpower: 5

Combat Agent

Attributes: Strength 3, Dexterity 3, Stamina 4, Charisma 2, Manipulation 2, Appearance 2, Perception 4, Intelligence 2, Wits 4

Abilities: Alertness 2, Athletics 2, Brawl 3, Computer 2, Drive 1, Dodge 2, Firearms 2, Intimidation 1, Investigation 1, Melee 2, Medicine 1, Stealth 2, Streetwise 1, Survival 2

Willpower: 6

Lab Scientist

Attributes: Strength 2, Dexterity 2, Stamina 2, Charisma 2, Manipulation 2, Appearance 2, Perception 3, Intelligence 4, Wits 3

Abilities: Alertness 1, Animal Ken 2, Computer 2, Drive 1, Investigation 1, Medicine 1, Science 4 (Choose from Genetics, Biochemistry, Biology or Chemistry)

Willpower: 5

Unusual Aptitudes

In various roles, such as educational anthropologists and school psychologists, DNA has placed skilled social scientists in schools around the country. They've concentrated in particular on areas where GLS seems to be concentrated. The social scientists are on the lookout for classic misfits — preteens and teens who don't seem to fit in or exhibit antisocial tendencies. They're also watching out for any kids that seem to have unusual abilities, such as possibly enhanced levels of strength and dexterity. The scientists will make observations and interview the students. If warranted, they'll consult with the parents and encourage further testing. By these methods, DNA hopes to bring in more potential GLS victims for study, believing the disease, like cancer, may spread more quickly in a young person's body.

Going Native

In a few select communities, DNA has planted their own equivalent of deep cover agents. These individuals are highly trained, usually in anthropology or sociology, and with some hypnosis and total immersion in a particular culture, blend in almost perfectly. DNA sees these agents as an extremely long-term project; they know it may take years before the small communities trust and include these individuals. But eventually, they hope, GLS victims will slip and leave some sort of evidence of their condition out in the open. At that point, the agents can ask for retrieval, plus call in capture teams or other appropriate personnel. Sendlar and his colleagues are patient because they know that acquisition of even one victim in the full-blown stages of the disease will be well worth the painstaking efforts.

They've Got That Glow

Knowing that pregnant women undergo a bevy of prenatal testing (several blood tests, frequent urine tests and sonograms, for example), DNA realized they could have a built-in screening mechanism for GLS. They've capitalized on the fact that a lot of prenatal testing is outsourced from various doctor's offices to private labs, most of which are extremely overworked. DNA has quietly stepped in to help lighten the workload of these labs—and help themselves to a plethora of samples. In theory, all such samples are immediately destroyed as biohazards after the tests are complete. DNA, however, has kept many of the samples after delivering results back to the physicians that ordered the tests. They're currently seeking to serve as an outsource lab for amniocentesis and chorionic villi sampling as well, tests that reveal the genetic makeup of fetuses. Such a move would open up a whole new venue of data for the scientists.

Cyberelectrochemical Armor (CBT)

CBT armor is highly experimental, but holds great promise. It works by inserting microthin needles into the wearer's epidermis. The suit can thus send the body electrochemical signals to increase or decrease adrenaline and endorphins, suppress seritonin and even cause blood clotting. The suits nonetheless have two major drawbacks. First of all, the lightweight batteries can only sustain power for about 30 minutes. Second, the suits' monitoring devices sometimes misfeed information to the wearer's brain, causing complications such as heart attacks and strokes. So while it's nice to have enhanced strength and speed, sometimes wearing the suits has a pricetag too high for most agents.

Story Seeds

How to best use DNA in your chronicle is ultimately up to you, the Storyteller. Consider what kind of players you have; if they like investigation, confronting the dangers of conspiracy and superscience or the occasional lab raid, they'll enjoy facing off against DNA. Here are a few ideas to get you started on bringing this organization into your games.

New Neighbors

This story will require some patience and a little long-range planning on your part, and it probably works best for werewolf packs that have regular contact with civilization. A new couple moves into the neighborhood or small town near where the pack resides. These are *nice* people, too. They're friendly and helpful, and they work hard to become sterling members of the community. Over the course of several games (and don't rush things), they befriend a member of the pack. Everything is innocuous and aboveboard; the newcomers in no way are obsequious or oily. But of course all is not as it seems. Months later, they make their move; the couple are agents of DNA. Perhaps one is an anthropologist, interested in studying the culture of GLS victims. The other probably has more combat training. In any case, they'd like to capture a werewolf or Kinfolk and bring the unfortunate "patient" in for study. Alternatively, they may just continue biding their time, slowly but effectively gathering more and more information, all of which is relayed back to their home lab.

Troubled Teen

The werewolf characters have kept an eye on a prospective new recruit, a teen close to her First Change. In fact, they are getting ready to swoop down and take the young one off for training and eventually, a Rite of Passage. But some event — an attack by Black Spirals or an Umbral journey, perhaps — delay their acquisition of the teen. By the time they get ready to make their move, a DNA representative has already stepped in as a supportive school counselor. He's warned the would-be werewolf about her potential illness and also about strangers who may want to kidnap her. The teen consents to get help at a DNA lab, so not only must the pack rescue the newbie, they've also got to spend some considerable time re-educating her as to what's *really* going on.

Two of a Kind

DNA really hits the jackpot; they manage to bring in both a Kinfolk and his Garou sister to perform a detailed

comparison study of their genetic makeup. If the Kinfolk is unknowing, he may be a willing patient; such action would not stand him in great favor with any rescuers, of course, though the Kin is innocent of any intentional betrayal. Even if he is in the know, and unwilling to help DNA, he's still going to be a lesser priority to the werewolves than his sister, a fact he may not be happy about. This seed should raise a couple of moral dilemmas for the werewolf characters revolving around the treatment and value of Kinfolk.

Bait and Catch

Realizing that GLS victims, for some unfathomable reason, tend to travel and work in small groups, DNA has made elaborate plans for a large-scale capture. Past experience has shown them that the werewolves tend to take care of their own. DNA purposely captures a werewolf and doesn't make any secret of the fact. They may even leak some information to insure that other victims of the disease know about it. The werewolf characters are all set to come in and rescue the unfortunate prisoner, but what they don't know is that DNA is ready for them. They've planned to bring down as many of the rescuers as possible, alive preferably but dead if necessary. They're interested in analyzing the group's combat techniques and how they work together as a unit. Any samples and data collected

will be worth the cost and potential fatalities of personnel (a bonus is in order for any volunteers). It should be a rude surprise for the pack to find out that they're expected.

The Traitor

This scenario sort of reverses the "New Neighbors" story seed. Here, the DNA deep cover agent has been in the local area probably longer than the werewolves have. She's an integral part of the community, and she's discovered a lot of truths behind werewolf society. The problem is, this agent is having serious second thoughts about what she's doing. Her reports back to her home lab have slowed; moreover, she may have falsified some information to protect those she's spying on. In any case, the agent can't keep doing this forever. Eventually, DNA is going to get suspicious and come to collect her, with or without her permission; the agent's time is running out. She needs help and takes a big risk; she approaches one of the werewolves and confides her predicament. What happens next is up to the player characters. Do they gut her then and there? Or do they try to help her, either providing a hideout or helping her fake out her employers? To complicate things, make this agent have some use to the werewolves; perhaps there are worse consequences if they kill her outright rather than help her. In any case, this seed should provide some interesting roleplaying opportunities for your troupe.

Chapter Five: Breaking the Mold

In the middle of the journey of our life I came to myself
within a dark wood where the straight way was lost.
— Dante Alighieri, *The Divine Comedy*

Werewolves in Historical Settings

When did the first Garou walk the earth? Was she a creation of Gaia? Was he part of a ritual uniting wolves and men? Was the first werewolf a spirit cursed and trapped in mortal form by gods of men and wolves? The legends of the Garou never say clearly how they came into being, only that they did. Werewolves have existed for a long time, at least as long as humans and wolves. And with that ancient heritage comes realms of possibility.

Werewolf offers great opportunities for role-playing in historical settings. Garou have been around forever. In every time, every place where people have lived, so have werewolves. They've suffered through all the tragedies and disasters and witnessed all the triumphs and glories.

Werewolves of most tribes also have the ability to experience directly the lives of their ancestors, or at least to call their ancestor-spirits to them to learn of bygone eras. If you don't want to run a full chronicle set in an alternate history, you can have characters relive the trials of their ancestors. You could also have them play different roles in the life of an elder or recreate the imprisoning of an ancient spirit.

Most werewolves, if they aren't slain in combat, can live long lives, retaining their youth for decades. A chronicle set in the 70s and one set today could have the same main characters. Storytellers could even follow the experiences of a pack from their early years through part of the 20th century until they become elders.

One of the most important things to remember is that you should convey to the players how you intend to approach the setting. If you're running a chronicle set during the Roman Republic, make sure they know the differences between patricians and plebeians, and understand just how large the empire is. They don't need to know everything about the setting, but they should know enough to feel comfortable. The Storyteller can help by explaining rules of etiquette or current technology as they come up.

Perhaps you like historical settings, but you don't feel like doing hours of research in a library. Maybe you like myths and fiction and you want to base your version of the past on a favorite movie. There's nothing wrong with that, just make sure that the players know ahead of time that you're playing more loosely. That way no one will get distracted by pointing out that Cleopatra couldn't have visited the Coliseum since it hadn't been built.

Using variant histories can be awesome amounts of fun. What if D-Day never took place or Stalingrad fell during World War II? What if the Confederacy had won the Civil War? Or what if the British had won the American Revolution? Maybe Carthage could build an empire spanning the known world instead of Rome? Or perhaps Asian powers could have colonized America before the Europeans? Maybe the Shadow Lords took over leadership of all werewolves?

The most important thing is that this is your game. As a Storyteller, you owe it to your troupe to make sure that they have fun, and you owe it to yourself to have fun. Don't be afraid to explore the past and even rework it in your own image. Have fun, explore the possibilities and enjoy your game.

Finally, the sections that follow describe different time periods and possible interpretations of them for your chronicle. These are far from complete. They are meant more to inspire than to educate. If you decide to use one of these settings, a little bit of research goes a long way, whether it's in **Werewolf** game books checking on the Garou legends or actual history texts detailing events.

Mythic Times

These are not so much periods of time as mythical ages known to werewolves. As far as when they happened in relation to human history, none can truly say. Human prehistory is hundreds of times as long as modern history. Most of the time that our species has existed is lost to us in forgotten ages. Perhaps civilization rose and fell many times before the history that we know started. However, the Garou were there. Their legends live on.

It's the Storyteller's privilege to place the any of the mythic time settings during any historical era that they find appropriate. If ancient Egypt holds a strong attraction for you, run the War of Rage with the pharaohs and their monuments as a backdrop. Some werewolves could have enforced the Impergium into Roman times. Use these settings as you will.

The First Times

In the beginning, the Umbra and the earth were as one. Traveling between worlds was easy; you just set out in an appropriate direction. There was no Gauntlet; spirits roamed freely over the face of the Earth. Different tribes didn't exist. Metis were extremely rare. The Litany only half-existed. All werewolves belonged to the same tribe. They lived in harmony with nature.

Humans also lived in harmony with nature; it was too early for the Impergium to be even be necessary.

During this time, werewolves can live among their human and wolf Kinfolk, helping them in the struggle for survival. Great and terrible spirits roamed the world freely, and werewolves fought against them, protecting their Kin. A vast untouched wilderness stretches out in all directions for Garou to explore.

If you use the current theories about our prehistory to base this mythic time, there are many things for werewolves to contend with. Saber-toothed cats, dire wolves, giant boars, cave bears, and other large prehistoric mammals filled the world. Monsters did exist and humans faced them with spears, while wolves had only their teeth and claws. The weather was much more volatile. Climatic changes occurred that made the American "dust bowl" look minor. Storms greater than the strongest hurricanes battered the land. Great sheets of ice flowed down from the Arctic. Life was harsh.

Other species of humans existed, including Neanderthals who competed with the modern humans. They may have had their own shapeshifting protectors. Also, humans that feared the werewolves may have had access to magic or their own allied spirits.

Powerful spirits roamed the earth in the First Times. Some may have demanded worship as gods. Other shapeshifters may have challenged the Garou as protectors of nature. Omens of the sundering of the Umbra from the material world haunted werewolves during these days. Characters could even experience the fracturing of the Garou nation and the forming of the first tribes. Maybe they could have helped inadvertently start humans on the path to civilization.

The Impergium

The Impergium was a time of strife and conflict for the Garou. The tribes shattered apart. Humans had gotten out of control. Ancient cities now grew up in river valleys throughout the world. Werewolves stood divided on enforcing the Impergium. Some followed the Impergium to the letter, culling humans evenly to protect Gaia. Others went too far, exterminating entire cultures, removing humans from history. A few fought against the Impergium, refusing to enforce the rule. Another select few carefully used the Impergium as an excuse to grab power for their Kinfolk.

In many ways, this is the darkest time in Garou history. The imprisoned Wyrm begins birthing increasingly deranged offspring. Corruption lurks among the humans. Rage runs deep in werewolves. As the culling continues, humans turn to the powers of darkness to aid them against the werewolves. They worship vampires as gods. Dark Wyrm-spirits receive sacrifices. Gaia herself rises up in anger against humanity, bringing the Great Flood, volcanic eruptions, and many other disasters.

Werewolf characters, especially homids, will have many moral dilemmas to face in an Impergium chronicle. How do they deal with packs that selectively enforce the Impergium? What do they do when other werewolves go too far, driving humans to summon dark powers? Can they bring themselves to slay their own Kinfolk if necessary? Are the signs of Gaia's displeasure evident? For troupes that enjoy moral issues and troupes that like continuous conflict, the Impergium has plenty to offer.

An exact historical date has never been set for the Impergium, only that it took place before humans began building cities. In order to add a little more cultural flavor, you might choose to extend the Impergium's life even into the birth of civilization — thus you can set an increasingly ineffective Impergium against a backdrop of ancient Egypt or Sumeria. Minoan civilization and the legends of the Greek hero Theseus can easily become stories of the Impergium, as the Minoans sacrifice to the creature within the labyrinth. Biblical events and histories can work as well for the setting. What did the cities of Sodom and Gomorrah do to bring about their destruction? Ambitious Storytellers could even pit Garou against the legendary First City of the vampires as a crossover. It would be hard beat a time when vampires are mighty, but no Leech has lived long enough to become invincible and the Garou are young, but in great numbers, for the conflict to start the ancestral war.

The War of Rage

The Garou blamed the other Changing Breeds for the Wyrm. The Gurahl strayed from Gaia because they woke the dead. The Bastet forgot their roles as protectors and served only their individual whims. The Mokolé took the very shape of the Wyrm. The alien nature of the Rokea and the Ananasi was easy for any to sense. The Ratkin skulked in the darkness, spreading filth and disease. Even the Corax could not be trusted.

Most accounts have it that werewolves started the War of Rage with little provocation. They attacked every one of the other Changing Breeds. The others retaliated in kind. Soon, events were out of control, reason was lost to all sides, and the War of Rage became a struggle for survival. Characters could be werewolves hunting down the other Changing Breeds during the War of Rage. They could also take the role of defenders, struggling to survive against an onslaught of attacks by other shapeshifters. For troupes that like action, this chronicle has the potential for great fight scenes.

Against the backdrop of the War of Rage, humanity gets more out of control. While a pack concerns itself with a Bastet, the Wyrm continues to corrupt. As a Storyteller, you could set a chronicle where the characters are trying to end the War of Rage and get back to fighting the Wyrm. This could give them allies and enemies on both sides. Many Garou are hardened veterans of the War of Rage; it's all that they've known in their lifetimes. They won't easily consider backing down before their enemies. The other shapeshifters have decades of hate, grief and rage to vent on the werewolves. They won't trust their enemies easily. Meanwhile, Gaia suffers, the Wyrm corrupts, and the Weaver's webs close more tightly on the world.

As a Storyteller, the War of Rage also gives you an opportunity to create new Gifts, fetishes, and talens, specifically created for the War. Some werewolves learned Gifts from the spirit allies of their enemies. Weapons designed to kill members of other Changing Breeds could exist.

This setting makes a good flashback for an existing chronicle. Modern Garou must still deal with the guilt and the scars left behind from the War of Rage. For many of the others, the War of Rage continues even today. Spirits allied to the other shapeshifters have not forgotten what the werewolves did. Items and weapons created by Garou to fight the War of Rage may still exist. What if some of these fetishes fell into the hands of hunters or Black Spiral Dancers? It's also an opportunity to show the war from the perspective of both sides. The Garou were the worst offenders, to be sure, but in keeping with the World of Darkness' shades of gray, it might be a good idea to show your players that not all Fera were innocent victims. If your players encounter other shapeshifters that actually *were* abusing their powers, then the context of the War of Rage itself shifts slightly. Instead of the Garou as mindless aggressors, their mistake becomes at least understandable, if not forgivable — making the War of Rage a more relevant and realistic story.

The War of Rage makes a good backdrop to any chronicle involving ancient Garou. Like many of the mythic times of werewolf legend, the exact dates aren't specified. The war would have started and ended at different times in different lands. It's hard to deny that Bastet and Mokolé battling werewolves across the scaffolding of a pyramid under construction in Egypt would be a wonderfully cinematic scene. A showdown during a druidic ceremony at Stonehenge would also be dramatic. This conflict should also make the players think about whether werewolves are always the good guys — or, if you have some players who are convinced that werewolves are always the *bad* guys, you can rattle *their* perceptions, too.

Historical Times

Werewolves have witnessed important events and even had some influence on history, but primarily, they have concerned themselves with events on the periphery of civilization, in the shadows of history. This means that almost all major historical events in the World of Darkness have generally happened, as in the real world, without the assistance of werewolves.

Try to avoid the temptation to make all historical figures into werewolves or Kinfolk. While it may seem like a good idea at the time, a story about how historical events indirectly affect the lives of the Garou makes for far better stories than having a pack assassinate Napoleon or Christopher Columbus. Allowing humans to guide history without too many supernatural influences makes the world seem more real, more believable.

Having said that, Storytellers should not be afraid to have historical figures appear in historical chronicles. Just be careful. The best way to handle historical figures is to keep them off screen and have them act through non-historical characters, such as servants or friends. Remember that anytime you have a historical figure appear on scene, there is a chance a player may take an action that would kill him. If that's an unacceptable risk, remember that players have a hard time killing anyone who does not actually appear in a scene. For example, the characters could certainly be aware of Napoleon through proclamations, laws, news events, and trophies brought back to France by his armies. His life could have a major impact on a chronicle, yet he never has to interact with the characters. You could even use a meeting or a glance at a historical figure as a reward to a pack or a player for a job well done; think of Hitler's cameo in *Indiana Jones and the Last Crusade*.

The Great Passage

About 10,000 years ago, the Bering Strait was a land bridge connecting Asia with North America. As tribes of hunters crossed following game, so did three tribes of werewolves, the Wendigo, the Uktena, and the Croatan. The journey was fraught with dangers and hardships, but when they arrived on the new continent, they had the vast untouched Pure Lands open before them. What spirits came with them? What conflicts arose between the different tribes? Were the Wendigo, Uktena and Croatan already split or did events occur which divided the tribes after they arrived in the Pure Lands?

When these people arrived in North America, they didn't find a land filled with milk and honey. An untamed wilderness filled with Ice Age mon-

PRESCOTT

166

sters loomed before them. Tidal waves hit the Pacific Northwest. Miles of ice covered much of the North. Dire wolves and saber-toothed tigers hunted Columbian mammoths and humans. Animal spirits that had never dealt with Garou saw these newcomers as a threat.

No one knows what happened to the people during the centuries that immediately followed their crossing of the Bering Strait. They appear to have been excellent hunters, as the megafauna, especially the large predators swiftly disappeared following the arrival of humans. The Garou made peace with the spirits of the Pure Lands. Over the years, the werewolves opened caerns and like their Kinfolk, they lived in harmony with nature. They still faced challenges. Warfare between tribes of Kinfolk and werewolves claimed many lives. Dark spirits gained influence over some of the great civilizations that formed in South America, forcing packs of werewolves to journey south to drive out the evil. Deadly Bastet claimed the great southern rainforests, slaying Garou that would trespass in their domains.

Classical World

The Ancient World spans Phoenicia, Greece, Mycenae, Persia, and Rome. It was a time of myths, legends, and the creation of great civilizations. Advancements in learning and science occurred along with the spread of humans and the destruction of the wilds. Both the Weaver and the Wyrm gained power during this time, as beliefs were tested and challenged and roads and cities erupted throughout the Mediterranean.

Classical Greece

Athens, Sparta, Thebes and Corinth are just a few of the Greek city-states. Athenian democracy and culture blossomed, while the Spartans took the military state to a new level. Many stories and myths came out of Classical Greek culture. The Iliad and the Odyssey are probably the most famous, referring to a time of Mycenaen culture before the rise of Athens. The Amazon legend surely arose from the influence of the Black Furies. Storytellers have a wealth of mythic beasts from which to draw (or to corrupt; imagine, for instance, the Harpies as fomori!). Any good book on Greek mythology should provide material to last a full chronicle and then some. The Persian Wars also provide good background. The Battle of Marathon and the Spartans' holding of the pass at Thermopylae come quickly to mind.

Classical Greece is an area where Storytellers shouldn't feel compelled to limit themselves. Much of what we know of the Greek city-states comes from Herodotus, who wrote about giant insects and mythical beasts in his history. Centuries later, Romans with political agendas wrote many of the other histories. There is far more that we don't know about Classical Greece than what we do.

Alexander the Great

The son of Philip of Macedon, Alexander the Great, may have been the greatest commander who ever lived. He forged a powerful army, surrounded himself with excellent generals, and just happened to conquer the known world. Alexander ruled the Greek city-states and their colonies, Egypt, the entire Persian Empire and parts of India. Although he was a great conqueror, he did not live long enough to enjoy his rule, dying at the end of his conquests.

Alexander brought many cultures together. Werewolves following Alexander's armies would find themselves on a whirlwind tour of the ancient world. They could fight the Wyrm at every stop, take a day to appreciate the culture and move on. A pack could discover lost caerns in India or explore the tombs of long dead pharaohs in Egypt. Conversely, the characters might take up the role of locals whose Kin are being adversely affected by Alexander's conquest — perhaps leading to a "The *real* reason Alexander stopped at India" chronicle.

Republican and Imperial Rome

Rome changed the world, uniting cultures around the Mediterranean. The Roman Empire at its height reached from the Middle East to the British Isles and back down into Northern Africa. As the old adage goes, Rome wasn't built in a day. The Roman world changed extensively over time.

The early days of Rome are the subject of myth. These were the times of the Roman kings. According to legend, Romulus founded Rome in 753 BC along the Tiber River, after slaying his twin Remus. A wolf, the sacred animal of Mars, had raised the twins. In the World of Darkness, Romulus is one of the few figures that could easily figure for at least Kinfolk and possibly a werewolf. Characters could be some of Romulus and Remus' warriors, uniting the Latins into a single people, instead of a scattering of tribes. During Romulus' reign, the Romans parleyed with the Sabines and then stole their women away. The Sabines came after the new Romans with a vengeance, but the women pleaded with their fathers and brothers to make peace with their new husbands. This is one of many legends about the early days of Rome.

After a set of terrible kings, the Romans established the Republic. The Senate made up of members of the noble class, or patricians, passed the laws that governed the city. Two elected officials, consuls, shared the duties of ruling the city, particularly commanding the armies. In times of extreme crisis, the Senate appointed a dictator who held absolute power. During this time, Rome expanded throughout Italy. They fought the great Punic Wars with Carthage, which ultimately led to the destruction of that vampire-controlled city. After salting the earth where Carthage once stood, Roman legions conquered Greece and expanded into the East. Leeches with great political skills manipulated their way into positions of power, but they never held the influence over the Republic that they had in Carthage. Chariot racing and gladiatorial games were part of daily life, but not at the level of extravagance present during the Empire.

The Roman Republic held a number of strong values, focused on hard work and the rights of all citizens. There was, however a distinct difference between the patricians, who were descendants of the first families from the time of kings, and the plebeians who came from families of the conquered. This class difference was the cause of many conflicts and riots in the city. As Rome expanded, slaves taken from distant lands entered society. People in the outlying provinces were not given the rights of citizens of Rome unless they did something to earn them. Over time, the Roman concept of the hard working citizen-statesman-farmer ceased to exist.

During the Republic, characters may struggle against the dark influence of the Wyrm as corruption slowly builds. Disease followed along the paths of Roman conquest as well. The advancing Roman armies often destroyed sacred sites belonging to other cultures, or remade them in the image of Roman gods. What protections might they have destroyed? What angry spirits wanted vengeance for the deaths of their people? How many caerns did the Romans violate? Did Shadow Lords enslave Black Fury Kinfolk in their conquests? Were Bone Gnawers responsible for the plebeian uprisings?

Storytellers could easily run stories based around the Punic War. According to **Vampire: The Masquerade**, Carthage was a city completely run by vampires. Werewolves sent to wipe this Leech-ridden blight from the world could help fight the war, either in the Senate, on the battlefield, or in dozens of secret locations around the Mediterranean.

As armies grew larger and conquests greater, the fall of the Republic became inevitable. Julius Caesar, a popular and successful general and statesman, formed a Triumvirate with Pompey, who was arguably the greatest of Rome's military leaders and Crassus, a man whose personal income exceeded the rest of the Republic. The trio seized power and then fought each other for ultimate control. Caesar survived and became dictator for life. Although a group of senators assassinated Caesar, the stage was set for his nephew Augustus to become the first Emperor of Rome.

Emperors held absolute power in Rome. The Senate offered opposition, but ultimately, if the Emperor had the support of the military he dictated events. The Roman Empire was a place of hedonism, decadence and suffering among the citizenry. While the government built grand monuments to celebrate military triumphs, people lived in firetrap high rise wooden apartments called insulae. The elite gave out food as largess to hungry masses. Emperors threw greater and more extravagant games in order to keep the people distracted.

Madness and corruption plagued the Roman Empire. Many of the Emperors went insane, ordering atrocities to be performed, sending armies to gather seashells, and even believing that they were living incarnations of Greek mythic heroes. Few Emperors named heirs, so civil war often broke out after the Emperor died, as generals across the Empire declared themselves the new Emperor. While the people living in Rome were repulsed, they at least had their games. In the far provinces, rebellions occurred, especially among the Celts. Fianna, Get of Fenris, and the White Howlers all raised their claws against the Romans. It was during a fateful battle near Hadrian's Wall that the Wyrm consumed the White Howlers, transforming them into the Black Spiral Dancers.

Christianity took root in the Roman Empire and spread throughout the Western world. During the early days of the Empire, the Romans persecuted Christians, and accused them of baby sacrifice and fish worship. Finally, during a civil war, the general Constantine converted to Christianity and won the throne. He made Christianity the state religion. He also renamed the city of Byzantium and divided the empire into the Eastern and Western Roman Empires. **Constantinople by Night**, a product for **Vampire: The Dark Ages**, has copious source material that could be converted for use in a **Werewolf** chronicle. Later Emperors persecuted non-Christians and destroyed pagan sites. The Olympics in Greece ended because they honored false gods.

The Roman Empire is fertile ground for Storytellers. It was a city founded by a man raised by a wolf. The Empire rose to greatness before falling to infighting and corruption. Just look at big budget Hollywood films over the years. The tragedy of the White Howlers is easily worth a chronicle. The eruption of Mount Vesuvius and destruction of Pompeii has been the subject of various books, movies and even mini-series. Exploring the Christian destruction of pagan sites, many of which were caerns, would be an excellent subject for a **Werewolf** story. The games of Rome, chariot races and gladiatorial matches, of course, make exciting material for any chronicle. The barbarian invasions that ultimately destroyed the western Empire in 476 AD surely had werewolves fighting alongside the invaders. Roman politics featured assassinations, bribery, arranged marriages, affairs, exiles, and all manner of examples of corruption. Although a political chronicle isn't necessarily adhering to the themes of **Werewolf**, Roman politics could drive antagonists to consider any sort of unholy grab for power. These are only some of the ideas that come from the Roman Empire. The fall of Rome became the beginning of the Dark Ages, but many of the ideas and stories of the late Empire carried on in Constantinople.

Medieval World

After the fall of the Western Roman Empire, Europe slid into the Dark Ages. Although the Roman Empire fell, the Roman Catholic Church did not. The Church reigned virtually supreme in the medieval world. It was the repository of all learning and knowledge. Nobles needed the blessings of the Church to maintain their authority. Rome became a center for faith and for hunters. **Vampire: The Dark Ages** and **Werewolf: The Dark Ages** both contain far more information on this time; however, they primarily focus on the end of the 12th century. While those supplements are useful, they are not essential to running games set in this period.

The Inquisition

The rise of the Catholic Inquisition heralded a difficult time for Europe. The Inquisition hunted down heretics and devil worshippers. Inquisitors searched long and hard for anything that they believed was infernal or anti-Christian. The Inquisition would interrogate suspects, using all manner of torture to force the truth from them. One particularly vile form was water torture. The subject would swallow a long cloth that would be slowly saturated with water. As this happened, the cloth would swell. Then the torturer would pull the cloth out of the subject, usually finding it covered in blood. The Inquisition turned neighbor against neighbor, husband against wife, and children against their parents.

Although the Inquisition's tactics were horrifying, they produced results. Some of the people that were caught were actual heretics and infernalists. Many vampires fled for their lives, as the Inquisition killed their pawns while seeking out the Leeches. The werewolves of the time didn't suffer as badly, of course; there were few inquisitors who could survive enraging a werewolf, much less do anything about the wrath of an entire pack or caern. But the Garou couldn't be everywhere at once, and isolated Kinfolk were at a great deal of risk. A story set among these events might make a good social challenge rather than a physical one; what if a fervent churchman incites a

whole village against a Kin family? Is the pack willing to slaughter the town to save their loved ones? And if they do, what sort of things will come to investigate such an overt display of supernatural violence?

The Black Plague

Sweeping through Europe with a vengeance, the horror known as the Black Plague killed a quarter of Europe's population. Death filled the streets. People cowered in fear, hiding in their homes, praying that they wouldn't be the next victims. Superstition gained control of the hearts and minds. A homid cub undergoing her First Change during this time might well believe that she was dying. These thoughts of doom and death brought about a spiritual malaise.

Werewolves may have had enough strength to resist the plague, but not all of their Kinfolk did. Many people looked for a cause, some secret sin that brought about the horror and death. Every time another victim fell to the Black Death, a potential hunter was born. These misguided people would seek out anything that they felt could be responsible. As so many died, the undead feasted and the Wyrm's promises of safety in exchange for services drew many followers. Banes flocked to the suffering, making the urban spiritscape a very dangerous place for even werewolves.

Renaissance

The Renaissance saw an ebb in the superstitions of the medieval world. The Church lost influence as the Reformation spread across Europe, and England established its own Church based on the divine right of kings. Learning and inventions spread through the lands, especially after the creation of the Gutenberg printing press. Knowledge was no longer exclusively in the hands of the Church. The Glass Walkers (then Warders) had the largest stake in the advances of human civilization, obviously; in particular, they were active around their homeland of Italy during the height of the Italian Renaissance.

For most werewolves, the most important event of this period came in 1492, when Christopher Columbus arrived in the New World. According to some stories, a member of his crew was a Bone Gnawer. Many Garou already knew about the Pure Lands. The Get of Fenris learned of it from Norse explorers centuries before Columbus. But, now word spread through Europe and all of the countries wished to carve empires out of this unexplored wilderness.

European werewolves flocked to the New World in the guise of furriers, soldiers, and even missionaries. They did not realize that they also brought agents of the Wyrm with them in the form of contagion and plague. For the Croatan, Uktena and Wendigo tribes, the start of the European invasion marked their own apocalypse.

The Age of Exploration

Disease spread into the Pure Lands faster than any European invaders. As when the Black Plague devastated Europe, thousands died. Entire cultures vanished as diseases killed and killed again. More Native Americans died from disease than from all the fighting with Europeans combined.

The Wyrm's onslaught against the Pure Lands was utterly devastating to the werewolves that had protected the lands for millennia. Theurges summoned spirits to help cure the sick, while conquistadors looted the Aztec and Incan Empires for their gold. The worst was yet to come.

The Eater-of-Souls, avatar of the Wyrm, came to the Pure Lands. For the werewolves of the Americas, the end was nigh. Disease had slain their kinfolk and thinned their ranks. They could not tend their caerns nor mount a defense against the coming waves of invaders. They could not stop the Eater-of-Souls, at least not without a terrible price.

The Croatan tribe paid that price. In a ritual that destroyed the Eater-of-Souls, the Croatan sacrificed their entire tribe. In a moment, an entire tribe of werewolves died. Spiritual shockwaves tore across the Umbra. Theurges in Russia clawed their eyes out in madness. For the Uktena and the Wendigo, the loss of their brothers and sisters was like the end of the world. Many members of the surviving tribes slipped quietly into mourning, then Harano, and died.

When the werewolves of Europe arrived along with human colonists, they found the Croatan caerns abandoned. The Get of Fenris zealously seized control of many of these sacred sites in order to protect them, since the weak Uktena and Wendigo obviously didn't know who to fight the Wyrm. Other tribes had similar feelings about the tribes of the Pure Land. For their part, the Wendigo and Uktena found targets for their rage in the invading Garou. Intertribal war raged in the forests of the Americas while colonists fought first to survive and then to gain independence from Europe. (The supplement **Croatan Song** contains much more information on pre-Colombian North America.)

While this was going on, werewolves renewed some acquaintances from the War of Rage around the world. The European powers wished to claim the world, and they would spend the next century doing so. Wherever they went, the Garou went with them.

The Rise of Reason

As time passed, intellectuals began to question nobility and the rights of the individual. The French Revolution was a major turning point in the history of Europe, as the common people rose up against the nobility. Ultimately, events led to executions of the nobility and a reign of terror in the streets of Paris. While the triumph of reason had lasting effects in the hearts and minds of Europeans, Napoleon would seize the reigns of power and bring order to the chaos for a time.

Napoleon's conquests transformed Europe, forging alliances between old enemies and redrawing political boundaries. His ultimate defeat left Great Britain as the most powerful of the European nations. The stage was set for the dominance of the British Empire.

Most werewolves watched the events unfold in Europe with a sense of apprehension. The world was changing quickly. Many of the elders did not know how to adapt. Napoleon raised an army of a size that no werewolf had ever seen. The French rational movements seemed to be the work of the Weaver, replacing religion with reason, transforming the world into clockwork mechanics and formulae.

American Civil War

Although historically the Garou were not dramatically affected by the Civil War, setting a story against the backdrop of the bloodiest conflict in American history is just too good an opportunity to ignore. Representatives of all tribes but Stargazers and Bunyip were present in America, allowing for a great diversity of characters. The most obvious story is a pair of septs that go to war against one another for some reason, mirroring the fratricidal conflict of the time. As North battles South, brother fights brother, and tribemate fights tribemate. Other plots might entail Garou involving themselves in the underground railroad (Uktena, Children of Gaia and Black Furies are all good choices for this), the Pure Ones taking some measure of revenge under cover of the war, or Garou of any tribes trying to protect their Kin from being caught up in all the bloodshed.

The Wild West

The war between the Uktena, Wendigo, and the European Garou finally ended with the coming of the Storm Eater. Long trapped in a spiritual net woven by the three tribes of the Pure Lands, the deaths of the Croatan weakened the Storm Eater's bonds enough for it to break free. Originally a massive Wyrm-spirit, the Storm Eater became something more when it devoured a powerful Weaver-spirit, becoming a blasphemous hybrid of both. Wherever it passed, the Umbra was shredded into new forms, creating Broken Lands where the Gauntlet was all but absent, or warping spirits into parodies of their former nature.

Amidst this chaos, the Wendigo and the Uktena fought to protect their remaining caerns from the

encroachment of European settlers and other werewolves. All the while they needed help to stop the Storm Eater, which was powerful enough to remold the entire Penumbra of the American West into a storm of its own creation. The desire to stop the Storm Eater won out in the end.

The struggle to win the West was one of epic proportions. Mix all the regular trappings of the West, outlaws, gamblers, gunfighters, and a horde of Storm Umbra twisted monstrosities and you've got a lot of material for a chronicle. **Werewolf: Wild West** covers this period in a detail and provides a good basis for adapting any time period to **Werewolf: The Apocalypse**.

Industrial Revolution

The Industrial Revolution promised empowerment for the people. A common person could become rich. Industry would lead to lives of luxury and plenty for everyone as production increased. But the empowerment of the people came at the expense of the rest of the world.

The Industrial Revolution saw the destruction of forests. It brought terrible pollution. Workers became slaves to their companies, working long hours in dangerous conditions for little pay. Advances in technology came with the Industrial Revolution, but only after people paid a high spiritual cost.

Werewolves had never experienced attacks on the environment. By destroying forests and polluting water and air, the Industrial Revolution was slaying spirits. Most werewolves did not know what to do, other than attack these new factories in the hopes of shutting them down. The spirit essence of the workers was slipping away. The Wyrm's minions gained power from the suffering and despair, finding their way into the souls of humans, creating fomori in numbers never before seen.

In many ways, the Industrial Revolution was the major turning point in the Garou's struggle. The Weaver's power surged to new levels, making raids into the cities all the more dangerous. The Wyrm, too, grew fat and powerful. A chronicle set in this time period could focus on how the world changes forever, the first true sign of the Apocalypse.

The Twentieth Century

The last century saw a technological boom coupled with a population explosion across the world. Many werewolves feel that the Apocalypse is here and now. Wilderness is disappearing at an alarming rate. Technology has brought consumption and waste, destroying the environment. The Industrial Revolution was just a portent of things to come. Humans now have weapons of destruction that put them nearly on par with the Garou. Modern firearms can bring down any animal. Nuclear war could destroy the world with a touch of a button. Turmoil wracks werewolf society, because obviously, somewhere, something has gone terribly wrong.

World War I

The innovations and inventions of the late 19th century continued in the early years of the 20th century. The world became a smaller place. Colonialism continued as empires clashed, evidenced by such events as the Spanish-American War and the Russo-Japanese War. Travel made the world smaller. The telephone, the automobile, and the airplane all found widespread usage during these years. In many ways, it was a time of optimism and nationalism.

No one was truly prepared for what would happen when a Serbian assassin killed the Archduke of Austria-Hungary. The First World War changed the world. Modern technology changed the way nations fought wars. For the first time, weapons of mass destruction saw action on the battlefields. Mustard gas and other toxic poisons killed not only enemy soldiers, but also everything that lived. Strategists invented trench warfare creating inhospitable no man's lands between the trenches. Land mines saw their first use, remaining deadly testimonials to military innovation long after the fighting ceased. Mechanized vehicles, the first tanks, rumbled onto the battlefields. Death flew in the skies as biplanes dueled each other for aerial supremacy and spied out enemy positions. The Garou saw the power of the Industrial Revolution in terms of raw carnage for the first time. The Wyrm grew stronger in Europe, forcing the Garou to desperate measures.

Werewolves fought on all sides during World War I. Some fought for their nation. Others fought to protect their homes. A few Garou even tried to kill as many soldiers on both sides as possible in the hopes of alleviating the suffering. The Communist Revolution in Russia tore the attentions of the Silver Fangs away from the other tribes. As monarchies ended across Europe, many werewolves found themselves without the leadership of the Fangs. Most septs chose to celebrate their independence.

World War I also brought back the specter of global disease. An epidemic of influenza killed the young and healthy in the United States and returned some of the fears forgotten since the time of the Black Plague. When American troops reached Europe, they brought the flu with them. No one, soldier or civilian, was safe from the plague which continued to kill even after the warring nations made their peace.

Roaring Twenties

The end of World War I brought an economic boom to the United States. Women gained the right to vote, a triumph rightly celebrated by the Black Furies.

Prohibition prevented legal alcohol from getting into the hands of the rich and powerful, and consequently, organized crime decided to help out. The rich lived a lifestyle of extravagance with few boundaries. The '20s make a fun time period for a troupe that enjoys gangster movies. Federal agents and mob bosses fought a not-so-secret war to keep the drinks flowing. When thugs with Tommy guns performed mob hits, it was one thing, but get a few werewolves involved and then you'd see something. In particular, Glass Walkers and Bone Gnawers would have a lot of fun. Such a chronicle is probably a little more pulp-action than the usual savage horror of **Werewolf**, but that's not necessarily a bad thing — playing a strong-jawed, corn-fed, all-American Get of Fenris fighting Wyrm-cults with his two good fists can be a delightful change of pace. The **Adventure!** game, while not fully compatible with **Werewolf** mechanics, contains more setting material on this time period and the next decade than you could ask for.

The Last Days of the Bunyip

An entire tribe died in the early 20th century, wiped out in an act of mass fratricide. It might be hard to base an entire chronicle around the fall of the Bunyip, but a long story arc set during the Bunyip's last days might bring home the tragedy of their loss in ways that simple narration can't. If you're willing to play with the Bunyip during their decline but prior to their actual final hour, you set the chronicle slightly earlier; Australia in the 19th century was very similar in mood to the American West, and could provide many a brutal frontier tale.

Great Depression

When the great stock market crash of 1929 occurred, it sent the world economy spiraling. Banks failed, wiping out people's life savings. Jobs disappeared. Money followed. Poverty existed on a nearly incomprehensible level. Homeless filled the city streets. Suffering, despair and hunger became the rule of the day. Once again, the Wyrm crawled into the hearts of humans. The Bone Gnawers were the most resilient tribe, and were the best at finding food to feed their hungry Kinfolk. However, the main trouble for the Garou wasn't food — werewolves are less reliant on a functioning economy to feed themselves — but the upsurge in Banes. As the humans' despair climbed, so did the fortunes of the Wyrm-spirits that fed on negative emotion, leaving the werewolves with much work to do. Finally, F.D.R.'s New Deal began to reverse fortunes, although the Depression ultimately ended in a way that no one wanted.

World War II

It's hard to understand today what World War II was like, although watching the first twenty minutes of *Saving Private Ryan* isn't a bad way to get in the mood

PRESCOTT

for a chronicle set in the war. Hitler isolated England and rained terror and death down upon its citizens. Fascist governments ruled Europe with an iron fist. Stalin ground the bodies of Russian soldiers under the wheels of the German blitzkrieg in the hopes of slowing it down. These madmen took mass slaughter and raised it up a notch to genocide. May no one ever have to experience anything like the concentration camps again. Africa was in flames as the Axis fought the Allies. Japan ran over the rest of Asia. The United States remained caught up in isolationism until a Japanese sneak attack on Pearl Harbor destroyed the entire Pacific fleet. No one knew how the war would end, and the Axis could have won.

The Garou fought against both sides early in the war, but as time went on, most of them realized that the Axis powers were Gaia's true enemies. The Get of Fenris became instrumental in sabotaging the Nazi war machine. Werewolves were in the South Pacific along with the troops, battling spirits of war woken in the jungles along with Japanese shapeshifters. The Wyrm never stopped fighting its war against Gaia during the struggle. Just when Allied victory seemed inevitable, the Wyrm achieved its greatest triumph as well in an isolated area near Los Alamos, New Mexico.

The atom bomb gave humans unimaginable destructive power. Hiroshima was the first city to suffer a nuclear attack. Even after the United States destroyed Hiroshima, the Japanese government had difficulty believing what had occurred. They thought that whatever had happened couldn't possibly happen again. Nagasaki convinced them that peace was the only option. Although the Japanese surrender spared thousands of lives from the horrors that would have followed an invasion of Japan, Pandora's box was open. No one, anywhere in the world, would ever be completely safe again.

The Cold War

After World War II, old allies quickly became rivals. The two superpowers, the Soviet Union and the United States, began to carve the world up into communist and democratic states. Once both nations had nuclear weapons, the threat of nuclear war loomed over every living being. Gaia's defenders were now absolutely helpless to stop the end of the world if the leaders of the two superpowers decided to go to war.

It was a time of distrust and fear, carefully hidden away behind censors who believed that they were protecting morality. During the heyday of McCarthyism, neighbor informed on neighbor. For werewolves, unexplained disappearances or voicing any anti-government sentiment meant visits from federal agents. Garou started to infiltrate some government agencies, but these attempts did not always go well.

The economy boomed, but minorities were left out of the bounty. Civil rights advances began, but in many places, especially the South, African Americans weren't treated as true citizens. Segregation, separate but equal, was the policy. It would take a great deal of courage, bloodshed, and resolve over the next two decades to change this.

A large teenage population swelled the schools as the post-war Baby Boomers grew up. They discovered a new type of music, rock and roll, which horrified their parents with its suggestive lyrics and hip-swaying musicians. This rebellious form of music may have helped prime the Baby Boomers for the years of protest to come.

The Cold War reached a crescendo during the Cuban Missile Crisis. The United States Navy moved to intercept Soviet transports carrying nuclear missiles to a base in Cuba. For days, the world teetered on the brink of nuclear war. Threats flew between the two superpowers. People huddled in bomb shelters hoping to wait out the attack. Cartoons taught children to duck and hide under blankets in case of nuclear attack. After a number of tension-filled days, the Soviet ships turned around. The crisis ended. However, the fear generated by the threat fed more power to the Wyrm. For decades to come, people around the world would carry the fear of global destruction with them.

The Vietnam War began as one of America's attempts to stop the spread of communism. The longest and most intense jungle fighting ever known took place as American soldiers tried to protect South Vietnam from the North Vietnamese army and the Viet Cong. From all accounts, veterans of the Vietnam War lived tension filled days and slept with nightmares. They fought an enemy that would never give up, dying to claim hills out in the middle of a trackless jungle. Unlike World War II, many soldiers did not understand this war. They did not know why they fought. A few werewolves found their way to Vietnam. They fought against the war-spirits and Banes that fed on the suffering, but they could not find a way to end the war.

Post-Apocalypse and Other Variations

Werewolves are obsessed with the Apocalypse. The fanatics among them believe that it's coming, and these are the final days. Unless, of course, it has already happened. What does a post-Apocalyptic world look like? What do the Garou do once they've failed? A post-Apocalypse setting allows you to explore several themes with a different perspective than you would in a standard game of the End Times. Post-Apocalypse adventures can be as simple as outcasts trying to survive in a hostile world. Young werewolves could be seeking redemption for all of Garou society, constantly trying to make up for their ancestors' failure to prevent the Apocalypse. Perhaps the Stargazers are correct, and the Apocalypse is just another stage in an eternal cycle.

Changing the setting from the standard World of Darkness presents the Storyteller with both opportunities and challenges. You now have the chance to truly personalize your world — it can be whatever you want it to be. You can change the rules without worrying about a player complaining "but it says on page 68 that it will work if I roll 4 successes!" Changing the setting, especially if the group is made up of veteran **Werewolf** players, can help encourage roleplaying and give a new perspective on Garou society. It keeps the players on their toes and gives them new areas to explore. That does lead, however, to the challenges. Not all players are willing to let you pry the rulebooks from their protesting fingers. Some players may feel confused or uncomfortable. A good idea for any game, but especially one where you plan to tweak the rules, is to warn your players ahead of time that not all will be as they expect.

The World of Darkness is a comfortable setting for many players —similar enough to the real world for them to be able to relate to it without too much trouble. That familiarity is part of what lends **Werewolf** its horror value. Players suddenly have the themes and morality of **Werewolf** confronting their perceptions of the real world. As a result, changing the setting can cause the plausibility of your game to suffer. Most alternate settings work best when the players can still relate to something — human emotions, a particular place, or anything else that lets the players connect with their characters. Of course, every rule has its exception, and it is perfectly possible to create an alternate setting that will completely disorient the players. Just make sure you are prepared to deal with the consequences.

If you need some inspiration, watch a few of your favorite apocalyptic movies, or read a few books. Pay special attention to the messages — they often center on survival, redemption, and rebirth, all of which are great themes for **Werewolf**. Below are some ideas for post-Apocalypse campaigns, and other variant settings. Use them as the beginnings of your own stories, or as visions of the future for standard settings.

It's the End of the World as We Know It

It's the Big One. Someone punched the big red button, and mushroom clouds sprouted throughout the known world. The remaining Garou, instead of being united to save Gaia, disintegrate further into warring factions. Some blame the madness of the Wyrm, others the Weaver's out-of-control technology. Skeptics blame human folly, claiming that humans were trying to kill humans, and good riddance. A few packs turn on their fellow werewolves, blaming everyone else for what has happened. The typical post-nuclear war setting provides opportunities for the characters to see the effects of war gone mad. A variation of the end-of-the-world scenario allows the Wyld to seek its vengeance — instead of nuclear war, an asteroid or other celestial body hits Earth (perhaps directed by Rorg, the Planetary Incarna of the asteroid belt).

A world in which many (if not all) existing caerns have been destroyed, and their sept members killed, provides an excellent opportunity for the Storyteller to bring together many diverse Garou. Elders and pups of all different tribes may gather together and either work together, or fight amongst themselves. This is a great reason for a multi-tribe pack, as whatever young are available find themselves thrown together. The pack can then roam the world, battling the forces of the Wyrm. Eventually, they may be able to discover the truth behind how the nuclear Armageddon started, and learn some ways to rescue Gaia from destruction.

You might want to make the setting realistic, or go with the pulp science fiction "twisted wasteland." Along the way, the pack may find strange mutants roaming the earth, including twisted creatures that were once werewolves. They could have to deal with the effects of nuclear winter and a terrifying climate. Imagine forests of wilted trees or coastlines swept clean of human structures by giant tsunamis.

Strange cults of survivors form, banding together for survival. These survivors will generally be scavengers and opportunists. Cannibalism wouldn't be unheard of in a world with little food. The survivors will gather weapons and turn them on anything outside the group. Insane survivors are easy prey for the Wyrm. Just think about escapees from a Mad Max movie and give them some Wyrm taint.

Not everyone who survives is a whacked-out paranoid psycho. More pacifistic survivors may try to unite everyone in peace. Some may seek out the spirit world. Others may welcome the chance to build a new and better society. They would be determined not to repeat the mistakes of the past.

Naturally, in such an environment, the spirit world will have suffered just as much as the physical world, if not more so. The background radiation strengthens the Gauntlet, cutting the Garou off from the Umbra except at the most powerful caerns. More Blights form in the Penumbra, making it far easier for Banes to enter the physical world. Hellholes form on earth where Nexus Crawlers lure wanderers desperate for any sign of hope. Damaged spirits of Gaia rampage through the Penumbra seeking self-destruction after witnessing the horror of nuclear war. Many of them lash out at anything in their final dying agonies. Tragically, the werewolves have to fight and slay spirits that were once their allies, but now are too far gone to save.

The Weaver's web has collapsed. Pattern spiders work desperately to fix the structure. Many have become Wyrm-tainted and savagely attack their crystalline counterparts. The Wyrm could even break free, heralding a time of hell on earth.

You could also run a nuclear apocalypse chronicle as a single setting. Maybe everyone's safe in a shelter that no one can leave without fear of exposing the community to dangerous fallout. A chronicle focusing on the development of player and Storyteller characters, Garou and human, who have to survive together in an isolated space would challenge roleplayers. How can a lupus keep herself out of Harano, when she knows that in all likelihood every wolf on Earth is dead? A number of isolated shelters could exist with a few cables connecting each other. After a few weeks, a group may want to try to venture out. What happens as food supplies run out? If the werewolves lose control, what will the community do about them?

As Storyteller, you may want to modify the skills available, depending on how long after the bombs fall you set your story. In the immediate aftermath of the Apocalypse, the Garou would obviously have all of the modern skills, and would have to learn whatever new ones they needed to survive in their new world. A generation or two later the characters would have had the opportunity to learn those new skills from childhood. New flora and fauna arise in the aftermath. Spirits that survived may have new Gifts to teach in order to help the werewolves survive a hostile planet. A lost world awaits discovery and rebuilding.

Silent Spring

The world's population has been devastated by an unknown, fast-mutating disease. Very few humans survived contact with it, but the Garou and their Kinfolk seem remarkably resistant. Werewolves have a nearly uncontested ability to dominate the planet. They no longer need to worry about the Veil, as most of those remaining are their Kin. The Garou have lost their natural leaders, as the Silver Fangs alone seemed vulnerable to the disease. Even more disturbingly, the Bone Gnawers and the metis proved to be the most resistant, suffering very few losses of either Garou or Kinfolk.

While the Garou fight for dominance, the forces of the Wyrm have grown much stronger. The disease was their ally (perhaps even their doing), and they were prepared for its effects. The Leeches who once ruled the cities find that they now have only one good source of blood — the Garou

Kin. The Garou must try to defend their Kin from the depredations of the Leeches, who are now fighting amongst themselves for the few human "cattle" that remain. Many of them also want to protect the few humans who remain, over the protests of the Red Talons and others that are happy to see humanity destroyed.

Such a scenario presents an excellent opportunity to turn players' views of Garou society upside down. The Bone Gnawers and the metis can take leadership roles never before available to them. This opportunity would likely bring about sweeping changes in Garou society. How likely are metis leaders going to be to enforce the section of the Litany that prohibits Garou from mating? The Bone Gnawers could be of split opinions. Some of them will want to do away with status entirely, while others want to lord their new status over the rest of the Garou, as had been done to them for so long.

This is a setting that has a lot of potential to upset players, especially veteran players who think they know how Garou society is supposed to work. Unless you just like unhappy players, make sure that they don't go into this game with plans to make a Silver Fang Ahroun who will one day rule the world on the strength of his birthright. On the other hand, if they wish to play the last of the Silver Fangs, trying to retain nobility and honor, it would provide a great roleplaying challenge.

Another possibility is that the disease hasn't finished its work. Maybe it's mutating and slowly killing off the Kinfolk and infecting select werewolves. The characters could have to determine the source of the plague and find a cure. Scenes of characters walking through quiet cities littered with corpses would be very eerie.

For a different variant, the disease could kill off all the wolves instead of the humans. Can the characters find a way to preserve the few remaining wolves? What happens if the Garou lose all of their wolf blood?

Death of the Spirit

The Umbra has been fully sundered from the material world. People everywhere have lost their spirit and their passion. Humanity no longer produces music, laughter, or joy. Humans have become capable of little more than despair and hopelessness. Though more resilient, the Garou have been affected also, and in some ways even more greatly. The Garou can no longer connect with the Umbra, nor do they have contact with the spirits. The influence of the spirit no longer tempers the werewolves' Rage, and many have rampaged through the throngs of human sheep that now occupy the world. The Theurges and Philodox have suffered greatly, and many have succumbed to Harano.

In the eyes of the Garou, the world has become a lifeless place. Colors have faded to a dull, dusty pallor.

The air has become thick and stale, an oppressive weight in the lungs with every breath. Lakes no longer sparkle in the sunlight, but instead lie stagnant under an overcast sky. The werewolves still remember the way the world used to look, and mourn the loss of the spirit world. Even some Garou have begun to forget. Most of the Glass Walkers have succumbed to this gray deadening.

As long as there are some that remember, Gaia has not completely lost Her defenders. The characters should be among those that remember, and are trying to restore the world's connection to the spirit. A chronicle set in the spiritless post-Apocalypse can become a story of inspiration and rebirth. As the characters search for ways to regain Gnosis and reawaken the spirit, they may inspire others and help them reconnect as well. Although this is an extremely dark and depressing setting, a theme of hope and renewal would help to balance the tone.

What happened? Did the werewolves fail? Could they be responsible for the sundering? One of the first actions that packs will want to take is to find out what happened and why. Has the Wyrm freed itself? Is a powerful spirit back from ancient times? Has the Umbra separated from the physical world in the past?

Perhaps a lost ritual or fetish could provide the way to reconnect the Umbra with earth. Maybe the werewolves must force their way into the spirit world and undertake a dangerous vision quest to restore the connection. Another idea would be to have a few single caerns remain the only connections to the Umbra. Septs that have lost their caerns prepare to seize the remaining ones from the defenders.

The Wyld Triumphant

The world's environment was a lot more fluid in the past. The Apocalypse may have very little to do with the Weaver and the Wyrm at all. Perhaps the Weaver has been able to hold the Wyrm in check… and maybe this really isn't a good thing. The spiraling influence of the Weaver's mad dance with the Wyrm has drastically altered nature's course. Perhaps the Weaver and the Wyrm have driven the Wyld berserk.

As the Wyld unleashes its vengeance, hurricanes the size of the Atlantic form and last for years. The world experiences ten-year droughts, earthquakes, huge volcanoes, melting glaciers, severe coastal flooding… any and every natural disaster you can think of. Whole continents may seize up or go down beneath the waves (was that Australia sinking?) The werewolves may find themselves in the unfamiliar, and uncomfortable, position of fighting against the Wyld.

The Garou may disintegrate into the predictable rounds of blame and recriminations… or they

might be finally forced to recognize that no one tribe can bring Gaia back into balance alone. The Wyld is an indiscriminate killer, and shows no mercy to animals or humans. This gives you a chance to put members of all the tribes together peacefully, united for a common purpose. A variant of this setting would allow you to have your player characters be tribeless, perhaps Gaia's plan to recreate the One Tribe.

This type of natural disaster lets the Storyteller literally rework geography. If you like the idea of the flame from the Statue of Liberty just breaking the surface of the Atlantic Ocean, go for it. Want to turn all of Florida into the Everglades? It's your world. Sea levels could drop, revealing ancient ruins long forgotten, possibly releasing imprisoned evils from the distant past. Maybe the secret to stabilizing the weather and appeasing the Wyld lies hidden somewhere in the world.

Perhaps nothing can be done to stop the weather. Werewolves and humans must learn to adapt. Gaia may create a sanctuary — a place like Summer Country on Earth, which the Garou have to find. The werewolves not only have to get themselves to this hidden sanctuary but their Kinfolk as well.

We Who Forget the Past...

Werewolves have been born, lived, and died in the post-Apocalypse world for many generations. Only stories remain of the Time Before, and those few have taken on the character of myths. Surely, a world like that could never have existed in this bleak, dark, devastated place. The characters should be well prepared for a harsh life, with suffering in the past and the prospect of more suffering for the future. Attacks by Wyrm-creatures, Black Spiral Dancers, and renegade Garou occur with depressing frequency.

Amidst all of this pain, one pack of young Garou finds a spirit gate that will let them journey to the past and possibly stop the Apocalypse. Of the many problems this raises, one of the first is that none of them knows what they would have to fix. How did the Apocalypse start in the first place? While they know that the gate will take them to the proper time and place, they do not know what they need to look for once they get there. According to the myths, the werewolves of the time were great heroes who died trying to defend Gaia. They failed, so how could this young pack hope to succeed? And yet, it would be worse for them to have a chance and not even try.

This scenario suggests an epic campaign where if the young werewolves succeed in changing the past, they may cease to exist. Heroes of the past could be the ones that they have to stop. Maybe they need to aid the minions of the Wyrm in their efforts to wreak havoc to break a series of events that leads to Armageddon. Other possibilities include a second pack being sent from the future to stop them. Does the spirit gate work in reverse? What happens if Black Spirals take over the future? Depending on your troupe, a nasty sequel to this type of chronicle might be a return trip when the actions that the Garou take only lead to a less destroyed but darker future.

As an important note with this type of scenario, don't get too wrapped up in causality. If you allow questions like "well, if we fix it, we won't exist so we wouldn't have gone back so we wouldn't have fixed it" to be commonplace in your chronicle, you'll only end up with a bunch of frustrated players. It's a time travel chronicle — it's not meant to be realistic! One option is to create a spirit guardian of the gate that explains that if the pack changes the past, the changes will be permanent, even if the timeline is changed. End of discussion and everyone goes back to worrying about what to do instead of trying to wrap their heads around the space-time continuum.

Victory!

The Wyrm has been healed — or even destroyed! The werewolves have survived the Final Days! Gaia's defenders did it. So, now what? What happens after the Wyrm is defeated? Without the constant threat of the Wyrm, do the tribes turn on each other? Does Gaia need the Garou at all? They always focused their rage against the Wyrm and its minions. Without the destructive power of the Wyrm, the Garou slowly lose their rage. Inter-tribal warfare rears its ugly head as the different tribes try to dominate in this time after the Wyrm.

For deep roleplaying, werewolves could slowly lose their ability to change forms. They have to choose which form to stay in, because like a child making silly faces, they could freeze that way. The Corrupter Wyrm may be gone, but not all of its human servants. Evil still exists in the world. For example, vampires are not necessarily Wyrm creatures. Can werewolves still protect their caerns or live their lives if Gaia no longer needs them? Does the Weaver become the big enemy? Glass Walkers may find themselves in a very bad light with the other tribes.

And if the Wyrm was actually *destroyed* — not healed, but wiped from the universe — what then? Without a force of Balance at all, the universe might quickly become unraveled as the Weaver and Wyld fight for dominance with nothing to keep them in check. Can something else be restored to the position of Balancer? Could the Garou themselves be the ones to find a way to replace the Wyrm?

Welcome to the Apocalypse

The Eye of the Wyrm is fully open; the time has come for the Final Battle. Werewolves must try to summon the spirits of their ancestors and gird themselves for war.

Nothing must be held back, because the Wyrm's agents are coming in force. This chronicle takes place in the last of the Final Days. The final signs come to pass on Earth and in the Umbra signaling the end of the world.

This is an ambitious setting, filled with high drama and desperation. **Werewolf** characters in this chronicle might be far more powerful than a starting character, generated using the rules presented in Chapter One, or they might be footsoldiers in the Final Battle. Don't pull any punches: this is the big one, the end. A sense of urgency should surround the characters' every action. The Black Spiral Dancers, fomori, and the like should have a similar sense of desperation, or overconfidence if you prefer.

The chronicle should build to a final battle, taking place in the Umbra and on Earth. Ultimately, it would be nice if the Garou won, but not totally necessary. Perhaps the end should be like Ragnarok in Norse legend. The warriors all die great and noble deaths, slaying their enemies, leaving behind only a few survivors, the peacemakers, the kinder and gentler sorts who can build a better world for the future. How successful the characters were in the stories building up to the final battle should help determine the final result. Maybe they die from wounds suffered in the battle, but only after they have a chance to see victory. Maybe the good guys lose, but they somehow survive to try to rebuild werewolf society and keep fighting until the bitter end.

Running the Apocalypse allows you to do a tour de force of all the major heroes and villains from your chronicle. Take every character you've ever liked from every Werewolf sourcebook and run with them. Let the characters journey to the surface of Anthelios, or gather the greatest heroes from each of the Near Realms to aid them. Enjoy yourself and make it an event for your group to remember. If you want to go really overboard, get cheap buttons made saying "I survived the Apocalypse" or "I died in the Apocalypse." Your players will wear them with pride for years to come.

Impergium?

The Stargazers were right. The Apocalypse was only another stage in an eternal cycle. That cycle has turned. Humanity sent itself back to the Stone Age eons ago. Now, the Garou find themselves confronting an exploding human population… one that has developed agriculture, is beginning to form cities, and is rapidly expanding across the globe. So now what?

The werewolves remember the stories of the Impergium. Will they let it happen again? Can they stop the cycle from repeating itself even if they want to? This is much like a historical chronicle of the Impergium, but this time humans may be a bit more prepared. Spirits may oppose the idea of a Garou Impergium. Hard-line werewolves may see this as a time of necessary action.

After all, if the Impergium had remained in effect, the Apocalypse would never have happened.

You can use this variant in conjunction with some of the other post-Apocalypse settings. Perhaps nuclear war was the Apocalypse, and human civilization has finally begun rebuilding a few thousand years later. The characters may all have memories of the Apocalypse from their ancestors.

Other Variants

Post-Apocalypse settings are not the only variants to the **Werewolf** world. Changing parts of the **Werewolf** mythology provides plenty of ways to change the tone of your chronicle, while still having it be about werewolves. Above all, your chronicle is a way for you and your players to have fun, while telling a story together. Never let the rules or the "official" storyline get in the way.

Werewolf's rules and themes can translate into alternate settings that may not be recognizable as a **Werewolf** game to outsiders. This can be a great way to wake up players and get them to think. In addition, it provides a special challenge to the Storyteller. By creating your own world as a Storyteller, you have greater control. Also, if you've run a number of **Werewolf** chronicles, it gives you a chance to do something different, but still enjoy your favorite (we do hope it's your favorite) game system.

Look at settings from fiction and find elements you like. You could throw all pretense of a serious game out the window and send a pack to the stars to fight giant bugs in some kind of *Starship Troopers* with fangs. If you want to do high fantasy or sword and sorcery, having characters with the ability to turn into werewolves should make that horde of orcs or barbarians think twice. They could be the holy warriors of the Great Wolf. Maybe being a werewolf is a true curse, not a gift, and the characters are fighting to free themselves.

The selections that follow are only a few ideas on possible variant **Werewolf** games. They are more meant to fire your imagination than anything else. If you like an idea but don't want to unbalance or radically transform your current chronicle, use the setting as part of a dream or a realm in the Umbra. Many of these settings have a particular theme or tone and could be used as analogy or symbols for events in an existing chronicle.

The bottom line is this: don't be afraid to do whatever you want with your game. As the Storyteller, it's your world, your creation, and your plot. Although we've said it before, it bears repeating: the only rule is to have fun.

The Last Defenders of Gaia

In the distant future, scientists have created the perfect soldiers. Mixing unstable DNA from wolves and humans, werewolf warriors now wage war upon their country's enemies. Cybernetic implants and combat drugs help them reach a state where they become nearly unstoppable killing machines. Science celebrates werewolves as the ultimate triumph of technology and nature. They inspire fear in their enemies, regenerate from nearly any wound, and depend on scientific treatments to ensure their loyalty and keep them breathing.

In a dark cyber future, werewolves serve as a special police force and elite soldiers. They receive orders from "The Man" with ruthless efficiency. Their forms are as much meant to engender fear as to serve practical purposes. Alternatives to werewolves exist, in the forms of slayer androids and other genetically enhanced cyborgs, but none of them inspires the visceral terror of the werewolf.

In this variant, the Garou don't exist. These aren't the spirit-loving naturalistic wolves we know and love. Maybe the last Garou died defending the final caern decades ago. The Veil still exists, but it's much weaker. People know about the werewolf project. Werewolves may scare the hell out of them, but no one denies their existence. Gifts are special implants or cyber drugs given to the characters to help them complete their missions. Werewolves can expect to be outfitted with a full compliment of modern weaponry and receive official or unofficial sanctioning from their creators. Everything's all set for a kill-fest of corporate warfare and amoral carnage. Woe to anyone who gets in the way. Oh, silver's not any more of a problem than any other metal.

Some Gifts aren't found in this world. Who needs to talk to spirits that don't exist? Gnosis shouldn't matter much. The Umbra doesn't exist, so no one needs to worry about Gaia… or do they?

Dark future settings usually wind up with the main characters finding out some kind of nasty secret that could hurt "The Man". Corporations always need a reason to turn on their creations and vice versa. Why should we be any different, especially when we've got a whole set of books full of them?

The Resurrected

In this variant of the Garou-as-engineered-soldiers, Gaia and the Umbra do exist. Perhaps the Garou are long gone, victims of the Apocalypse or simply hunted into extinction ages past. Gaia has not forgotten her protectors. Now, modern science has found a way to bring them back. Gaia's spirits want them back, and they don't intend to leave them alone. What happens when the artificial werewolves of the future tap into the Umbra? Do their creators decide that the creations are going insane? What happens when they realize what the Weaver and the Wyrm have done to the world? Do their loyalties lie with the government and scientists who created them or with a spirit world desperate to have

them back? How do their employers deal with spirit magic and real magical Gifts? As the werewolves rediscover the past, they may gain weaknesses to silver, but they also regain Gifts and fetishes. Also, no one said that the Wyrm and its lovely servants ever went away.

This variant can cover many different government-conspiracy type settings. For example, werewolves could be police officers or bounty hunters, created to track down criminals and some people that just know too much. Werewolves could be government enforcers, created with a way for them to instill terror into normal people, as if the Veil were pierced. What would happen if a group of these werewolves rebelled?

Wolfweres

What if no homids existed? Everyone's a lupus or metis in this chronicle. The homids are gone, slaughtered to the last — or perhaps they never existed, and werewolves were never meant to treat humans as relatives. Furthermore, the humans know about werewolves. Forget the Veil, humans have learned that werewolves do exist, and they aren't happy. The thought of giant werewolves terrorizing the night is enough to alarm any government.

In this setting, the Garou desperately try to keep their wolf Kinfolk and themselves alive against a human race determined to find and exterminate them. Some werewolves infiltrate their enemies, using human forms to pass among their enemies. Special units of werewolf hunters armed with high frequency sirens, flame-throwers, and silver bullets search out the Garou. They have government support, including helicopters, radios, and support teams. Some may even have psychics in their employ.

In this world, the Red Talons are the greatest and most respected of tribes. Humans have proved them right, time and time again. Glass Walkers and Bone Gnawers live on the verge of extinction, yet they still dare to enter the cities and sabotage their hunters. It is a time of war, a war that the Garou stand little chance of surviving.

The Children of Gaia realize that humanity is too powerful to defeat simply with fang and claw. They hope to open a dialogue and negotiate with the humans. They believe that their enemies will listen to reason and stop this genocide. Red Talon leaders suspect the Children of Gaia of plotting to betray their society. They don't care how good the Children's intentions may be.

If that weren't enough, the Wyrm still seeks to destroy the Garou. Fomori aid the hunters in their attempts to find and kill the werewolves. A group of humans, the Silver Circle, has discovered the truth about the Wyrm. They know that only the werewolves hold to key to stopping the Wyrm. However, the Circle's attempts to contact the Garou have only led to dead members. Furthermore, they can't convince politicians and paramilitary hunters not to kill the werewolves.

A chronicle built around this setting focuses on the themes of overcoming hatred and prejudice as well as the struggle for survival. As wolf packs flee from the humans, the werewolves must protect their Kinfolk and lead them to safety. A poignant romance could arise between a character and a human fighting the Wyrm. Perhaps some Garou will mate with humans in the hopes of having a homid breed again. The Red Talons would not take that well.

Raging for a Cure

Lycanthropy has nothing to do with heritage or being a defender of Gaia. Werewolves pass on this chronic disease when they bite a person. True to the werewolf horror movie genre, a werewolf can't control himself on nights of the full moon. Difficulties are lower on Rage rolls, making it more likely that the werewolf will lose control.

All of the characters should start as a human, preferably with established connections to each other. Each one of the characters survives an attack from a werewolf. They contract the disease. It progresses slowly at first, leading to sudden bursts of temper, unusual hair growth, and sharper canines. Maybe the original werewolf still lurks outside their town, maybe not. Is there a cure if they find and kill the beast?

Over time, the problem becomes worse. You should play the personal horror aspects of transformation to dramatic effect. The characters have to find a way to save themselves and their families from the raging beast within. If they aren't careful, they may pass on the disease to others. Over time, the wolf starts craving fresh meat. They pose a grave danger to their friends and loved ones.

A sinister corporation or government agency starts asking questions. They want to hunt down the werewolves for their own purposes, possibly planning to vivisect the beasts. If they find out who the werewolves are, they would be willing to stop at nothing to find a way to take one alive. They'll threaten the friends and family of the characters, all the while staying strangely out of reach of the law.

Eventually, the werewolves may organize and take the offensive. They could discover that the investigators are the ones who created the virus. They may even have the cure hidden somewhere in their labs. If the characters are willing to venture into the lion's jaws, they may find a way out of their nightmare.

This setting revolves around finding a cure. Gifts and tribes don't exist in this world *per se*. The infected werewolves may possess certain physical Gifts if they make sense; for example, Razor Claws would be plausible. The Umbra also doesn't exist. No one gets to step sideways. The new werewolves will have to struggle to balance using their newfound abilities with finding a way to cure themselves. Of course, a cure has its price as well. It would be tragic if someone found a cure, only to discover that the bad guys were still out to get him. A cured character might have to seek out an infected friend to re-infect her so she can protect her loved ones or put a final end to this plague.

The Eternal Pack

Some battles never end. If you as a Storyteller want to use all the historical settings, this may be the chronicle idea for you. No matter what happens, the eternal pack always arrives to fight the darkness. The chronicle could start with a pack of werewolves in the distant past fighting a terrible enemy. The pack fights to the end, but they can't stop the creature. With their dying breaths, the pack members swear an oath to Gaia vowing that if they can have the strength, they will use it to fight against her enemies throughout all of their lives. Gaia grants their request, but now they reincarnate time and time again to fight her enemies, always appearing in times of great need. Alternatively, the pack could have failed their sept or tribe, unleashing a terrible avatar of the Wyrm upon the world, perhaps even an Urge-Wyrm. They may not find true rest as long as the spirit remains free. Though they may imprison it again, each time throughout the years that it gets free, the spirits of the pack return, taking physical form to return the spirit to its prison. Only when they ultimately destroy it will they find peace. Also, like any good ghost story, the Garou could be tied to a person, like the true king of the Silver Fangs, or a place, like the Caern of the Sacred Spring. Whenever those things are threatened, the Eternal Pack returns to defend them.

Each story in this type of game could take place in a separate time period. The chronicle ends whenever the characters manage to permanently slay their foe or accomplish their goal. With this type of chronicle, you don't have to worry about not killing any of the player characters. They'll be back next story, although you may want to throw in a way that the pack can be permanently destroyed or made to suffer eternally. You want to avoid players growing too world-weary and attempting to sabotage the pack, although it might be amusing to watch one individual try it for a story or two. Also, characters that carelessly throw away their lives might get old after a while, though a few heroic sacrifices could be lots of fun.

The characters become the stuff of legends among the Garou. Future generations may even become lax, expecting the Eternal Pack to arrive and save them. They may have other problems when they arrive. Skep-

tics may accuse them of being imposters attempting to curry favor by impersonating great heroes of the past. They'll have to learn new skills as customs and cultures change. Imagine the surprise the first time someone pulls a gun on one of the pack. They will also find themselves worshipped and holding positions of honor among the ancestor-spirits. Theurges and Philodox may grow angry when the pack fails to offer them divine insight into the workings of the spirit world. The Garou may expect them to bring back the dead or perform other miraculous tasks. Some packs may take offense at having these saviors come to protect them.

A well-developed recurring villain or group of villains will strengthen this chronicle. As the pack learns how their foe operates, he will learn about them as well. Nothing adds to a fight scene quite like the good guys and bad guys calling each other by name or pointing out the mistakes that their opponent made last time. Storyteller characters can reappear in different stories as well, perhaps being a young cub in one story and a revered elder in the next. Some werewolves could remember the eternal pack through their Ancestors Background.

For a fun variant on this concept, maybe the characters switch auspices each time they return or even switch bodies. Be careful though, this will work well with some troupes and go over very badly with others. Don't surprise the players with more than they can handle or you'll hear things like, "What do you mean I'm so and so's character? I hate Bone Gnawers."

What's So Special?

Everyone is a werewolf. *Everyone.*

In this type of setting, the characters are part of a Silver Pack or have some other advantage over most people, but everyone is a Garou. People keep their arguments under tight control, lest the Rage grow too great. Doctors give their patients special medications to help them retain control. Sports take place with the participants in Crinos form. Fur-coloring shampoos are all the rage (pun intended). Instead of a space program, werewolves are colonizing the Umbra with special moon-bridges. Everyone reveres Gaia. Universities teach classes about conversing with spirits. Instead of cities being urban sprawls, Garou have built them up around caerns and designed them to harmonize with nature. Politicians settle disputes with klaives. Society may handle divorces the same way. Possession of silver requires a permit.

Metis don't really exist. Everyone's technically a metis, but breeding works fine and there's no trace of deformities. Anyone may take Gifts from either the homid or lupus list. Of course, children could occasionally be born as metis. People would consider them handicapped and give them special care and sympathy. In other words, they'd grow up angry and bitter as usual. As a story idea, maybe true metis start to be born in greater and greater numbers. Something may be going wrong in the hospital.

Fomori don't exist. Instead, anyone who falls to the Wyrm becomes a Black Spiral Dancer. Underworld legions of Black Spirals wage a perpetual war against the rest of the world. Anti-Black Spiral packs form specifically to combat the threat.

This setting probably makes for a better short chronicle than a long one. But again, it should make players think, especially if they have a tendency to push normal humans around. Another option, more suited for a one time adventure than a full chronicle, would be to make the player characters into humans or wolves in this world. For some reason, they are the only ones who aren't Garou. This may make them outcasts or make them more trustworthy, since they don't struggle with Rage. They may need to go on a quest to attain their Garou heritage and join society.

Servants of the Dragon

Want to really turn **Werewolf** on its head? Try this one.

The Wyrm, or Dragon, desperately struggles to save an insane Gaia from the warring powers of the Wyld and the Weaver. The Dragon's not imprisoned anywhere or insane. His agents of balance, the Garou, try to purify the corrupt spirits. Failing that, they cull the threats to Gaia. All of the tribes pay some reverence to the Dragon.

Fomori are noble humans who've sworn themselves to the service of the Dragon. Unfortunately, each one of these individuals knows that the human body can't contain the power of the Dragon for long. Over time, they slowly suffer physical and even mental agony, but they're willing to do it to help save Gaia from Herself. Fomori are the ultimate martyrs, true heroes, in every sense.

The Wyrm isn't a force of corruption, more like a purifying flame. He does his best to try to save Gaia but such is his power that he could just as well destroy Her. Therefore, he needs the werewolves to help him try to heal and save Gaia. The Dragon's power can corrupt the weak-willed, so Garou must gain Renown to prove that they have the strength of will and character to handle the Dragon's Gifts. The Spiral Dancers are one of the greatest tribes of werewolves, while the Silver Fangs succumbed to the madness of Gaia ages ago.

Alternatively, just move the Wyrm from its position as the main antagonist in **Werewolf**. The Weaver or the Wyld could easily replace it. The Glass Walkers or Red Talons could assume the role of the fallen tribe. Gaia Herself could lash out against Her children as She suffers from environmental and spiritual damage. The Triat could stand united in their attempts to save Gaia.

Caern sites are locations where Gaia's spirits pass between worlds before they rampage on earth, killing all in their wake. Werewolves must seek out alternative places to gain spiritual energy, possibly getting gnosis from the Weaver's labs in this alternate world.

Alien Invasion

In the midst of looking into mirrors, seeking out corruption and the like, werewolves sometimes forget to look up. Well, in this alternate setting, prepare to put the Triat on the back burner. A much more physical threat has found its way to earth. The Garou may be the only chance we have.

Source material for alien invasions is everywhere. You can find movies like *Independence Day*, *Evolution*, and the *Alien* trilogy at a nearby video store. Literature is everywhere as well, but H.G. Wells' *War of the Worlds* was probably the first.

Aliens could be giant insects, spindly creatures with great mental powers, artificial lifeforms, or best of all, shapeshifters. They should have technology beyond that of earthlings; after all, they did manage to get here. However, it shouldn't be so powerful that the human race, and more importantly the Garou, can't put up a fight.

During classic alien invasion tales, the invaders always have some type of weakness that the heroes can exploit. The hard part is usually discovering this weakness. Maybe their ships are impenetrable by modern weapons, but they have no wards against attacks from the Umbra. Packs of werewolves could slip through the Umbra and make their way inside the alien vessels. The aliens may have studied humans, but they don't even have an inkling of the existence of werewolves.

Alien invasions also have the wonderful effect of turning mortal enemies into best friends. After all, if they destroy our planet, what are we fighting over? Hunters, vampires, and Black Spiral Dancers could all unite with werewolves to fight off the invasion. Once the aliens leave, things may return to normal, or perhaps the former enemies will have found a common ground.

Of course, the invasion could be a misunderstanding. Alien starships forced to land for repairs may inadvertently release high levels of radiation into the atmosphere, which the military may interpret as an attack. The pack may need to help the aliens get what they need to repair the ship and flee the planet. Perhaps an unconventional way for aliens to get home would be to take a long trek through the Deep Umbra.

Invasions can come from any direction. They don't have to be from space. Aliens could come from another dimension, deep with the earth's core, or from the future. Invaders could be from an alternate world, like any one of the other settings listed here. For real fun, the

invaders could be evil counterparts of the Garou. Characters would have to clear their names and stop the invasion. Letting a player in on this sort of thing and having her play her villainous counterpart can really throw a troupe's paranoia into overdrive. If you do this, give everyone a chance to play a bad guy at various points if you can. That way the troupe doesn't shun one person out of paranoia, and everyone in the troupe has to be a bit nervous.

For another change of pace, aliens could capture the pack and take them out into space. The pack could break free and escape, but would then have to find their way home. Not the easiest of tasks, but certainly an unexpected challenge for a werewolf game.

Totalitarian Society

In the near future, people live in a totalitarian dystopia. The government watches, monitors, and censors everything. All laws are absolute. It executes anyone who challenges its authority by word or deed. Even the slightest hint of dissatisfaction results in swift punishment.

Werewolves, by their very nature, are subversives, hiding their true nature from the government. Yet, even dystopia is not free of the Veil. Garou use their Crinos forms to evade the authorities. Glass Walkers are especially good at using their Gifts to sabotage the world government.

Caerns exist outside of the closed cities, but packs must risk their lives to free cubs and Kinfolk trapped in the living prisons of the world government. Going in to rescue those who've grown up brainwashed by the state is extremely dangerous. The greatest threat is often the target, whom the government has indoctrinated to believe everything it tells her. Many times the subject of the rescue has set off the alarms, attempting to save herself from kidnappers. A few werewolves have fallen into the hands of state interrogators. Every time this happens, the threat to the remaining caerns grows.

The Get of Fenris want to attack and destroy the world government. As long as the world suffers in the chains of total control, the Weaver's web tightens. The Fenrir believe that war is the only option. The Black Furies, Shadow Lords and Fianna agree with the Fenrir. The Bone Gnawers and the Children of Gaia believe that working to slowly foster seeds of dissent will ultimately destroy the state, but patience is the only answer. The Red Talons just want the humans to stay locked in their cities and out of the wilds. If humans suffer as a result, so be it.

George Orwell's *1984* and Aldous Huxley's *Brave New World* are required reading for this type of world. This setting allows players to explore philosophical and political questions. Where do the rights of individuals fall against the needs of the state? Is a life without freedoms worth living? If the state has trained its agents from birth to serve its needs, is it right to blame them for their actions? Of course, some players won't care. They'll be enjoying themselves too much trying to tear down the world government.

Steam Punk

Imagine werewolves doing battle with steam-powered monstrosities in the Victorian era. Although not a true historical setting, a number of sources exist about the Steam Age. Basically, they all function under the premise that the steam engine has reached its ultimate potential, usually coupled with a touch of magic. The writings of Jules Verne and Edgar Rice Burroughs provide solid source material for this type of setting. Steam Punk settings usually pit the benefits and dangers of science against each other. This is a very easy alternative way to play Werewolf: Wild West. Just add a few Steam Punk conventions to the setting and you're ready to go.

Criminal masterminds, dirigibles, lost worlds filled with dinosaurs, hidden alien races dwelling beneath the world or the waves are all part and parcel of a Steam Punk world. Werewolves have to foil the plots of noblemen intent on taking over the world. Giant steam-powered robots threaten national capitals. Black Spiral Dancers attack caerns and make their getaways in steam driven airships. Oil wells drilled deep into the Earth's crust reveal a lost civilization and its powerful spiritual guardians. Just about any part of the 19th century can be super-charged with the addition of steam.

Keep in mind that technology in this era shouldn't be reliable, even for the villains. Large clanking metallic devices with lots of steam whistling from gears are the rule of the day. Science usually creates more trouble, not less. Action should try to run at a Saturday morning serial type pace, with heroes escaping one death-defying situation to leap into another. Give players a chance to catch their breath, then launch them on the path to adventure again.

It's also a setting for revolution and new ideas. Challenge the status quo, but in a manner that doesn't get you completely thrown out of society. Young members of the European nobility discuss revolution. Inventors propose concepts for devices that could shift the balance of power between nations. With the help of technology, the downtrodden can make themselves downright dangerous.

Leaving Out What You Don't Like

Another way that you can create alternate settings is just to remove anything that you don't like. For example, perhaps you hate crossovers with other World of Darkness games. Remove them. Vampires, mages, and mummies — none of them ever existed in your world. They are all just myths.

You could target a particular tribe. In your world, the Silent Striders could have vanished centuries ago in Egypt. Maybe the Bone Gnawers didn't survive the Black Death. The last of the Silver Fangs committed suicide during the Russian Revolution. Think about the implications of losing any of the tribes. If the Silent Striders didn't exist, who or what opposed the dark powers in Egypt? Have the Glass Walkers filled the niche that the Bone Gnawers held, or are the urban poor and homeless shepherded by wererats instead of Garou? Did the Shadow Lords take over the tribes immediately upon the fall of the Silver Fangs or did they wait a short while out of respect? More seriously, how would the other tribes react to the fall of the Silver Fangs?

Storytellers can also change a tribe. The Black Furies are the traditional leaders of the Garou instead of the Silver Fangs, and suddenly the Garou Nation takes a matriarchal turn. The Fianna join the White Howlers and fall to the Wyrm. The Glass Walkers have completely fallen to the Weaver in the same way that Black Spiral Dancers fell to the Wyrm. The Glass Walkers have reached their limit on technological advances and now work to try to stop humanity from moving any farther forward. The Black Furies allow male werewolves in their ranks. The Red Talons decide that humans are part of nature as well and welcome homid breeds into their ranks. The Silver Fangs prey on other tribes of werewolves, conducting their own small scale War of Rage.

What if the Veil never existed? Hunters would exist in far greater numbers. Caerns would survive in far fewer numbers. Werewolves would have to have a masquerade, much like vampires, if they wanted to survive for long. Players would have to be careful about their characters' actions. How would the tribes find a way to control their rage?

You can change the breeds. What if the metis didn't have deformities? Make the metis stronger than normal werewolves. Give them a few attribute points for free. These super-werewolves could try to replace the Kinfolk, creating a society of pure Garou. How would the other werewolves handle this? Without a reliance on Kinfolk, what kind of check would the metis have to prevent the extremists among them from culling wolves and humans indiscriminately? "We

don't need the others" could well be their attitude. Even if it's not, would the other breeds oppress them out of the fear that they might take over? How would Gaia's spirits react to them?

Take abilities away from werewolves. Garou that regenerated at half the normal rate would live in a much deadlier world. Werewolves may have lost the ability to shift into Glabro or Hispo in the distant past. Werewolves who could only change under the light of the moon would have a real problem during the day. Wolfsbane could actually repel wolves, and belladonna might prevent a werewolf from changing forms. Of course, enough belladonna might just kill them.

Remove Gaia and the Triat. Spirits could just exist without belonging to more powerful spirits out in the Umbra. Werewolves might serve their own individual purposes, maintaining a loose community. Daily survival would replace a shared purpose. Storytellers could also replace Gaia and the Triat with entities of their own creation. Fenris could rule all Garou. Maybe the mythic Greek or Norse gods are real and they command the werewolves. These are just a few ideas that you can develop into different worlds for werewolves. Mythology from all over the world provides most of the source material that we use for the World of Darkness. Take what you find and make it your own.

Add What You Do Like

Conversely, you can always pile more into your games. Create your own tribes, being careful to balance them with the existing ones. A patriarchal tribe could exist to counter the Black Furies. A tribe infected with chaos dedicated to the Wyld is another idea. Old tribes thought extinct could still exist. Have players make up White Howlers, Croatan or Bunyip characters. A new auspice could exist, like the rare children born under a lunar eclipse. Maybe they rage more easily than an Ahroun, but have even less control. Or they could be pariahs, distrusted and disliked by elders who can't easily classify them.

The War of Rage may never have taken place. All of the Changing Breeds could be welcome at caerns, working in harmony with each other. Maybe the united shapeshifters have Gaia's enemies on the run and the majority of Garou have an optimistic worldview.

Werewolves could be immortal. They may never age once they reach maturity, only finding death through battle. Garou could also continue their fight as spirits long after their bodies have fallen.

As Storyteller, you could increase the power level of all werewolves. Detect Wyrm could be a free

Gift that all werewolves possess. Silver may not do any more damage to a Garou than any other kind of metal. Werewolves who regenerated at twice the normal rate would find the world much less of a threat to them.

Historical Variants

As mentioned in the section on historical periods, there's nothing to stop you from playing in a world with an alternate history. Imagine if the Garou lost the War of Rage and werebears were Gaia's primary defenders. Werewolves fighting as an underground resistance against the Nazi world government would make a fun game as well. Even simple changes to history can have far-reaching effects. What if computers were never invented? It's a subtle change to the game, but it makes quite a difference in the modern world.

Nazi Earth

World War II is over and the Axis won. Everyone lives under fascism. Werewolves could be resistance fighters struggling against the Axis tyranny. They could also be more concerned about the Wyrm and the world government may simply be getting in their way. The Nazis could also be servants of the Wyrm. The only opposition to Hitler could come from his former Axis partner, the Japanese. This setting would work well with the Hengeyokai sourcebook and characters.

The Second American Civil War

The Confederacy won the Civil War some time ago. Now, the Union has decided that it can no longer tolerate the division, and its factories have produced enough weapons to have a second try. Disputes over western states have pushed diplomats on both sides too far. If your group likes dealing with a lot of tense moral issues, the threat of a modern civil war will make even the most isolated werewolf pay attention.

Welcome to Mars

The United States wasn't satisfied with being the first country to reach the moon. The space program remained in high gear until the establishment of the first Mars colony. Now, young werewolves travel to Mars in an attempt to open the first caerns and make contact with strange Martian spirits.

The Colonization of Europe

What if the people of North and South America discovered and colonized Europe instead of the other way around? Would we have Incan temples in Spain? How would the Wendigo and Uktena treat their oppressed European brethren?

Getting Stranger

There is no end to the types of strange reasons werewolves could be running around the world, none of which necessarily have anything to do with Gaia. Perhaps werewolves are the result of alien genes mixing with humans, as a precursor to an alien invasion. Maybe you have to be asleep in order to be a werewolf, and you stalk your prey in their dreams. Maybe wolves evolved into intelligent beings and are running the earth, with humans a subjugated race. In the end, as we've stated several times before, do what you enjoy. Make sure you and your friends have a great time exploring all the potential **Werewolf** has to offer. It doesn't really matter if your chronicle conforms to the "official" **Werewolf** world, as long as it works for your troupe.

Crossover

The options to explore in a **Werewolf** chronicle are near endless. Politics on the pack, sept, tribal and even global level. Struggles against the Wyrm, Weaver or even Wyld. Umbral Realms from the immense to the pocket-sized. A near-infinite supporting cast of mortals, Kin, spirits, werewolves, fomori and more.

And yet there's the potential for more — the rest of the World of Darkness, to be precise. The temptation to bring in other Changing Breeds is fairly powerful; and the temptation to loot the other World of Darkness game lines is sometimes even stronger.

The main problem, though, is that these alternate character types and societies don't always blend well with a **Werewolf** game. Not all supernatural types are interested in (or would even believe in) the war against the Wyrm. If the players consort with allies incapable of traveling the Umbra, they might find themselves barred from spirit quests in the interests of fairness.

So you have a few challenges ahead. But if you're reading these words, you're interested in trying anyway, right? More power to you. This section is meant to give you some assistance in wrangling a crossover chronicle into something all your players will enjoy as much as you do. Use these rules as guidelines, adapt them as inspiration, or ignore them completely if you decide something else would work better — you're the boss.

The Fera

"Each of the Fera has — or had — a purpose under Gaia. Some of them seem redundant, some mysterious. I have to confess that the Garou's purpose seems simple, and yet it is the Garou who have developed a complex and overreaching culture. Of course, the other Fera's growth in this regard may have been stunted."

— From the journal of Martin One-Name, Glass Walker Philodox (deceased)

As the name of the game suggests, **Werewolf** is about werewolves. However, other shapeshifters do exist in the World of Darkness, and it would be somewhat hypocritical to publish books about them and then not expect people to want to play them. This section is meant to show the Storytellers how to integrate the Changing Breeds into **Werewolf** games, either as plot hooks or as player characters.

Fera as Storyteller Characters

Fera can work nicely in supporting roles to the pack, either as allies or contacts (even if the pack is unaware of the true nature of the Fera) or as adversaries. They may show up as one-time plot devices (especially as adversaries) or as recurring characters in a chronicle.

Portraying the Fera

Something to consider about using Fera is that, with only a few exceptions, the other Breeds distrust the Garou at best and bitterly hate them at worst. These bad feelings are usually reciprocated. While the Corax and the Nuwisha, as the two Breeds that deal with the Garou but were least affected by the War of Rage, may enjoy the ability to announce themselves to the werewolves and not expect to be met with fang and claw, this goodwill is not at all universal. Many Garou have heard stories of the other Breeds, but those stories are mostly propaganda (from the maligned Fera's perspective, at least) and rarely cast the Breed in a positive light.

When introducing the Fera to a pack of werewolves, stress their strangeness. A Gurahl should not come across as a gentle defender of the wilderness. She should embody the she-bear's rage, a monstrous, snarling beast. The non-mammalian Fera — especially the bizarre Ananasi — resemble Wyrm-monsters in their middle forms, and the Storyteller shouldn't draw too much of a distinction between these creatures and fomori or other beasts that the pack may have encountered. If the pack does not attack right away, but tries to identify the threat (especially by using a Gift such as Scent of the True Form), then the "monster" might be revealed as one of the Changing Breeds. This doesn't mean that everything is suddenly smoothed over, however.

A lone Fera should never stand and fight against a pack of Garou; all of them know this to be suicide. This means that the werespider they surprise during its nightly feeding turns and then dissolves into a mass of tiny spiders, or the Pumonca they meet by chance on the plains calls on a Gift (one the Garou have never seen) and vanishes. The first meeting with a Changing Breed shouldn't involve the Fera and the werewolves sitting down and chatting about what a mistake the War of Rage was. The first meeting should be laden with fear — remember, as far as most of the other Fera know, the Garou are still out for blood (which is not always untrue!).

If the pack asks the elders of their sept for advice about the Fera, they are likely to hear horror stories. See this book's **Legends of the Garou** for the sort of thing elder Garou are likely to say about even the gentle Gurahl. Stories of the Mokolé should focus on huge, slavering dragon-like monsters, not the fact that the werealligators are not meant to be Gaia's warriors, but Her memory. A tale about the Ratkin might feature a brave Garou who faces the hordes of wererats to save his Kinfolk from disease. Remember, too, that many of these legends are oral history, meaning that while they've changed with time, they also are not entirely false.

Fera as Allies

How each of the Fera might fit into a **Werewolf** game is covered below. In general, however, if you plan on letting the pack have an ally of another Changing Breed, consider what the ally is getting out of the deal. Remember: The Garou effectively committed genocide on the other Fera, and while the younger generations of werewolves might be very sorry about the whole thing, that hardly makes the Fera feel comfortable around them. Each of the Breeds, therefore, has found ways to hide from the Garou and further their own ends. If a Corax is going scouting for a pack, he might be doing it simply because it's his job under Gaia — or he might be planning to lead the Garou into a conflict with his own enemies. A Mokolé might consent to use her Mnesis to try and find the answer to a problem the Garou seek, but she may well require an entire quest to prove the pack's good faith.

In general, the hardest part of getting the help of one of the Fera should be getting them to sit down and talk (as discussed above). Even if the Fera trusts the Garou not to suddenly tear her in half, she will *never* lead the Garou to her home (especially true in the case of a Gurahl's Umbral glade or a Mokolé's clutch). Also, unless a Fera's home or Kin are threatened, they will usually not fight alongside the Garou. There are two good reasons for this. First, the

Garou's penchant for bloody Rage is widely known among the other Breeds, and no one wants to be on the same battlefield with a frenzied werewolf. Second, Gaia designed the *Garou* to be her warriors, not the other Breeds. Since the Garou went out of their way to demonstrate how efficient they were at their job, the other Fera have no compulsions to try and outdo them.

Fera as Antagonists

The motivations a Fera might have for working against the Garou are varied. Perhaps the Garou chased a Black Spiral Dancer right towards the Fera. Perhaps the Fera holds a grudge for the War of Rage (this grudge will be ideological for all except the Mokolé, some of whom might actually remember it). Perhaps the Fera doesn't hate the Garou in general, but loathes the pack (or one pack member) for a past slight. On the other hand, the Fera might simply be a sadistic, bloodthirsty monster and want to hurt the pack simply to see them in pain.

The Storyteller should clearly define the reason for the Fera's hatred if she plans to use such a creature as a pack's enemy. Going looking for trouble with the werewolves is not a safe proposition for anyone, and while certain Fera may not care, any action taken against the Garou by the other Breeds damages their already shaky relations.

If the Fera has a personal grudge against the Garou and/or the pack and wishes to see them come to harm, she can lead all sorts of trouble to the Garou's door. She can set up ambushes and lure the werewolves into dangerous situations, perhaps appearing to strike while the pack is busy fighting another foes and then vanishing again before they realize her presence. A truly vicious adversary may stalk the Garou's Kinfolk, perhaps using Animal Attraction to seduce them (imagine the horror of the werewolf who discovers that his Kin is carrying the child of a werespider!).

If the Fera's interests merely run counter to the Garou, however, he is unlikely to take violent action, direct or otherwise, against the pack. The Fera know how difficult werewolves are to kill, and doing so isn't a venture to enter into lightly. If the Garou are simply disrupting the Fera's territory or venturing too close to his home, he may stir up trouble elsewhere, to drag the werewolves away from his turf. If their battles are attracting too much attention from their enemies, the Fera may actually help the pack covertly for a time, but attempt to get the enemies and the Garou to finish each other off, simply to make the area safe again.

Caveats

When using the Fera as Storyteller characters, whether friend or foe, some dangers present themselves. Beware of:

Never Say Never

The reader may notice that reference is made to things that Fera "always" or "never" do. Of course there are exceptions. Of course those exceptions can — and possibly even should — appear in your chronicles. The idea, after all, is that the characters' pack is special in some way; that's why they're the stars of the show. So what if no pack in five centuries has seen — much less befriended — a Gurahl? The pack in *your* chronicle just might be the first.

Just make sure to stress exactly how rare and special an event that is.

• **"Monster of the Week" Syndrome:** During the last story, the characters ran afoul of an angry werebear, recently awakened from hibernation. During this story, the pack finds a newly-Changed Bastet, and must decide what to do with her. Perhaps next story, they will all realize that a raven watches them wherever they go....

Each of the Fera is special and creates its own unique mood. Using one shapeshifter after another cheapens this, and creates the illusion that the world is overpopulated with were-creatures. Of course, if the theme of the chronicle revolves around the various Fera, as shown in the examples in Chapter Three, more frequent meetings with the Fera become part of the mood. Unless this is a major theme of the chronicle, however, beware of bringing in more than one Fera.

• **Familiarity:** The Garou do not teach classes on the other Fera, and even if a Garou's mentor happens to be fairly knowledgeable about them, she certainly isn't going to use the **Mokolé** book as a text for the lesson. The Garou do not know creation legends and general philosophical outlook of each of the Fera, and frankly, the Breeds aren't going to be too keen on enlightening them. Information is power, after all, the Garou have enough already.

Even if the pack befriends another Fera, that shapeshifter should be constantly on guard. She might trust the pack, but not at all trust the other Garou at the sept. She will not teach them Gifts or tell them of her society, beyond some fairly useless (if interesting) tidbits. This isn't a matter of stubbornness (usually); the Fera see it, quite accurately, as a matter of life and death.

• **Fera ex machina:** The Fera have powers and Gifts that the Garou do not, and many of them are quite impressive (even "cool"). This does not mean that the Storyteller is free to let the pack's buddy, who just happens to be a Rank Five Bagheera, show up in *Juddho* form and lay waste to the pack's enemies. A Fera ally of the pack should be treated like any other ally with regards to avoiding *deus ex machina*, if not even more carefully. It pisses players off to have "the Storyteller's pet characters" hog the spotlight, and since Fera attract attention by their very nature, they should be used with caution.

Fera as Characters

If the Storyteller chooses to allow a player to have a non-Garou character in a **Werewolf** game, she should be aware that the inclusion of that character is likely going to be a major theme in the chronicle. A werewolf pack that goes on a quest with a Corax, of course, won't draw as much attention as a (non-Bone Gnawer) pack with a wererat companion. But even in the case of the more "Garou-friendly" breeds, a lot of explanation needs to go into why the pack has a Fera buddy and why the Fera wants to hang out with the wolves in the first place.

Agendas

Each of the Fera, as noted above, has its own concerns and agendas. The Gurahl, for example, are charged with healing and giving succor. This makes a pack that boasts three Ahroun and Griffin as its totem a rather poor choice for a Gurahl character. If a player wishes to play a Fera, the character's concept must give the Fera some reason to associate with werewolves. If the character is a typical member of her breed, then the pack's quest (and totem) should mesh with the Fera's purpose. If the character is some sort of rogue — on the run from her own people, perhaps, and seeking refuge with the Garou — then how does she view her Gaia-given task? Does the Nuwisha who has grown disillusioned and travels with the Garou pack continue to play tricks, or does she simply try to keep the Garou in good spirits?

And then there is the not inconsiderable problem of how the pack's elders view their odd friend. This will largely depend on the dominant tribe(s) of the sept, of course; the Get of Fenris would quite likely welcome a Corax into their midst, but if the kids bring home an Ananasi, the elders will justifiably be horrified. On the other hand, a sept of Glass Walkers might appreciate the knowledge of Weaver-spirits that a werespider could bring to the table, but the raw chaos that accompanies the Ratkin would likely be a cause for much consternation.

Despite what some Garou have been taught, there is no one tribe that relates well to any particular breed as a matter of course. Yes, the Bone Gnawers and the Ratkin share a totem, but if the pack is suddenly attacked by a swarm of rats, simply yelling, "I'm a Bone Gnawer!" isn't likely to get much of a response (other than "Really? We gnaw bones, too. Watch!"). This in mind, the reason for including a Fera in the pack needs to be more than "Well, my character is a Child of Gaia, and they get along with everybody, so we could have a Mokolé who feels secure around our pack." Maybe the Fera's prelude could coincide with one of the characters', or perhaps the Fera lends a hand on a whim during the pack's first mission. Whatever the reason, the relationship between the characters needs to be well thought-out; Garou do not mingle with the other Fera "just because."

Outside the Pack

Some Fera — Garou, Rokea, and Ratkin, for example — travel in groups, complete with totems. The rest are solitary beasts. Besides the obvious difficulty this presents for the loner Fera who must fight instinct to adventure with a pack of Garou, there are other issues as well.

One of the main problems this causes is that it tends to make gathering Renown difficult. The pack may praise the Fera at Garou moots, but Renown granted by the Garou is recognized minimally or not at all by the Fera's own kind. Worse yet, some breeds may actually lose Renown by associating too closely with the werewolves (notably the Mokolé and the Bastet). While Breeds such as Ananasi and Corax can report to their kind fairly easily and thus gain Renown, the often-bloody exploits of the Garou may not garner them the Renown they need to rise in rank (of course, it's all in how one tells the story).

Another problem is that of totem. As mentioned above, the pack's totem must at least approve of the Fera's presence, but unless something truly extraordinary happens, the Fera isn't going to receive the totem's benefits (if a Ratkin journeys with a pack that follows Rat, or some similar situation, this may change, of course). This poses several difficulties for the Fera besides not getting the same bonuses that the werewolves get from the totem. For one thing, the Fera cannot act in concert with the pack during combat. The Fera is exempt from pack initiative and any pack maneuvers involving her receive a +2 difficulty. However, this is not the worst of it.

Without the blessing and acceptance of a totem, the Fera is forever an outsider. The werewolves in the pack are bonded mystically, and therefore share a connection that transcends words and feelings. Even if the Garou aren't exactly best friends, they understand each other and are ready to leap to each other's aid at a moment's notice. Longtime packmates may finish each other's sentences or make inside jokes (just like any group of longtime associates) — but no matter how long the Fera has been traveling with the pack, he is always the odd man out. For the solitary breeds, this may prove little more than an annoyance, although a human-born shapeshifter might feel excluded. For the social breeds, however, it can be torture. A betweener Rokea who befriends a pack of werewolves may enjoy their company, but he will never truly fit in, regardless of how much he learns of werewolf culture. Over time, this can lead the Fera into depression, restlessness, and resentment.

Bending the Barriers

It's going to be inevitable. Sooner or later, a player will ask you if he can play a Garou/Bastet metis hybrid with the powers and Gifts of both, or another player may try to learn the upper-level powers of the Nagah to increase his ass-kicking quotient, or some similar situation will arise. The following advice is the official way that such things are addressed in the World of Darkness. You may decide differently; that's fine. Just remember that these rules are meant to keep each Changing Breed special, rather than letting homogenous blends of all the coolest powers rule the day. If you don't mind changing that principle, go right ahead. Either way, here you go.

Gifts and Lore

The lore of the Changing Breeds is full of tales about sharing and stealing Gifts and rites; the Gurahl claim to have taught the Garou rites of accord, the Bastet claim to have stolen Gifts from nearly everyone, and so on. Clearly, this kind of "cultural exchange" seems likely to have happened before. And it's still possible — with a few restrictions.

First, the Gift or rite in question cannot rely on the unique capabilities of its parent Changing Breed. A Garou could no more learn the Ananasi Gift of Spinnerets (which requires literal spinnerets) than could an Ananasi learn Song of the Dire (which requires a Hispo form capable of howling). Never let pure rules-lawyering override common sense.

Second, if the Gift is something that both species (or tribes) can use at varying ranks, the student can learn it only at the level he could normally acquire it. A werewolf must learn Catfeet at Level Three, whether he has a Bastet teacher or not. The varying levels of some commonly shared Gifts represent a Changing Breed's innate knack for some tricks — and this knack can't be taught. Nuwisha will always be better than Bastet or Mokolé at Umbral travel, and that is that.

Third, the Gift in question must be no higher than Level Three. Level Four and Five Gifts are the exclusive property of their Changing Breed. (Some Storytellers may also choose to extend this rule to learning Gifts across tribal barriers; it does seem silly for a Get of Fenris to be able to learn Call the Cannibal Spirit, no matter the circumstances.) Similarly, any rites that strike the Storyteller as completely exclusive to one type of shapeshifter — such as the Rite of the Birthing Plague — are off-limits.

Finally, you can forbid players to learn *any* Gift or rite outside their Changing Breed. It's up to you to determine which tricks can be shared and which can't — and your word goes. Period.

Cross-Breeding

Obviously, each Changing Breed can take human form, and thus representatives from any two Breeds are capable of mating. So the question is: Can they produce shapeshifter offspring? Specifically, hybrids.

The answer is generally no — two different shapeshifters can produce offspring, but the chances of breeding true to either Breed are greatly reduced. The official reasoning runs as follows.

Shapeshifter status is not solely genetic in nature; in fact, genetics take a back seat to the spirit part of the equation. Each werebeast is half mortal, half spirit; whether the spirit half comes from heritage, a Fetish Egg or the Birthing Plague is irrelevant. The spirit nature of a shapeshifter is unquestionable — and not easily diluted.

Generally speaking, if two shapeshifters of different Breeds conceive a child, the child has a 5 percent chance to be a shapeshifter of the father's kind, a 5 percent chance to be a shapeshifter of the mother's kind, and an 90 percent chance to be a normal Kin to either. If the mother is animal-born (a lupus, feline, etc.), however, any children will be normal Kin to her Changing Breed or shapeshifters like herself — a lupus cannot give birth to a Khan or to tiger cubs, or even to wolves that are Khan Kinfolk. She may only give birth to wolf cubs, and there's a 5% chance at best that one of them will be Garou. The reduced chance for true-bred children is one of the reasons that the various shapeshifter races consider cross-Breed matings dishonorable at best, insulting at worst. The werewolf who takes a Fera for a mate instead of a Garou Kin may not be betraying his race, but he's certainly ignoring an important duty. Blood feuds have broken out over less.

In no case can a shapeshifter be of two separate Changing Breeds; a Garou with Bastet blood is simply Kin to the Bastet and nothing more. There isn't room for two shapeshifter souls in one body. It also follows that the Ratkin Birthing Plague can't work on other shapeshifters; nor can the Rite of the Fetish Egg. Gaia requires only one duty from each of Her children.

And in case it need be said, Pure Breed is utterly diluted by such radical crossbreeding. If a Silver Fang with Pure Breed 5 takes a Bagheera who also has Pure Breed 5 for a mate, any children who breed true have no chance at so much as a dot of Pure Breed whatsoever. The purity is lost.

Thematic Integration

Each of the Changing Breeds — Garou included — have certain thematic elements about them. To ignore these elements is to disrespect the breeds. Therefore, when including a Fera in a **Werewolf** game, the Storyteller would benefit by knowing each species' purpose as granted by Gaia, as well as its basic flavor.

Ajaba

The werehyenas served a noble purpose, once. They made sure that sick and weak animals (and humans) did not die slow, lingering deaths under the African sun. Instead, they tore these unfortunates to shreds. Naturally, humans didn't often see the good that the Ajaba did. Neither, unfortunately, did the Bastet.

Playing a "Unique" Character

"I wanna be just like all the different people."
— King Missile, "It's Saturday"

As discussed in Chapter Three, all characters are unique. A player who wants to play one of the Fera simply so he can stand apart from the rest of the pack is probably a) trying to sponge extra attention from the Storyteller and b) not considering how difficult doing so will really be.

The Fera are part of the world of **Werewolf**. That does not mean, however, that the Storyteller must allow them as characters, especially without a strong concept. Furthermore, the desire to play a weirdo can be contagious. One player says, "I want to play a Corax!" And a moment later, you've got five players who want to play various Fera, but no one who wants to play one of the game's title characters.

The best thing to do if you don't want to host such one-upmanship is make it clear from the beginning that the game is **Werewolf** and the characters will be a pack of *werewolves*. Offer to aid any player who has trouble thinking of a unique concept. If the player is just looking for a character he feels is unique and special, that's fine. Offer to tie his character's back-story into the plot of the chronicle somehow, so that the player feels that his character is indispensable to the chronicle (all of the characters should be, of course). A player who just wants to be different will usually go along with that wisdom.

A player who is absolutely in love with a given Changing Breed, however, will attempt to plead with the Storyteller. She will arrange her concept, probably with the help and suggestions of other players, so that it makes some sense for her Fera character to be hanging out with Garou. If you find such a player — one who understands the ramifications of playing a Fera and is willing to help you make the character fit into the chronicle — you can probably allow her to play her chosen character type. If nothing else, it makes for an interesting challenge for the Storyteller....

The werecats (the Simba especially) never got on well with the Ajaba, and in 1984, the Simba lord Black Tooth led an assault on the Hyena King's home near Mount Kilimanjaro and slaughtered all present. Only a handful of survivors lived to preserve the line. Now, years later, as Black Tooth's corpse becomes fodder for worms, the Ajaba feel a sense of hope.

Themes: The werewolves may not have much left, but the Ajaba have *nothing*. They hate the Bastet with a passion that is truly frightening, and their Rage is, for the most part, righteous. However, since the slaughter at the Hyena King's court, some have searched for — and found — allies in strange places. Some Ajaba packs include Black Spiral Dancers, and a large number of werehyenas have given themselves over to the Wyrm in exchange for some protection. Their themes, therefore, include Rage, revenge, redemption, and corruption.

Ananasi

The Ananasi do not claim Gaia as their mother. According to the werespiders, Queen Ananasa — herself a creation of the Weaver — gave birth to them and charged them with their purpose. Their purpose is simply to love and obey their Queen.

All Ananasi must obey when given orders from Ananasa, but in lieu of direct orders, they do as they wish. The werespiders each follow one aspect of the Triat, and so some Ananasi emulate the Wyld, some the Weaver, and some the Wyrm (it bears noting, however, that the spider-folk try to emulate what each of the Triat should ideally be, rather than what they are). Most Ananasi are loners, watching and using others to their pleasure. Some are vicious predators, all are blood-drinkers. Ananasi are detached if not simply cold. Emotion — including loyalty — is rather foreign to them.

Themes: The Ananasi were never exactly friends with the other Fera and Garou (or "Ovid" as the werespiders call them), so they were already accustomed to hiding when the Garou began killing the others. As such, they don't typically strive for revenge. However, the wide variety of philosophies that they present (each Ananasi falls not only under one of the Triat's auspice but adopts a Faction within that auspice) makes for an equally wide variety of thematic possibilities. Some more general Ananasi themes include manipulation, harsh lessons, and horror (Ananasi are hard to beat for sheer scariness).

Bastet

The nine tribes of werecats have been the Garou's rivals for time immemorial. Meant to be the "Eyes of Gaia," the Bastet scour the globe ferreting out secrets of one type or another. It would be hard to find a group of Fera that resent the Garou more.

Each of the nine tribes has had its own trials and tribulations in recent years, and space precludes discussing all of them here. However, the death of the Simba king Black Tooth and the peace agreement between Africa's Fera (called the Ahadi) has made the Bastet in other lands take notice. While the Garou and the Bastet might never be friends, perhaps they could agree to disagree…

Themes: Any cooperation between werewolf and werecat is going to be uneasy. It isn't just the old "cats and dogs" joke, either. The two species have never been comfortable with each other — each sees the other as a competing predator and a threat to territory. Possible themes using the Bastet include secrets, compromise, competition, ancient stories, seduction (possibly seduction based on power instead of lust), curiosity, and war.

Corax

The wereravens also claim to fact-finders for Gaia, after a fashion, and they frankly seem to be more generous with their secrets than do the Bastet. They share history with several tribes of Garou, and of all the Changing Breeds, they are one most likely to be welcome among werewolves.

Corax are not warriors, however, and don't pretend to be. A wereraven who travels with a pack of Garou had best be prepared for danger. While seeing a battle firsthand may yield some very intriguing secrets, they do no good if the messenger doesn't live to relate them.

Themes: Stories involving Corax might use themes of secrets (but of a more temporal, immediately useful nature than Bastet secrets), urgency, Pandora's box, or hope.

Gurahl

By most accounts, the War of Rage began because the Gurahl would not share their most potent healing Gifts with the Garou. They saw the werewolves as immature and didn't feel they'd use the Gifts — which included the ability to raise the dead — in the proper manner. Regardless of exactly how it started, the werebears were decimated in the War, and most of the survivors went into hibernation.

Now, many of them are waking up and some new cubs have begun to emerge. It is still a desperate time, but with Gaia in such dire straits, even the anti-Gurahl legends of years past don't always convince young Garou that the werebears deserved what was inflicted upon them.

Themes: If any breed is built to forgive, it's the Gurahl. Themes such as forgiveness, penance, renewal, and succor are appropriate to stories involving werebears.

Kitsune

The mysterious werefoxes are rarely encountered outside of the Far East, and when they are, it is to act as emissaries from the Beast Courts. See Chapter One for thematic information on the hengeyokai.

Mokolé

Designed to be Gaia's memory, the Mokolé are the oldest of the Changing Breeds. Many of them remember events from centuries past; some can remember the time of the great Dinosaur Kings. What all remember vividly, however, are the days when the Garou would smash their eggs and murder their hatchlings. The Mokolé do not forget, and rarely forgive.

While relations have improved between the Dragon Folk and the werewolves in some places, most Mokolé still think of Garou as "egg smashers", and most Garou still think of Mokolé as Wyrm-creatures.

Themes: Stories involving Mokolé might be stories of war, remembrance, justice, and truce.

Nagah

The wereserpents enforce Gaia's laws, and therefore act as her judges and executioners. Peerless assassins, they judge the other Changing Breeds and slay those found wanting. And, they do all of this in utmost secrecy — even the Corax believe them to be dead.

Themes: Any story involving the Nagah should involve a theme of paranoia. The pack should never know exactly what they face (if they do find out, it only gives the Nagah more incentive to hunt them down). Other themes include judgment (and punishment), corruption, and nobility (as the legends paint the Nagah as forthright and peaceful).

Nuwisha

The Garou might dismiss the werecoyotes are immature pranksters, but the truth is somewhat more complicated. The Nuwisha are meant to prank others, yes, but the reason is not simply to giggle about it later, but to teach a lesson. If that lesson must be applied in the target's next life, so be it. In many Native American legends, Coyote is not a gentle trickster, and those who cross him know his wrath.

Like the Corax, the Nuwisha have some hope for the Garou. Unlike their winged brethren, however, they don't work tenaciously at trying to help the werewolves. Instead, they travel the world, spreading their own brand of chaos, and eventually leave the Earth for the Umbra.

Themes: Laughter is a common Nuwisha theme, of course, but it is a derisive laughter, aimed at the weak and foolish. Other themes include poetic justice (see "Urban Legends" in Chapter Three), instruction and riddles.

Ratkin

The wererats look ahead the Apocalypse and crave the chaos it brings. Many of the rats are mad with Rage, others are simply mad. They have no

love and no trust for the Garou — the werewolves hunted them down and slaughtered them for doing their Gaia-given task. Now, rats flourish everywhere, while growing numbers of humans force wolves to extinction. The irony is not lost on the Ratkin. The Ratkin are also wholly devoted the Wyld, and while humans built their cities up to protect them from the chaos of the world, the rats (and the wererats) are always there, ready to show the humans that chaos isn't so far from home at all.

Themes: Ratkin themes include madness, retribution, chaos, violence, terrorism, and disease.

Rokea

The Garou are unlikely to encounter weresharks, unless they travel by sea or frequent the coasts. Even then, the Rokea keep to themselves. Theirs is a simple task — survive — and all they have heard about the Garou indicates that associating with the werewolves is not conducive to survival.

Even so, the Rokea war on each other. Those that choose to live on land are hunted by their sea-dwelling brothers, and sometimes the Garou find themselves witness to (or caught in the middle of) such a hunt. The Rokea are not mindless brutes any more than the Garou, but they can certainly appear so.

Themes: Appropriate themes for stories involving the weresharks include fear, culture clash, and frenzy. A less definable, but very appropriate theme, is the "other" — Rokea have a mindset completely different from humans (or indeed any land-dweller). The almost alien differences between Rokea and Garou can make for exciting stories when the two meet.

The Whole World of Darkness

Although integrating Fera into a crossover chronicle can be tricky, blending other game lines into a **Werewolf** game can be downright headache-inducing. Each of the World of Darkness game lines is designed, mechanics and all, to encourage and reflect a different theme, from "personal horror" to "modern fantasy" — resulting in mechanics that vary from system to system. The Humanity so important to **Vampire**'s theme of psychological degradation is utterly absent in **Werewolf**, where personal degeneration is the least of the Garou's worries.

The main trick, then, is to design a crossover chronicle to your specifications from the very beginning. If you decide that you want an electric, balls-to-the-wall, dynamic **Werewolf/Mage** chronicle, you'll

want to downplay the more introspective elements of **Mage**. If you want a crossover with **Changeling** to be a light-hearted departure from the usual **Werewolf** fatalism, you may want to reduce the chances of a Garou frenzying and ripping his friends limb from limb. Ask yourself what you want to accomplish, and then customize the chronicle's focus to that end.

The most important thing is to be flexible; some truly insane situations may arise, and you don't want to be reliant on the rules text when they do. In particular, it's good to be able to make thematic decisions quickly, when your players inevitably confront you with strange conflicts between game line tropes. It's also important to be consistent; once you've chosen the general pattern by which you want things to work, you'll just confuse and annoy your players by making rulings that depart from this pattern.

Just remember that crossover chronicles are by nature strange beasts, and none of the games involved can be expected to work exactly as you'd normally expect them to. Don't let your players browbeat you with cries of "But it doesn't normally work like that!" — vampires created with **Vampire: The Masquerade** rules don't normally slug it out with (or work side by side with) full-fledged Garou from **Werewolf: The Apocalypse**, either. All bets are off — the chronicle is in your hands, not the books'. As it should be.

General Guidelines

The crossover guidelines here are generally meant to represent werewolves encountering other supernaturals; there simply isn't room to address all the other Changing Breeds. Use these guidelines as a framework for similar judgements.

Generally speaking, when a power calls for a Rage or Gnosis roll to resist, a target without Rage or Gnosis is out of luck. If the Storyteller deems that a subject should have some resistance to a power of that nature, he may call for a roll on an appropriate Virtue or similar trait (such as substituting Courage for Rage). Gifts that use the target's Rage or Gnosis as a difficulty should generally have the default difficulty of 6.

Non-shapeshifters cannot activate fetishes, with a very few exceptions. A klaive in a vampire's hands is simply an awkwardly large silver dagger, for instance; and a fang dagger will do only lethal damage in the hands of a non-shapeshifter. Mages may use their Spirit sphere to activate fetishes, but generally no other entity can do so.

Other supernatural creatures are of course immune to the Delirium; their nature prevents them from feeling the fear ordinary humans do when looking at a Crinos werewolf.

Relative Power Levels

Sometimes creatures will use powers that contradict each other; a werewolf will use a Gift to detect his enemies, while a vampire uses a Discipline to remain hidden. Although it may be tempting to compare the relative power levels of the two powers in question and rule "higher level wins," this can be often misleading. For example, a thin-blooded young Leech who sank all his freebie points into gaining five dots in a Discipline would therefore be able to overcome the mighty Rank Four Garou who has been fighting vampires — and winning — for over a decade. Generally it's fairer to rule that the higher level power has a chance at overcoming the lower-level one, and assign a resisted roll. Feel free to adjust the difficulty for the two participants if you feel the power levels of the two clashing powers don't accurately represent the skills of the two contestants. It's your chronicle.

Vampires

It's rare that a **Vampire/Werewolf** crossover turns anything but violent; both sides have long memories, and are weaned on tales of treachery and murder from the other side. But it's this ancestral war that makes a crossover between the two games so interesting in the first place; after all, the conflicts and twists create themselves.

Vampires are considered innately Wyrm-tainted; the power that animates them is spiritually akin to that of the Wyrm. If the Leech in question has a Humanity score of 7 or more, the taint is not detectable to Sense Wyrm; Paths of Enlightenment, however, cannot mask Wyrm-taint no matter the rating. A Cainite on a Path is embracing his vampiric nature, not resisting it. This Wyrm-taint cannot be removed in the usual fashion, as it is literally part of the vampire; a Rite of Cleansing or similar remedy will cause a vampire great pain, but cannot remove its taint. Any vampire with detectable Wyrm-taint is considered a Wyrm-creature for the purposes of Gifts and other powers that specifically target such.

Shapeshifters are not considered mortals for the purposes of most powers. They may, for instance, roll Willpower to resist the Kiss. Most shapeshifters are considered to have a blood pool of 20 (25 in Crinos or similarly larger forms); this is thanks to the potency of their blood, not an excess quantity. Storytellers may adjust this figure up or down for larger or smaller forms of various shapeshifters; a Ratkin in Rodens form should have a significantly smaller blood pool, for instance.

Werewolves are allergic to vampiric vitae, and are more difficult to ghoul or blood bond. Only a few can ingest the stuff without violently vomiting it back up. If you like, you may call for a Gnosis roll, difficulty 3, the first time a werewolf tastes vampire blood. If the roll succeeds, the Garou in question is among those allergic to the stuff; if it fails or botches, the werewolf has a tolerance for vitae.

Disciplines and Gifts

The following are guidelines to resolve the most common conflicts that might arise; use these as the basis for resolving disputes based on more esoteric powers. As a rule, Disciplines that target an opponent's Virtue use the werewolf's Willpower instead.

• **Animalism** powers treat Garou in Lupus form as if they were werewolves, not ordinary animals; no Animalism power that specifically affects only animals will have any effect on a shapeshifter of any breed. The only difference is communication; Feral Whispers would allow a vampire to communicate with werewolves using wolf-speech. Powers that affect a werewolf's Beast function normally.

• **Auspex** powers can be used to pierce Gifts of stealth and the like. The Psychic Projection power is somewhat problematic, as it doesn't presume a multi-layered Umbra. For convenience's sake, presume that the "astral plane" the vampire accesses is the Shadowlands, the "Penumbra" of the Dark Umbra.

• **Chimerstry** illusions must be carefully crafted to affect a Garou's heightened senses; assume that the werewolf gains an automatic attempt to "prove" the illusion's falsehood (**Vampire**, pg. 154) unless the vampire possesses Heightened Senses himself, and can accurately construct the extra layers of scent and other careful details.

• The **Dominate** power of Possession is not as effective on werewolves, who are not truly mortal; if a werewolf target achieves three successes more than the vampire on the resisted roll, the attempt is broken. If the werewolf achieves five successes before breaking the attempt, he becomes immune to Dominate attempts from that vampire as if the vampire had botched.

• **Obfuscate** does not reach into the Penumbra; a werewolf who peeks from the Penumbra will see a vampire in its true form, not as it wishes to be seen. (This information is tucked away in this book for a reason! Don't let your players abuse this privilege, sneaky gits that they are.)

• A Garou is at -1 difficulty on frenzy rolls when **Obtenebration** powers are active nearby; the Discipline contacts the stuff of the Abyss, which sets Garou on edge.

• Shapeshifters may soak the damage inflicted by the **Protean** power Feral Claws. Their natural ability to soak aggravated damage is considered "a power such as Fortitude."

• The **Thaumaturgy** power Theft of Vitae inflicts one health level of lethal damage on the Garou for every two blood points stolen. Cauldron of Blood inflicts one level of aggravated damage on a werewolf for every two blood points boiled.

• Garou heal **Vicissitude** alterations as if they were aggravated damage.

• No Gift can restore a vampire's lost health levels; healing Gifts such as **Mother's Touch** do not work on the undead, and vampires are not inanimate objects (and hence not subject to **Reshape Object** or the like).

• **Resist Toxin** cannot prevent ghouling, although it gives a Garou four extra dice to soak the effects of Disciplines such as Quietus that inflict damage through supernaturally "poisonous" blood or other substances.

• The Silver Fang Gift: **Mindblock** works against Presence and Dominate as direct mental attacks, and Obfuscate as a "more insidious psychic assault."

Abominations

Occasionally some foolish Leech tries to make a pet of a Garou, usually by means of the Embrace. Because almost all werewolves are violently allergic to vitae, they are accordingly hard to ghoul. By the grace of Gaia, they are just as difficult to Embrace: Most werewolves die upon the attempt. Sadly, the Embrace works in a few rare, rare instances — and the miserable results are the rightly named Abominations.

Vampiric werewolves are literally things that should not be. Shapeshifters are the purest form of primal life on the face of the planet — vampirism is living death. The Embrace disconnects Garou from the world's soul, their very reason for existing. As a result, the leading cause of Final Death among the dozen or so Abominations that exist at any given time is suicide. An Embraced Garou has lost far, far more than the average once-mortal childe.

Abominations are created in mostly the same manner as all vampires, save that even the most depraved Black Spiral Dancer isn't inclined to sacrifice willingly his higher spiritual being for the powers of the grave. Virtually all Abominations were taken prisoner as living beings, then Embraced to enslave them to their sires.

Garou receive one final chance to escape the living death; upon the Embrace, the Garou makes a reflexive (and instinctive) Gnosis roll, difficulty 6, to die quietly. If the roll succeeds, he dies without pain and his spirit travels to its destined place. If the roll fails, he dies in torturous agony, but his spirit is free. If the roll botches, the Garou becomes an Abomination and cannot hope ever to see his Tribal Homeland. No Discipline, Gift, magic or any other sort of power short of direct intervention by a Celestine can affect this roll, save one — the werewolf can spend a Willpower point to gain an automatic success as usual (and is almost certain to do so).

A newly Embraced Abomination takes on the clan of his sire, learns three dots of clan Disciplines and gains the clan weakness as does any other neonate. He may spend blood points to increase his Attributes or heal himself like any other vampire.

The advantages of the Embrace end there.

Becoming an Abomination results in the immediate loss of two permanent points of Glory, three permanent Honor and three permanent Wisdom. The Embrace usually causes even mighty Garou elders to fall at least two places in rank; indeed, a newly-turned Abomination can even fall below Rank One. Unless the werewolf was previously a Black Spiral Dancer, she cannot gain Renown or rise in rank again. Only the depraved Dancers acknowledge their undead relatives, and even then the Dancer gains only one-quarter of the standard Renown awards for her deeds. Abominations also cannot spend experience to raise their Gnosis Trait.

Upon death, the Garou's connection with the spiritual whole of Gaia is irreparably severed. This loss means that Abominations cannot regenerate their wounds as do Garou; Abominations may heal themselves only by spending Blood Points.

This severing from the wellspring of life also has severe repercussions on the Abomination's relationship with the spirit world. Although Abominations retain knowledge of the Gifts and rites they possessed before their Embrace, they cannot make any rites other than Wyrm-rites work; only the most corrupt spirits ever answer a call made by a dead thing. Abominations also cannot learn new Gifts from any spirits other than Banes, and these spirits are spiteful, devious teachers. At the time of the Embrace (or, more precisely, of death), any dedicated items or attuned fetishes lose their connection to the once-Garou. Gaian spirits, even those bound in fetishes, chafe at the presence of the undead. To attune himself to a Gaian fetish after the Embrace, the Abomination may still roll Gnosis as usual — but at difficulty 10, and a botch results in the Abomination losing a permanent Gnosis point.

Abominations may not spend blood points for any purpose in the same turn that they spend Gnosis, make Gnosis rolls, spend Rage or make Rage rolls. Rage, Gnosis and vitae all interfere with one another's use, and an undead Garou can draw on only one of the three at any given time. Abominations have blood pools according to their Generation, as usual — their doubly potent Garou blood was drained during the Embrace, and they must make do with normal vitae.

Abominations exist in a state of perpetual Harano; *every scene*, an Abomination must spend a Willpower point to spend the scene with his dice pools at full. If it will not or cannot do so, its dice pools are halved for the scene. What's more, the spiritless Abominations may not spend Willpower points to gain automatic successes on any dice rolls.

Having been something other than human, Abominations don't use Humanity as a system of morality. They have a far greater stake at risk — their Gnosis. It is the only thing keeping them from acting on the vile impulses that grow within them in undeath: not natural urges, but seeds planted by the Wyrm during their Embrace. An Abomination's Gnosis Trait determines how soundly it sleeps during the day and in most cases acts as Humanity would. (Of course, the Abomination still checks for frenzy by rolling Rage.)

Whenever an Abomination transgresses against the ways of the Gaian Garou, whether deliberately or unconsciously (such as in a frenzy), it risks degeneration. The higher the Abomination's Gnosis, the more likely that even a minor transgression can tear more of his spirit from him. This is true even for Black Spiral Dancers — their usual customs and tactics are a sure road to degeneration. The chart below is a rough guide to what actions force an Abomination to check for Gnosis loss. If the vampiric Garou takes an action that requires a check, it rolls Gnosis, difficulty 7 (with modifiers at the Storyteller's discretion — particularly callous deeds might make degeneration much easier). Failure means that it loses a point of Gnosis *irrevocably*. A botch grants the hapless creature a Derangement. When all the Abomination's Gnosis is gone, it can no longer step sideways or use *any* Gifts or fetishes.

There is only one way to prevent this degeneration — the Abomination can fully offer what's left of its soul to the Wyrm (more accurately, a powerful intermediary thereof, such as a Maeljin Incarna). After making this black pact, the Abomination becomes a Storyteller-controlled character. Its Gnosis is no longer at risk; the Wyrm sees to fueling its spiritual energy. However, the Abomination no longer has any free will whatsoever; every action it takes is at the direction of its patron.

Other Changing Breeds are, if anything, even less suited to vampiric life. A Bastet, for example, begins losing permanent Gnosis, one per moon upon the Embrace and can never recover her loss. Eventually, the undead cat is cut off from the spirit world entirely, unable to do so much as activate Gifts. Nuwisha, by comparison, cannot undergo the Embrace — indi-

Gnosis	Minimum Wrongdoing for Gnosis Check
10	Accidentally breaking the Litany
9	Purposefully breaking the Litany; refusing a rightful challenge; cannibalism (drinking the blood of humans or wolves)
8	Refusing to acknowledge loss of a challenge (lack of instinct); teaching Garou lore to Wyrm minions (including vampires)
7	Unjustly killing a Garou; using vampiric mind-control powers (Dominate, Presence) against a Garou; betraying a Garou to Wyrm minions
6	Trafficking with or binding spirits to evil purposes
5	Destroying a natural place (harming Gaia); causing a Blight to grow or fester
4	Allying with Wyrm minions (including vampires)
3	Cannibalism (drinking Garou blood); sadism and perversion (Black Spiral virtues)
2	Warring against any of the tribes
1	Destroying or helping destroy a caern

viduals who try to force vampirism on the coyotes find that the Nuwisha die quietly, one and all. Mokolé and Corax have it even worse, with their ties to the sun — both die the Final Death within one day of the Embrace, their loss of connection with Helios killing them irrevocably by the next sunset. Unfortunately for everyone around him (including the vampire parent), a Mokolé Abomination spends the rest of his existence in a brutal, mindless frenzy, which almost always results in the would-be sire ending up as so much reddish goo spread across the ground. Thankfully, all shapeshifters at least receive the standard Gnosis roll to avoid the Embrace and die quietly.

Mages

In strictest **Werewolf** cosmology, reality is not consensual; it is animistic. The spirit world reflects the physical, and can influence it as well, but reality itself is not subject to being molded by a sufficient force of belief. In particular, humanity is not the center of the universe — they are a very influential species, but not the reason reality is what it is. This can do some serious thematic damage to the **Mage** elements of a crossover, and is one of the reasons that Mage and **Werewolf** don't play together as well as some might assume. But on a technical level, very little is changed. Whether Paradox is caused by the Weaver's rigid attempts to keep reality constant or by a cosmic level of disbelief

doesn't really matter when it comes to determining whether the dice system works the same or not.

Although shapeshifters are not as hostile toward mages as they are toward vampires (as a general rule, at least), there's still millennia of bad blood between the two groups. Allowing a mage, even a Kinfolk mage who's one Garou's sister and another's wife, into a caern is a violation of the Litany. Werewolves are quite aware that *something* reacts poorly to mages using their powers, and the common interpretation is that a mage isn't intended to have that power in the first place. This makes relationships difficult — but not impossible.

The Umbra

Werewolves do not take any notice of the Avatar Storm; whatever trait mages possess that puts them at risk, the werewolves don't have it. They step sideways as normal.

Outer space has a physical presence in **Werewolf**; the Gauntlet is likely no higher than 1, but outer space and the Umbra are not one and the same.

The **Mage** concept of the "Bygone" does not apply in **Werewolf**; the existence of freakish monsters such as Thunderwyrms and Vhujunka (the morbidly curious are directed to the Book of the Wyrm) seems to indicate that monsters can exist quite nicely in the face of human disbelief. Most fantastic "beasts of legend" translate well into spirits, perhaps with the Materialize Charm.

Damage

Most of the usual ways of creating aggravated damage — fire, Prime-fueled effects, and so on — work just as well against werewolves as they normally would. Most effects that would involve conjuring silver are vulgar, and the silver must be genuinely pure to have any effect on the Garou; alloys and trace amounts are little more than an irritation.

Werewolves' half-spirit nature gives them a measure of protection against some magic; in particular, Life effects will not affect a werewolf unless paired with an equal amount of Spirit.

For their part, werewolves have little difficulty causing aggravated damage to mages.

Countermagic

Magi may use countermagic to defend themselves against Gifts or fetish powers that are directly targeted at them. This is usually a matter of Spirit, although you may choose to allow other Spheres to cancel certain other effects, such as using Mind to counter the Gift: Roll Over. The Arete roll uses the opposing Garou's Rank + 3 as a difficulty number; each success counters one of the werewolf's successes.

You may choose to allow a mage to use countermagic against Gifts that aren't targeted directly at her, so long as she has sufficient knowledge of Spirit or other Spheres to do so. The difficulty to use countermagic against a rite is always 8; the rite is empowered not by the werewolf ritemaster, but by the spirits he invokes.

A few Garou Gifts can be used as countermagic against a mage's effects; for instance, Exorcism may be used to counter Spirit magic. Such efforts are entirely at the Storyteller's discretion, and are not as effective as a mage's countermagic would be; the werewolf removes one of the mage's successes for every *two* successes he scores on his "countermagic" roll.

Shapeshifters and True Magic

The Changing Breeds are, one and all, incapable of using True Magic as mages know it. Since shapechangers are all born with shapechanger spirits, their half-spirit nature, even before the First Change, makes them Awakened beings from birth. They don't possess individual Avatars as mages know them. Instead, they tap into the wellspring of Gaia's blessings to work their own miracles — "static magic," as mages define it. Sphere magic is the province of humans alone; the Changing Breeds are given gifts of a different nature.

Some rare shapeshifters are able to learn certain paths of hedge magic, Sphere magic's poor cousin. However, it is hardly common practice; when all's said and done, the shapeshifters' Gifts and rites are at least as potent, if not more so. Only the most curious or completist of the Changing Breeds feel the need to learn such human wizardry.

Creating New Shapeshifters

Mages often like to claim that they can do anything given time, and some players like to try proving it by "fixing" the Garou's "problem" with breeding true. As the argument runs, one mage could make sure that the Garou breed true almost all the time.

It isn't as easy as that.

The fashion in which shapeshifters propagate their own kind has nothing to do with genetics or, apparently, evolution. Trying to beat the odds and ensure that a child is born Garou is a very dangerous form of "playing Gaia." Theoretically (and it would take something along the lines of Occult 6 to piece this together), ensuring that a cub is born Garou would require the ability to find wherever it is that the spirit half of a newborn shapeshifter comes from (and Garou theorize it's Gaia Herself), slice off an appropriate amount, and bind it perfectly to the child at the *exact moment of conception*. Even the so-called demigod status of an Archmage is probably insufficient for such

an exacting operation, and it's damn unlikely the Garou would be willing to let them try.

A more reasonable approach would involve using Entropy to mess with the "odds" of conceiving a true Garou rather than Kin. A generous Storyteller might allow each success on the roll increase the odds of breeding true by 1%, (an extended roll is not possible). However, the mage would have to be present for conception, and most shapeshifters are sufficiently protective of their Kin and young to remove a mage's arm just for looking funny at the honeymoon suite. Assisting on the battlefield is one thing — using their powers to potentially draw down the Weaver's wrath on a cub is flatly intolerable.

Wraiths

The werewolves most likely to interact with wraiths are the Silent Striders, who have often served as intermediaries with the human dead. However, the war for Gaia causes a lot of casualties, and a crossover **Wraith** story is an excellent way to confront trigger-happy Garou with the consequences of their actions, or to showcase the evil of their opponents by emphasizing the ghosts their foes leave in their wake.

Wraiths do not typically detect as Wyrm-tainted unless their Shadows are particularly strong; if a wraith's permanent Angst exceeds her permanent Willpower, she gives off the "scent" of the Wyrm. Spectres count as full Wyrm-creatures, each and every one.

Wraiths do not generally count as spirits for the purposes of rites or Gifts; they cannot be bound into fetishes, summoned with the Rite of Summoning, ordered around by Command Spirit, and so on. You're welcome to make exceptions if they would fit the story, however; it might be thematically appropriate for the Gift: Exorcism to affect wraiths, or for a set of sanctuary chimes to prevent wraiths from materializing. Just be conservative; werewolves have a *lot* of ways to mess with spirits, and allowing too many of those measures to affect ghosts would be a bit much. Similarly, remember that wraiths are not living beings; their Corpus forms may render certain Gifts such as Bloody Feast or Heart of Ice useless.

On the flip side, werewolves are not wraiths and are not treated as such, even when traveling through the Dark Umbra. Moliate does not work on Garou, who are not made of plasm; the power of Oubliette will not hurl them into the Tempest, and so on.

Arcanoi

Some Arcanoi that work on mortals have no effect on werewolves; others function normally. The main differences are listed below.

- If the Storyteller is using the optional rule that werewolves gain Shadows in the Dark Umbra, **Castigate** powers may be used on these Shadows, though at +1 difficulty.

- Werewolves doomed to die do not manifest deathmarks, and **Fatalism** powers that focus on deathmarks (Kismet and Fatal Vision) are useless on werewolves.

- Wraiths may not use **Inhabit** to possess fetishes.

- **Keening** is often more effective against werewolves, passionate beasts that they are. Five successes when using Dirge will drive a werewolf into Harano for a week, while Crescendo and Requiem force Garou listeners to make frenzy checks.

- Practitioners of **Lifeweb** cannot establish a Soul Pact with a werewolf.

- A wraith cannot use **Moliate** to shape a werewolf's form, but the weapons formed with Martialry inflict aggravated damage.

- The **Outrage** power Stonehand Punch inflicts lethal damage on werewolves; Obliviate inflicts aggravated damage.

- The **Phantasm** powers Elysia and Agon do not work on werewolves, who do not possess the same sort of "soul" that wraiths are used to.

In the Dark Umbra

The Dark Umbra isn't reached by stepping sideways in the usual fashion; it takes a special rite to do so, or following dark paths from the Middle Umbra can lead a werewolf there. But once there, werewolves function fairly normally. They regenerate, spend Rage and so on; the main differences lie in the atmosphere.

A werewolf is a creature of vibrant life, and the energies of the Dark Umbra conflict with his own being. The difficulty to use any Gift is increased by 1 while in the Dark Umbra; Gifts that do not require rolls function normally. Garou appear as robust, luminous beings to a wraith's Lifesight, which makes traveling incognito rather difficult. A werewolf may spend a Gnosis point to "drop out" of the Shadowlands into the physical world at any point; if farther from the Shadowlands, the Gnosis expenditure only gives the werewolf a sense of the closest route back to the Middle Umbra proper.

At the Storyteller's discretion, shapeshifters may acquire temporary Shadows (usually of the Abuser, Freak or Monster sort) for the duration of their stay. A shapechanger's Shadow has Angst equal to the shapeshifter's Rage (minimum of 1), and whatever Thorns the Storyteller deems appropriate.

Shapeshifter Wraiths

Upon death, a shapechanger's spirit half usually travels to her Umbral homeland, there to become one with Gaia. Even individuals that return to aid their friends and descendants (usually through riding someone with Past Life) do so as Ancestor-spirits, not as wraiths.

However, there are a few exceptions. Rarely, when a shapeshifter dies with just a touch of Wyrm-taint on his soul — just enough of a touch to break him away from the natural way of things — and a powerful desire to complete some business unfinished in life, he awakens in the Shadowlands as a wraith.

The wraith of a former shapechanger gains no special abilities from her former life. She is considered a wraith like any other; even so simple a thing as shapeshifting is impossible without the aid of Moliate. Her Corpus takes the form of her self-image, whether that be humanlike, a wolf, or even Crinos form. However, her Attributes are not altered by whatever shape she finds herself in — her form is a matter of self-perception, nothing more. The character becomes a wraith in all aspects, with her base Homid Attributes, her usual collection of Abilities (although some, like Primal-Urge, are now useless to her) and nothing more. She no longer possesses Rage or Gnosis. Her Gifts no longer work; nor do her rites or any other ability outside the ken of wraiths. In essence, she is nothing more than a wraith. However, the new possibilities of wraithly existence allow her to explore areas rarely seen by any other shapeshifter. The fight against the Wyrm, as personified by Spectres (to a wraithly Garou's perception, anyway), continues even in the Shadowlands.

The worst fight of all, of course, comes from the tiny seed of Wyrm-taint that lay within the Garou's soul at the time of her death — from which soon blossoms her Shadow. A shapeshifter's darker half is more bestial by far than that of most humans.

Changelings

The stereotype presumes that the Fianna have the most truck with changelings, and that other tribes couldn't care less. However, a **Changeling** crossover can easily defy this stereotype. A Silent Strider could strike up a friendship with an equally nomadic eshu; a sidhe delegation might demand to strike bargains with the Garou's own nobility, meaning the Silver Fangs; Bone Gnawers might make the acquaintances of the goblins of the inner city, and so on. Although Garou have little interest in the changelings' conflicts, and the fae would likely avoid being drawn into the werewolves' war, this actually works out for the best. A crossover chronicle could be a wonderful dance of diplomacy and truces, with each side trying to enlist the other's aid without committing to too much in return. After all, deals with the fae are legendary for their risk — and only a fool approaches negotiation with ravening werebeasts without being at least a little nervous.

Arts

Obviously, the Actor Realm is necessary to affect shapeshifters or spirits (although the Fae Realm may at the Storyteller's discretion, affect certain Chimerlings).

• **Chicanery** powers such as Veiled Eyes cannot reach into the Penumbra, and do not affect observers there. Certain applications of Haunted Heart may provoke a frenzy check when used on werewolves.

• To use **Legerdemain** to control a fetish, the changeling must beat the fetish in a resisted roll — the changeling's Willpower versus the fetish's Gnosis.

• The **Primal** art of Holly Strike inflicts aggravated damage, which can be soaked by shapeshifters.

• Any changelings within a mile of a Fianna using the Gift: **Faerie Kin** may make a Willpower roll, difficulty 8, to resist the summons. Those who answer the Fianna's call do not have to obey the werewolf without question, but disobeying without good reason may make the changeling some enemies among other fae who want to see the ancient pacts upheld.

One or the Other

Changelings are fae souls born into human bodies; the Changing Breeds are shapechanger souls born into shapechanger bodies. A newborn is one, the other or simply human. Although it's possible to have changelings who are technically Kinfolk (though with no access to Gifts or other Gaian powers) or werewolves with a touch of the fae blood in them, no creature can be fully both.

Hunters

Most crossover stories involving **Hunter: The Reckoning** are likely to be hostile, although the short-lived "team up against a common foe" chestnut is also popular. Hunters can hardly hope to match a werewolf in outright combat, but their powers can make them credible opponents — if they're clever about it.

Conviction will protect a hunter against all manner of illusory or mind-affecting Gifts, from the humble Blur of the Milky Eye to the mighty Obedience. Even shapeshifters in Homid form can be detected as "monsters." Physical effects (such as the mist summoned by

Curse of Aeolus) can affect a hunter's senses, but purely supernatural effects don't work. At your discretion, you might rule that particularly powerful entities (such as manifested Incarnae or Rank 5 shapeshifters) might have a chance of overcoming this immunity; in such a case, you can call for a primary Virtue roll against an appropriate difficulty (6 for a Rank 5 shapeshifter to 8 for an Incarna).

However, a hunter's second sight does not reach into the Umbra; a werewolf in the Penumbra is as good as invisible. A hunter's Conviction *does* protect against supernatural attacks targeted from the Umbra, such as the Possession Charm. The only exception is that imbued are able to target ghosts in the Shadowlands.

Second sight marks Kinfolk as "off," while Discern, Witness and Illuminate all reveal Kin as the blood relations of shapechangers.

Edges

Most Edges are written with the various powers of supernatural beings in mind. Only a few require clarification. Unless otherwise stated, an Edge cannot cross the Gauntlet and affect spirits or werewolves in the Penumbra.

• **Illuminate** works even on shapeshifters who have used Gifts such as Thousand Forms to take wildly different forms.

• **Ward** extends into the Penumbra; spirits and other Penumbral denizens cannot approach the hunter's immediate area. The mark left by **Brand** remains in all forms.

• A shapeshifter may step sideways to negate the effects of **Burden**. **Balance** can be used to prevent the use of Rage or Gnosis. Shapeshifters revealed to onlookers by the use of **Expose** typically induce Delirium as if they'd shifted to the appropriate form.

• Heightened Senses allows a werewolf to detect a **Trail**.

The Imbuing

For obvious reasons, werewolves cannot be Imbued. Ever. However, neither can Kinfolk. Whatever force is empowering the new breed of hunters with their strange gifts, it apparently is able to recognize Kinfolk, and never chooses them for the Imbuing. Even those Kinfolk ignorant of their nature are never chosen; they are simply too close to the supernatural, and therefore not sufficient guardians of humanity.

Chapter Six: Odds and Ends

Kami: Gaia Made Manifest

In the times of Gaia's first stirrings, the Mother looked upon Her new creation and felt a great longing within Her. "I want to see and hear and touch and taste and feel everything that I have made," She whispered to Herself. And with this thought, Gaia gave birth to Her very first children, spirits wrapped in the stuff of the physical world. Parts of Herself came forth from Her womb and took material forms. Gaia's spirit children ran with the deer and the tiger, swam with the fish, flew with the eagles and raged across the land with the hurricane winds. Every day, Gaia found a new way to give birth to Herself and exulted in the richness of Her creation. The animals and plants, in turn, accepted their spirit brothers and sisters as natural, for they knew no difference between one world and another.

The Wyrm changed all that. His madness broke the worlds apart and his corruption taught the creatures of the physical world to fear the spirits they once trusted. Gaia's spirit children grew troubled and withdrew from the company of their former comrades. Some of them fled forever into the Umbra, returning to their spirit forms and turning their back on the physical world. Others chose to remain in their manifested forms but hid themselves in the wildest

places of the world or cloaked themselves in disguises, trying to pass themselves off as true humans or animals or plants.

The appearance of the Gauntlet made it difficult for Gaia to infuse Her spirit directly into the world, yet She saw an even greater need to touch Her creation. Now that the Wyrm and the Weaver threatened to upset the delicate balance of the Triat, Gaia realized that She would have to find a new way to create a link between the physical world and the Umbra. Thus, out of Her sorrow and Her rage and Her love, Gaia created Her second children, the Garou and the other Changing Breeds.

— Ariana Maker-of-Stories, Black Fury Galliard, "How the Kami Came To Be"

The creatures known as Kami occupy a unique place in the universe. Some Garou describe them to cubs as "Gaia's fomori," an imperfect way of describing the unique blend of spirit and material existence. Like fomori, most Kami exist as spirits embodied in physical hosts, fusing together the material and immaterial world. Unlike the fomori, however, in which the melding of Bane and flesh (or matter) results in the corruption and eventual degeneration of the physical host, Kami form a seamless union between the physical and the spiritual, one that works for the express purpose of manifesting Gaia's love for Her creation.

Kami are excellent elements to add sparingly to a chronicle — they are the rare and wondrous manifestations of Gaian spirits, living reminders that the Mother and Her children are not defeated yet. The presence of a Kami indicates that Gaia still touches Her creation, that the Garou are not wholly without allies in the physical realm. Although an encounter with a Kami should be appropriately singular (these entities are not ones to overuse), it is this very rarity that can leave your players with the feeling that they've just participated in an encounter that few people are worthy of experiencing.

Gaia's First Children

Ancient legends speak of a time when Gaia filled the whole world with expressions of Her spirit. Before the Garou, before the other Changing Breeds, the Kami walked the earth in their many forms. Because the Gauntlet had not yet risen, so the stories go, the barrier between spirit and flesh did not yet exist. Spirits could manifest whenever they wanted, and Gaia gave them permission to take on the forms best suited for them whenever they chose.

Kami delighted in the profusion of forms their Mother had created, expressing themselves as the spirits of mountains, rivers, trees, plants, animals and other growing things. Kami even assumed the shapes of humans, enjoying the many forms of communication and expression available to those creatures.

The insanity of the Wyrm and its growing power have made the creation of Kami increasingly more difficult for Gaia. Today, new Kami appear only rarely. When such a momentous event occurs, all the spirits in the vicinity gather to witness the miraculous birth. Most Kami are created when a Gaian spirit possesses a human, animal or even plant host in a symbiotic joining such as that of a fomor, although a few actually come about as a result of more-or-less permanent materialization, or as the awakening of a portion of land.

Family Relations

In modern times, Kami have little occasion to interact with the Changing Breeds. Usually solitary and shy creatures, Kami preserve their secrecy jealously, fearing the wrath of those that discover their true identity. Only the wisest Theurges know their lore, and only the most accomplished Galliards know the legends that tell of the Kami. These elders, hailing from a proud race as they do, seldom tell the stories of children who predate them in their Mother's favor.

The same holds true for the Fera, who frequently share the Garou's reluctance to acknowledge (or believe) that others came before them.

Occasionally, when the need arises, Kami interact with the Garou or with other Changing Breeds. These encounters always depend on the individuals involved. Kami can usually sense whenever one of their distant cousins will react with favor — or at least without hostility — to their appearance.

Because of their nature as lesser manifestations of Gaia, Kami rarely work directly against the Garou or any of the Mother's other children unless given a direct command by Gaia to do so. Occasionally, Kami find themselves in need of assistance from the Garou or from other Kami. In these instances, they emerge from isolation and make their desires known. Because Kami tend to live as recluses, however, they seldom know the ins and outs of Garou culture or philosophy. They know nothing of the Litany, of Garou tribes or auspices and even less of the internecine squabbles that make up much of Garou society. The same holds true for the Kami's knowledge of other Fera.

Manifestations of Gaia's Bounty

All Kami share certain benefits granted to them by Gaia. Every Kami possesses an intelligence that at least equals that of most humans, even though their thought processes may differ considerably from those of humankind. The thoughts of a bird-Kami, for example, while more cohesive and sentient, than those of normal birds, do not at all resemble the thoughts of a Kami with a human host. Instead, the thoughts reflect matters of concern to birds — wind patterns, the changing of the seasons, the abundance or lack of food, the presence of predators and possible threats to themselves.

Shapeshifters, spirits and other supernatural creatures with spiritually aware senses (which might include some mages, but would certainly exclude vampires) can sense an aura of holiness or spirituality emanating from Kami. This radiance has no tangible effect on other creatures that sense it other than to announce the presence of one of Gaia's special children. Anyone feeling this emanation knows that something wondrous is nearby.

Most Kami have a vulnerability to some substance, such as fire, cold iron, glass, plastic, wood or metal. Any Kami injured by a weapon or object made from their particular baneful substance takes aggravated, non-soakable damage.

Like Gaia's other children, Kami possess Gnosis. Some, but not all, Kami possess Rage as well. Both Gnosis and Rage replenish themselves at the Storyteller's discretion. Kami that possess Rage have the potential for frenzy, just as Garou do, though the reasons for the frenzy may differ according to the nature of the individual Kami. Health levels depend on the size of the Kami. Kami with animal, small plant or human hosts have as many Health Levels as normal examples of those types would have. Large Kami, such as those inhabiting trees, boulders, or rivers have more health levels and are more difficult to destroy. Animate lands may prove almost impossible to destroy except through extraordinary measures such as chemical exposure, toxic waste, radiation or wildfires.

Some Kami may also possess a geas in the form of a prohibition, such as a ban on speaking above a whisper or the inability to wear clothing of a particular color or material (for Kami with human hosts). Violation of this geas may result in consequences that range in degree from serious to fatal, depending on the nature of the transgression.

Kami Powers

The powers listed below provide examples of the kinds of abilities Kami possess. Each Kami manifests its own unique powers, appropriate to its host. Storytellers may customize the powers enumerated here or may create their own to reflect the uniqueness of each Kami (Gifts provide more ideas, and are thematically sound). Even two Kami with oak trees as hosts may differ in their powers.

Since Kami are intended primarily as Storyteller characters rather than as player characters, no fixed rules for character creation appear. If a Storyteller wishes to allow one or more of her players to play a Kami character, she can adapt the character generation rules from **Werewolf: the Apocalypse** or else come up with her own guidelines. The number and type of powers available to a Kami should remain consistent with the Kami's host creature and should pertain to the Kami's purpose in the world.

• **Animal Affinity** — Kami with this power may influence animals. The affected animal views the Kami as a trusted companion or leader and will aid the Kami in whatever way possible, according to its natural instincts. No roll is necessary for normal animals. This power resembles the Philodox Gift: King of the Beasts.

• **Animal Communication** — The Kami enjoys the ability to communicate with animals of any kind, as well as the "beast tongues" of shapeshifters in their animal forms. The Kami possesses the knowledge of all forms of animal speech and may "speak" to them through the sounds and body gestures normal to each particular animal. Although the Kami may make sounds and movements, the actual communication takes place telepathically. This power is akin to the Galliard Gift: Beast Speech.

• **Animal Powers** — A Kami with this power may change its form to enable itself to take on some animal aspect, or its host form already possesses one or more of these powers. If a Kami must transform itself, it must spend a point of Gnosis for each transformation, regardless of the number of powers such a shift in form provides. For example, a Kami may gain a wolf's heightened senses by changing its facial features to that of a wolf. Even though this change affects three or more senses, the Kami need expend only a single point of Gnosis. If, however, the Kami wishes to achieve the benefit of claws in addition to heightened senses, it must spend two points of Gnosis — one for the heightened senses and one for the claws. A Kami whose host form is that of a wolf, however, gains the natural powers of its animal form without expending Gnosis. Additional examples of Animal Powers include fangs, prehensile tails, water breathing, wings and fins.

• **Animal Summons (Cost: 1 Gnosis)** — A Kami uses this power to summon animals to its aid. The Storyteller determines the number and type of animals that respond to the Kami's summons. Regardless of the number of animals that answer the call, the Kami's Gnosis expenditure remains the same. This power resembles the Lupus Gift: Beast Life.

• **Animate Self (Cost: 1 Willpower)** — Inanimate Kami may rouse themselves to action through the use of this power. Though most inanimate Kami use this power only for short bursts of activity, a few maintain it almost continually, allowing themselves the ability to walk, run or perform some other form of physical action at any time they so desire. If movement requires a Kami to detach itself from the earth or some other object, then it must spend two points of Willpower. For example, a Kami tree must uproot itself from the earth in order to walk; thus, using this power costs 2 points of Willpower. The effects of this power last until the Kami returns to its inanimate form or for one scene.

• **Aura of Tranquility** — Kami with this power radiate an aura of peacefulness that calms everyone within its area, whether allies or hostile creatures. Shapeshifters may not use Rage, vampires find themselves unable to frenzy and any others find it almost impossible to commit violent actions. In order to invoke this power, the Kami must roll Charisma + Empathy (difficulty of the target's Willpower). Targets who fail the roll may not act in a violent fashion. The Kami may affect more than one target with this power but must make a separate roll for each individual targeted. Most Kami that possess this power project it at all times.

• **Autumn's Blessings** — The Kami can bring about the appearance and effects of autumn to an area. Leaves change color, animals prepare for winter by storing up food and the weather takes on the aspects of autumn. Sudden changes, such as causing the leaves to fall at once from all the trees in the designated area, cost the Kami one Gnosis point to effect, but gradual changes carry no cost. Kami with this power become aware of individuals who have passed the prime of life and are nearing late maturity.

• **Child of the Elements (Cost: 1 Gnosis)** — Kami with this power may summon elementals of the type most suited to them. For example, a Child of Earth may summon an earth elemental, while a Child of Fire can call a fire elemental to its service. In order to do this, the Kami must roll Manipulation + Expression (difficulty 7). Each success allows the Kami to summon one elemental, although the Kami may only control as many elementals as its rating in Wits. Most Kami possessing this power can summon only one type of elemental, but Kami whose hosts combine elements may summon elemental of either sort. Thus, a Child of Steam may summon either fire or water elementals, while a Child of Mud may summon elementals of water or earth. Often, Kami children of the elements possess other powers appropriate to their element.

• **Command the Earth (Cost: varies)** — The Kami uses this power to subject the earth to its will. At the Kami's command, the earth can form itself into desert or quicksand or anything in between. The Kami can cause earthquakes, landslides, rockfalls or any other natural phenomena. This power costs one point of Gnosis for minor effects such as a small patch of desert or a minor rockfall. Major effects, such as the transformation of a large area into a quicksand mire or occurrence of an earthquake, cost two or more points of Gnosis.

• **Curse of Gaia (Cost: 3 Gnosis)** — Kami may use this power to place a curse on anyone that disrupts the will of the Mother or upsets the balance of the natural world. The Kami determines the nature of the curse, which may vary from relatively minor — such as a run of bad luck — to major impediments or fatal afflictions. The Kami may induce Harano in a Garou, turn a mortal offender to stone, inflict a wasting disease on an individual or cause the earth to engulf the cursed victim. The nature of the curse is up to the Kami (or the Storyteller). Most Kami can inflict only one major and one minor type of curse.

• **Enchanting Voice (Cost: 1 Gnosis)** — With this power, the Kami can enthrall anyone that hears its song. The listener must make a Willpower roll (difficulty of the Kami's Charisma + Performance) in order to avoid being drawn to the Kami's voice. This power does not grant the Kami any additional power over the victim. If the Kami wishes to enlist the victim's assistance or punish the targeted individual, it must do so through the use of other powers or abilities.

• **Gaia's Summons (Cost: 1 Gnosis, 1 Willpower)** — A Kami with this power may call to itself one of the Mother's forces or creatures. Kami may summon Wyldings, Great Beasts, totem spirits or, in some instances, a particular group of Garou or Fera (i.e., all Ragabash in an area). Summoned creatures feel inclined to act in the best interests of the Kami that called them. Those who wish to resist the summons must make a resisted Willpower roll against their summoner.

• **Great Destiny** — The Kami exists for a significant purpose and nothing short of the completion of that goal can stop it. Miracles occur in the vicinity of the Kami whenever something threatens the successful accomplishment of its purpose. Not even death can stop it until it has fulfilled the destiny chosen for it by the Mother. This is, for obvious reasons, one of the rarest powers, suitable only for Kami that are destined to play a significant part in the chronicle.

• **Heart Sense (Cost: 1 Gnosis)** — A Kami with this power can see into the heart or essence of an individual and ascertain whether that creature belongs primarily to the Wyld, the Wyrm or the Weaver. Additionally, Kami with Heart Sense can identify an individual's connections to the past (such as that granted by the Ancestors Background), determine a person's innocence or guilt, ferret out someone's dreams and desires or discover the true form of someone in another shape. The Kami must succeed in a Perception + Empathy roll (Difficulty 7). Each success provides the Kami with additional information.

• **Invulnerability** — This power provides the Kami with one to five points of Stamina (Storyteller discretion) for use in soaking damage. Kami with this power generally manifest it visibly in some way, such as skin with a faintly metallic appearance, a hard carapace or an exoskeleton. Kami with stone host bodies frequently possess this power.

• **Longevity** — Although Kami are not immortal, many possess this power, which greatly extends their "normal" lifespan, slowing down their life processes and causing them to age very gradually. Kami with human hosts may live for two or three centuries, while Kami insects may live for several months (a phenomenally long lifetime!). Mountain Kami or animate lands with this power have a life expectancy that might as well be infinite compared to those of mortal creatures. Without this power, a Kami "lives" only as long as its host's normal life span.

• **Lord of the Land** — A Kami with this power remains constantly aware of everything that takes place within its territory. The most common Kami to possess this power include plant or tree Kami, mountain or river Kami or animate lands. Kami may use this power at no cost.

• **Mask Presence (Cost: 1 Gnosis)** — For the duration of one scene, a Kami with this power can prevent others from seeing, hearing or otherwise detecting its presence. This power can manifest itself by making the Kami invisible or by camouflaging or otherwise disguising it. Occasionally, the power simply causes those in the vicinity of the Kami to ignore it as if it were not there.

• **Mega-Strength** — The Kami possesses an additional one to five points of Strength. Mountain Kami, shade tree Kami or Kami with large animal hosts tend to have this power.

• **Mother's Healing** — This power functions as the Theurge Gift: Mother's Touch.

• **Peaceful Fighting** — Kami with this power may defend themselves without causing lasting physical damage to their opponent. The Kami fights normally, but each health level of damage it causes lasts only as long as the remainder of the scene. The opponent heals completely when the scene is over. If the Kami deals a number of health levels of damage in one blow as the opponent has Stamina, the opponent falls unconscious, awakening at the end of the scene. In the meantime, the Kami has the opportunity to leave the vicinity or otherwise take itself out of harm's way.

• **Piercing Gaze (Cost: 1 Gnosis)** — The Kami can make whoever it looks at feel as if her soul has bared itself to the Kami. Victims of this power become agitated and tense. Occasionally they succumb to anger or some other injudicious emotion. Even Kami who do not possess physical eyes (such as plant Kami or animate lands) can use this power to make individuals in their vicinity feel as if someone or something is watching them. Kami use this power to repel intruders, drive unwanted creatures from their lands or force an individual to confess some hidden crime or great secret.

• **Plant Animation (Cost: varies)** — This power enables the Kami to animate plants, causing flowers, trees, shrubs or other forms of vegetation to move in ways not normally available to them. The Storyteller determines what each affected plant can do. Roses may lash out at an intruder, scratching the individual with their thorns. Vines may entangle the Kami's victims, while a tree's massive limb may reach out and wrap itself around an enemy, causing severe crushing damage. Plants possess one to three points of Dexterity and one to 10 points of Strength. A patch of animated grass may have only one point of strength, while an animated redwood tree would almost certainly possess maximum Strength (10 points). The cost in Gnosis to the Kami using this power varies in

relation to the number of plants affected and the potential for causing damage. Kami may use this power to affect a small number of trees or a larger number of smaller plants.

• **Plant Kinship** — Similar to Animal Kinship, this power grants Kami the friendship of all plants. Animated plants come to the Kami's assistance whenever possible. This power also grants Kami the ability to speak with plants. This ability resembles the Galliard Gift: Beast Speech, except that it pertains to plants rather than animals. Even though plants do not possess true sentience, the Kami can use this power to learn what transpires in any given area from the plants that grow there.

• **Regeneration** — Kami with this power have the ability to regain health levels at the rate of one per turn. This only applies to non-aggravated damage.

• **Silent Speech** — This power gives the Kami the ability to communicate without speech. Similar to telepathy in many respects, it bypasses language altogether. Thus, a Kami may use this power to speak to individuals from many different cultures at once, regardless of their native language. Each person or creature hears the Kami as if it were speaking the language most familiar to the recipient.

• **Skinchanger Kinship** — Kami with this power enjoy the friendship and confidence of one of the Changing Breeds, to which they are attuned. The most common version of this power is Garou Kinship (owing to the decline of the other Breeds), but a Kami may possess Kinship to any shapechanger race, even the Rokea or Ratkin. This power is the equivalent of a Pure Breed rating of three.

• **Spirit Awakening (Cost: 1 Gnosis)** — Kami with this power can awaken spirits in a manner similar to the Rite of Spirit Awakening, though the Kami only needs to spend one turn to rouse the targeted spirit.

• **Spirit Charms** — Some Kami possess certain spirit Charms, such as Reform, Break Reality or Airt Sense. Kami that use these powers may or may not assume certain aspects of the spirits that most commonly possess these Charms. Only those Kami possessing Umbral Passage may have this power. Kami tend to use Gnosis to power these Charms, but occasionally they may use Rage for appropriate Charms.

• **Spirit Sense** — The Kami can look into the spirit world and speak to any spirits it happens to see even though the Kami itself remains in the physical world.

• **Spring's Blessings** — This power functions in a manner similar to Autumn's Blessings, except that it enables the Kami to cause an area to take on the aspects of spring. Plants in the targeted area sprout and bud, animals emerge from hibernation or feel the urge to mate and the temperature takes on the mildness of spring. Using this power, Kami may also identify preg-

nant individuals or creatures that have not yet reached their true potential.

• **Strange Senses** — Kami with this power possess senses that defy definition in human terms. These Kami can see sounds, hear colors, detect invisible creatures or sense the emotions of others. Other manifestations of this power are up to the Storyteller.

• **Subtle Presence** — Kami with this power become difficult to keep up with and extremely hard to find. They leave no physical trail and people have a hard time keeping the Kami in their memory, forgetting they saw the Kami. Anyone who actively searches for the Kami must succeed in a Perception + Alertness roll (difficulty 9) in order to have any chance of locating it and even then, the searcher takes longer than usual to find her target.

• **Summer's Blessings** — The Kami causes an area to assume the aspects of full summer. Leaves become green, trees bear fruit, animals give birth and engage in hunting behavior and the temperature takes on the warmth of the season. Kami can use this power, if they so desire, to cause sunstroke in individuals. This form of the power costs one point of Gnosis and requires the Kami to roll Stamina + Primal Urge

(difficulty 7). The victim may make a Stamina roll to resist. Success means that the victim takes no damage. Failure means that the victim loses consciousness and takes one non-soakable health level of aggravated damage. Kami with this power can sense the presence of creatures that are in the prime of their lives.

• **Transformation (Cost: 1 Willpower)** — Kami with this power can change themselves into some other creature. Thus, a Kami may transform itself into a particular type of form (animal, plant, mineral) a select group (all canines, trees, insects) or a single form (Great Dane, eagle, willow tree). Some Kami may even choose several unrelated forms (a birch tree, a dove, a rock and a butterfly). This power works in both the Umbra and in the physical world.

• **Umbral Passage** — The Kami rolls Gnosis and uses this power to cross the Gauntlet in a fashion similar to the Garou ability to step sideways. Plant or animal hosts leave their physical forms in the material world and assume spirit forms in the Umbra. While occasionally, plant or animal Kami take spirit forms that mirror their earthly hosts, most often they assume human or some other form capable of movement when they travel to the Umbra.

• **Universal Tongue** — Kami with this power can speak the language of and communicate with all living creatures.

• **Winter's Blessings** — Kami can cause a designated area to manifest signs of winter. Plants wither and become dormant or die, water freezes in ponds and lakes, animals that hibernate seek places to undergo their seasonal slumber and the air becomes cold with the feel and smell of winter. Kami can create gusts of freezing air as weapons, similar to the Wendigo Gifts: Cutting Wind and Chill of the Early Frost, though they must spend one point of Rage to do so. Kami with this power can sense individuals who approach the end of their lives and some Kami can even use this power to see into the Dark Umbra.

• **Wyldkin** — Kami with this power tend to possess powers similar to creatures of the Wyld. These Kami can create elements and often manifest the Charms common to Wyldling spirits. Spirits of the Wyld consider the Kami as one of their own and feel an inclination to assist the Kami so long as it does not order them to do something that goes against their instincts. A Kami that attempts to force a Wyld spirit to act counter to its nature must succeed in an opposed Willpower roll and risks alienating the Wyldling. The Kami can also use this power to summon Wyldling spirits by rolling Charisma + Expression (difficulty 7). Each success attracts one spirit. The Kami may control a number of spirits equal to its Wits rating. It's entirely possible that a Kami might manifest a similar "Wyrmkin" or "Weaverkin" power, although the madness of Wyrm and Weaver has seriously eroded each Celestine's relationship with Gaia.

Kami Weaknesses

Just as Kami enjoy access to powers granted to them from Gaia, they also pay a price for these powers in the form of *geasa* or prohibitions. These bans or taboos serve several purposes within the context of the game. With regard to game mechanics, they provide a counter to the powers of the Kami, making these spirit creatures a little more than just a collection of neat abilities. Storytellers might want to assign one geas for every three or four powers or else content themselves with giving each Kami a single ban regardless of how many abilities it possesses.

Within the story itself, Kami take on an additional depth and a hint of tragedy when they exhibit certain weaknesses. Many legends ascribe bans or taboos to heroes, who often face their undoing through a trap based on these prohibitions.

The following list offers some examples of geasa appropriate for Kami. Not all of these bans will suit all

Kami. Storytellers should pick and choose the most relevant ones for their Kami characters or else feel free to make up their own. Storytellers also have the option, of course, to ignore the idea of Kami weaknesses entirely.

Penalties for violation of a geas can vary from loss of some or all of its powers, diminution of Attributes, loss of Gnosis, Rage or Willpower or utter dissolution, depending on the severity of the prohibition and the circumstances under which it was broken. Gaia enacts the penalty at the time (and the Storyteller determines the nature of the punishment).

• **Barefoot** — The Kami must never wear shoes or any sort of foot covering. This geas, needless to say, only applies for Kami with human or clothes-wearing hosts.

• **Color Ban** — The Kami may not wear clothing or ornamentation of a particular color. While this seems initially to apply to Kami humans only, this ban also includes animal collars, saddle blankets, ribbons tied around tree limbs and even spray painted graffiti on rocks.

• **Gender Ban** — The Kami may not speak directly to a man (or a woman). Any communication with the banned gender must take place through an intermediary.

• **Indirect Movement** — The Kami may not move in a straight line, but must always take an indirect path to its goal.

• **Question Ban** — The Kami may never answer a direct question.

• **Rover** — The Kami may not call any single place home. A Kami with this ban may not sleep in the same "bed" or spend the night in the exact same spot two nights in a row. Kami must have the capacity for mobility to possess this geas.

• **Silence** — The Kami may not speak while performing its appointed task. It must make its wishes known by other means.

• **Substance Ban** — The Kami may not come into contact with a particular substance, such as wood, silver, gold, plastic, water, etc.

• **Thankless** — The Kami may neither give thanks to anyone who assists it nor accept thanks for its assistance. In addition, it may not explain its apparent ungratefulness without violating the ban.

• **Whisper-Bound** — The Kami may never raise its voice above a whisper, even when calling for help.

Kami Characters

The following sample characters provide Storytellers with examples of several different types of Kami, according to their host forms. Storytellers may use these characters as presented here or may alter them to suit their chronicles. These examples can also serve as guidelines for creating Kami characters in general. As a rule of thumb, Storytellers should begin by designing a "normal" creature to serve as the Kami's host, then modify that creature by customizing Attributes and Abilities and adding appropriate powers and one or more geasa.

Plant and Animal Hosts

Plants and animals infused with Gaia's essence and her awareness make up the bulk of Kami existing in the world today. Most of these Kami possess telepathy and some may even have the ability to communicate in one or more human languages. While many animal or plant Kami are indistinguishable from their normal counterparts, a few have some unusual quality about them such as odd coloration (a blue squirrel), enormous size (a Volkswagen size cat) or strange shape (a mushroom ring). All plant and animal hosts have several powers given to them by Gaia and may also possess at least one prohibition.

Mow'ruth the Hunter

Kami Type: Animal Host (Feral cat)
Physical: Strength 1, Dexterity 4, Stamina 4
Social: Charisma 5, Manipulation 3, Appearance 3
Mental: Perception 4, Intelligence 5, Wits 5
Talents: Alertness 3, Athletics 3, Brawl 4, Dodge 4, Empathy 2, Intimidation 2, Primal-Urge 5
Skills: Animal Ken 4, Etiquette 1, Leadership 3, Stealth 5, Survival 5
Knowledges: Enigmas 4, Investigation 3, Linguistics 4
Backgrounds: Allies 4, Ancestors 5 (may contact prehistoric cats), Contacts 3
Powers: Animal Kinship, Animal Powers (Catfeet, Claws, Heightened Senses), Animal Summons (animals of the forest and field), Heart Sense, Long-Lived, Mask Presence, Mother's Healing, Piercing Gaze, Silent Speech, Universal Translator
Rage: 2; **Gnosis:** 8; **Willpower:** 10
Health Levels: OK, -1, -1, -2, -5
Attacks: Bite (Str + 1 aggravated damage); Claws (Str + 2 aggravated damage).
Bans: Rover, Whisper-Bound
Mow'ruth gets two attacks per turn, one from his bite and one from his claws.

Image: Mow'ruth appears as an oversized (25+ pounds) longhaired brown and black tabby tomcat. Many humans who see him mistake him for a feral Maine Coon cat. He has enormous paws, tufted ears, a ruff that lies close around his neck and a full, brush-like tail. His voice is almost non-existent, resembling a kitten's scratchy cry rather than a full-throated cat's meow. He purrs rarely and

inaudibly. He understands any language and can telepathically communicate his wants to others.

Roleplaying Hints: Mow'ruth lives in the wild country of rural New Hampshire. Gaia has charged him with overseeing the balance of "his" realms and making certain that the encroaching human population does not extend too far. He accomplishes his task in various ways — by appearing to lead lost humans to safety, by acting as a hidden menace and frightening off intruders and by conducting guerrilla warfare on unwary campers or hikers. He can and sometimes does befriend humans, but refuses any attempts at domestication.

History: Mow'ruth remembers the coming of the Europeans and their Garou kin to North America. He used to have contact with the Native Americans, who acknowledged him as a spirit-creature and gave him offerings from their hunts. He finds his Rage at the loss of the Mother's wild places growing by leaps and bounds and struggles to maintain his equanimity and focus.

Arbina, the Sheltering Maple

Kami Type: Plant Host (Maple Tree)
Physical: Strength 12, Dexterity 0/3 (when animate), Stamina 10
Social: Charisma 4, Manipulation 3, Appearance 2
Mental: Perception 3, Intelligence 3, Wits 3
Talents: Alertness 2, Brawl 2, Empathy 3, Intimidation 1, Primal-Urge 2
Skills: Animal Ken 5, Survival 3
Knowledges: Area Knowledge (South Carolina Piedmont) 5, Enigmas 3, Medicine 1
Backgrounds: Allies 5, Contacts 2
Powers: Animal Summons (nearby animals), Animate Self, Lord of the Land, Mother's Healing, Peaceful Fighting, Plant Animation, Spirit Charms (Break Reality, Possession), Spirit Sense
Rage: 4; **Gnosis:** 8; **Willpower:** 10
Health Levels: OK, OK, OK, -1,-1,-2,-2,-5,-5, Incapacitated
Attack: Branch Swat (Str + 1 bashing damage)
Bans: Substance Ban (plastic), Thankless

Image: Arbina is a large maple tree with broad limbs and a wide-spreading crown of leaves. She makes her home in the Piedmont region of South Carolina where she provides shelter for small animals and numerous species of birds.

Roleplaying Hints: Arbina watches with growing alarm as the expanding urban centers encroach on her home and threaten the small creatures that depend more and more on her for their survival. She has occasionally roused herself to walk in human form, exacting vengeance on those who deliberately despoil the wilderness and she may prove helpful to Garou who ask her politely for assistance. Her sap possesses healing properties (Mother's Healing).

History: Arbina is more than a century old and shows no signs of rot or blight as yet. Though she has not walked the earth in the last 20 years, she has seen the growing turmoil in the Umbra caused by the appearance of Anthelios and is considering taking on human form once again to do what she can to respond to its threat. She believes that the Garou may hold the key to fighting the red star, but she is reluctant to place herself in their debt.

Mortal Hosts

Mortals who become hosts to Kami retain their human souls but acquire an added dimension. Some humans do not realize precisely what they are but call themselves "messengers," "aliens," or even "angels." They blend reasonably well into human society, and sometimes give rise to local legends or "tall tales" similar to those of Johnny Appleseed and Paul Bunyan.

Old Man Fisher

Kami Type: Mortal Host
Age: 70?
Physical: Strength 2, Dexterity 3, Stamina 3
Social: Charisma 4, Manipulation 3, Appearance 2
Mental: Perception 5, Intelligence 3, Wits 5
Talents: Alertness 4, Dodge 1, Empathy 3, Subterfuge 3
Skills: Animal Ken (fish) 5, Craft (fishing) 5, Survival 4
Knowledges: Enigmas 4, Investigation 3, Science (Marine Biology) 5
Backgrounds: Allies (fisherfolk) 4, Resources 1 (odd jobs)
Powers: Animal Kinship (sea creatures), Aura of Tranquility, Gaia's Curse (causes trouble for those who over-fish the nearby lake), Heart Sense, Piercing Gaze, Mask Presence, Transformation (fish)
Rage: 1; **Gnosis:** 10; **Willpower:** 9
Health Levels: As a human
Ban: Barefoot

Image: Old Man Fisher stoops rather than stands. He appears in his mid-70's, though his build implies a hardier constitution than his years might suggest. He dresses in worn, patched clothing. His thinning hair is mostly white and he wears it in a straggly ponytail. He never wears shoes and his feet are covered with thick calluses.

Roleplaying Hints: Old Man Fisher lives near a large fishing lake surrounded by a small village and many vacation homes. He believes that aliens abducted him when he was young and charged him with protecting aquatic life of all kinds. He instructs local children in respect for water creatures and makes certain that no one over-fishes the lake he considers his territory. He can be a formidable opponent as well as a staunch ally.

History: When he was a teenager, Terry Fisher had his encounter with "aliens." A near drowning experience opened his spirit to Gaia's infusion of her own essence, giving the young man a new life as one of her Kami. Over the years, Terry has abandoned his first name and simply goes by the name "Fisher." He is a local "character" in his community and though many people make fun of him, none can deny his powerful aura of peacefulness when they come into his presence.

Animate Lands

Gaia occasionally infuses an entire region with her essence, awakening the very earth to consciousness. The land becomes one sentient entity and all the plants and animals that dwell on it act as part of the land's "body." Occasionally, humans may live on and work the land so long as they do nothing disrespectful to it. Animate Lands regain Gnosis more quickly than other Kami, replenishing their supply three or four times a day if necessary.

Primeval Forest

Kami Type: Animate Land (forest)
Physical: Not applicable
Social: Charisma 4, Manipulation 2, Appearance 0
Mental: Perception 5, Intelligence 4, Wits 6
Talents: None
Skills: Animal Ken 8, Plant Lore 8
Knowledges: Area Lore 10, Enigmas 5, Garou Lore 2
Powers: Animal Speech, Animal Summons, Autumn's Blessings, Child of the Elements (all), Command the Earth, Curse of Gaia (cause technology to fail in its vicinity), Heart Sense, Lord of the Land, Piercing Gaze, Plant Animation, Plant Kinship, Spirit Sense, Spring's Blessings, Summer's Blessings, Winter's Blessings
Rage: 5; **Gnosis:** 10; **Willpower:** 10
Bans: none known

Image: The Primeval Forest appears as a large tract of old-growth forest located in the Appalachian Mountains of West Virginia. It has the ability to become raucously loud or extremely silent and foreboding. Those who wander in it swear that the forest has eyes — and, indeed, it does.

Roleplaying Hints: The forest seldom takes action unless directly threatened by hunters, loggers, road builders and other usurpers. Then it springs into action, usually causing the violent and permanent disappearance of those who endanger it.

History: The Primeval Forest awoke when the first logging companies came to despoil the ancient trees that covered the gently sloping mountains of West Virginia. Though much forestland has fallen prey to forces of the Wyrm and the Weaver, the Primeval Forest has remained unharmed, due to its many Gifts from Gaia. Some Garou have just discovered this untouched forest and are trying to discover what makes it so different from the nearby lands.

Inspiration

Storytelling can be an art, a craft, a meticulous attempt to blend disparate themes and motifs into a careful and intoxicating melange that encourages your players to reexamine the way they look at the world — but it's also basically a way to tell stories you think are cool. There's no shame in borrowing motifs you see elsewhere, as long as they don't distract your players. (If you tell your players that the gruff Master of the Challenge looks like Hugh Jackman in *X-Men*, that's one thing, but if he starts quoting the movie or pops adamantium claws, your players may find that less than awe-inspiring.) Maybe you find that it's easier to plan stories if you have particularly appropriate music playing, or that watching one of your favorite werewolf movies always inspires you to craft a new scenario.

To round out the **Storytellers Handbook**, the following essays and recommended sources are presented to give your creative juices that last little nudge. With luck, something here will strike a chord with your Storytelling style, or present a few ideas you hadn't previously considered using.

Media at Large

Movies

We've said it before, and it bears repeating: The werewolf movie genre suffers from a dearth of quality offerings. Only a small percentage of werewolf movies move past the cheese factor, and the perfect werewolf movie is probably still waiting to be made. So rather than list every movie focused on werewolves (Teen Wolf? Teen Wolf Too?), we've gone for the ones most likely to contribute something, even if small, to your Werewolf game.

The 13th Warrior — Culture clashes, cannibalistic villains that lurk in underground labyrinths, and the themes of living honorably, dying bravely, and having your deeds remembered in song. This take on the Beowulf legend is rather more **Werewolf** than you might first expect.

An American Werewolf in London — One of the strongest entries into the genre of werewolf movies, this is worth watching for the transformation sequences alone.

The Blair Witch Project — Forget the hype; this movie is remarkably useful as an example of how ordinary humans *should* fear the woods in the World of Darkness. This is what the Impergium was all about.

Brotherhood of the Wolf (Le Pacte des Loups) — A French film retelling one of the pre-eminent real-world werewolf myths, the Beast of Gevaudan. Practically surreal in the number of elements it blends. Check it out.

Full Eclipse — Cheesy, but in a good way; "Adam Garou" and his lycanthropic task force merit at least a rental.

Ginger Snaps — An unconventional werewolf movie, not unlike *Heathers* on lycanthropy. Intelligent, witty and yes, savage horror.

Princess Mononoke — We couldn't make a more relevant movie if we tried.

The Howling — Perhaps the first "Crinos" on film, and certainly the most influential. There are a number of sequels, but all are legendary for their schlock status. Be warned.

Wolf — Although received with mixed reactions, this is still one of the better werewolf movies out there, whether you're a die-hard Jack Nicholson fan or not.

Wolfen — An interesting mood-setter for portraying wolves with human intelligence and how alien they would appear to humans.

Books

Black Elk Speaks — A must-read for anyone wanting to understand the Wendigo, as well as possessing a wonderful voice for those interested in the Galliard side of things.

Erdoes, Richard and Alfonso Ortiz, editors — *American Indian Myths and Legends*. Yes, it's relevant to more than just Pure Lands chronicles. This volume showcases much of the animal-people themes that run through **Werewolf**, as well as providing a glimpse at what the world must have been like before the Sundering.

Holland, David — *Murcheston: The Wolf's Tale*. A fun Victorian werewolf story with particularly evocative descriptions of the sensory experience of becoming a wolf.

Lang, Andrew — *The Green Fairy Book*, *The Blue Fairy Book*, *The Red Fairy Book*, et al. Although sanitized into proper "fairy story" format for children, these books are nonetheless surprising collections of folklore and weird stories, and can provide great inspiration for tales of a pack's ancestors. And yes, they go beyond Europe.

Leopold, Aldo — *A Sand County Almanac*. Very much merits a look for those interested in the environmental and conservation aspects of **Werewolf**.

Mieville, China — *King Rat*. A modern fable that blends legendary animal-human figures with the frenetic energy of urban culture. Of particular interest to Storytellers who enjoy using Ratkin.

Mowat, Farley — *Never Cry Wolf*. An excellent resource for understanding and portraying wolf Kinfolk and lupus alike.

Stieger, Brad — *The Werewolf Book: The Encyclopedia of Shape-shifting Beings*. Although heavily padded with entries only peripherally related to werewolf lore (such as serial killers and obscure mythical shape-changers), this is still a sound resource for a Werewolf Storyteller.

Music

Almost any sort of music can contribute to a **Werewolf** game, if timed properly. Fast-paced dance music such as the various offshoots of techno works well for urban stories, as does the more hard-edged hip-hop and rap; conversely, world beat is great for chronicles where there's a lot of travel. There's plenty of Celtic music to be found for the Fianna in your group, but authentic country music would work just as well (for the very same tribe, no less!). Metallica, Dead Kennedys and Slipknot are just as valid as Dead can Dance and Afro Celt Sound System; it's all a matter of how you handle it. Of course, you may want to avoid using albums or songs that your players have heard a thousand times before; nothing kills a song like overplay.

The advantage to wordless music, such as that from a movie's score, is that players are less prone to sing along — a real mood-breaking experience if ever there was one. Just be careful about some modern movie soundtracks that have the obligatory pop song at the end. The soundtrack to *The Mummy Returns*, for instance, can really get your players in the mood for a **Rage Across Egypt** story, only to demolish the atmosphere as it swings into the pop number at the end. This does more damage than good, and is to be avoided. Some of the better movies and miniseries soundtracks to be found include *500 Nations*, *Blade*, *Braveheart*, *Conan the Barbarian*, *Gladiator*, *Last of the Mohicans*, *Princess Mononoke*, *Rapa Nui*, *Rob Roy* and *The 13th Warrior*.

Moral Dilemmas

By Kylie Greenham

One issue that is underplayed in many **Werewolf** games is that of morality; black or white. Is a werewolf a sociopath by nature? Many players play them as such, happily plowing through witnesses and people who just happen to be in the wrong place at the wrong time, as if it doesn't matter and never will. After all, these *humans* are little more than obstacles that are here on sufferance at the best of times — and if they need be sacrificed, it's all for the greater good. At least, that's how the werewolves think, and there's no real need to challenge those assumptions. Right?

Wrong. Particularly for those who wish to set their chronicles within a city, human nature — and the morality of the Garou — is an issue that cries out to be examined in depth. The average Garou should *not* be a killing machine that is incapable of feeling anything past the anticipation of their next battle. Not only is a werewolf capable of feeling any and all emotions a human being would — love, sorrow, fear as well as hate — but the beast within ensures that a werewolf can often feel those emotions far more keenly than their human counterparts.

You can play on this fact to bring forth some incredibly intense scenes from your players. Take the following example, by a group of players I had the fortune to Storytell for a while ago.

The chronicle was set in a fictional city, and the players took the roles of a pack of Glass Walkers. One of the first stories involved family — a key element in **Werewolf**. Michael Lucas — the Ragabash — had the misfortune to discover his father worked for a Pentex subsidiary. Naturally, the pack did not take kindly to this. Michael Whitman — the Philodox and alpha — took the ruthless approach. The father was, after all, Glass Walker Kinfolk. Such treason was not to be allowed. The pack staged a kidnapping and interrogation.

The father wasn't necessarily evil; a lot of innocent people can be found to work for Pentex. But in this case, Lucas' father knew the significance of the tainted corporation he worked for. During the interrogation, it was found that his largest motivation for staying with the company was fear of his superiors. He attempted to bargain for his life with the pack, offering information if they would only allow him to leave the city. He played on his son's sympathy, claiming the company had threatened the rest of his family. Whitman flatly told him he was lying to a Philodox.

Whitman offered the man a quick and honorable death for the information he sought, a bargain to which he finally agreed. Despite Lucas' pleas to the contrary, Whitman then shot the man through the head, killing him instantly. In a knee-jerk reaction of grief, Lucas immediately challenged Whitman for the alpha position of the pack, claiming Whitman had no right to act like such an "inhuman bastard".

Whitman's acceptance was predictable; the challenge he set was astounding. He requested that the Sept's Master of the Challenge come up with a set of questions on Garou morality and ask them of the two disputants. The Master would then judge for herself who would make the better alpha of the young pack, based on the answers they gave.

I have to admit I was originally floored by this challenge. Working as the Storyteller, I had the Master accept this request, informing both parties that the challenge would take place in the board room, with witnesses, in two days hence. This gave me time between game sessions to work on a set of questions that I believed would not only force both characters to think, but ensure Lucas would be forced to *rethink* exactly why he had challenged. I also invited two other people to sit in on the game with previous characters they had played, as witnesses to the challenge.

The next session still stands out in my memory as one of the most intense roleplaying sessions that I have ever run. Dead silence hung over the pack as questions issued back and forth between the Master of the Challenge and the two disputants. They both stammered through the first two questions, not really answering them to anyone's satisfaction, but they settled down to it with the third:

MASTER: How many humans is too many to kill to protect the Veil?

LUCAS: One.

MASTER: One? Are you saying that you will walk away from a Veil breach and leave witnesses alive to tell the tale?

LUCAS: No. I would my duty and kill those witnesses. But one is still too many.

[Lucas won that round.]

MASTER: Would you sacrifice yourself to save a pack of wolves?

LUCAS: Yes.

MASTER: How about a family of humans?

LUCAS: Yes.

MASTER: I turn the question to Mr Whitman.

WHITMAN: No and no.

MASTER: Why not?

WHITMAN: Because I am more useful to the fight for Gaia alive. What is a family of humans or a pack of wolves going to do for Gaia except mate?

[There were nods from around the table. Whitman won that round.]

[Finally, it grew very interesting as we settled down to the questions that made Lucas think about the situation with his father.]

MASTER: Is the Wyrm evil?

LUCAS: Yes.

MASTER: Then would you say all who try to help and support the Wyrm are evil as well?

LUCAS: No.

MASTER: So the enemy is merely… misguided.

LUCAS: Yes.

MASTER: Does that give us the right to kill them? Are you saying the Black Spiral Dancers are just 'misguided'?

LUCAS: Um. Yes.

[By this point, I think he was trying to save his position on his father.]

MASTER: Does killing them make us any better than they are?

LUCAS: No.

[There was a lot of muttering on *that* reply.]

MASTER: Your question, Mr Whitman. Is the Wyrm evil?

WHITMAN: Yes.

MASTER: Are all who try to help and support the Wyrm evil as well?

WHITMAN: They may not necessarily be "evil", but they are at least pawns of evil, and thus we kill them because we are at war.

[Round to Whitman. Lucas was starting to get that doubtful look on his face. Was he wrong in his challenge? But he pressed on.]

MASTER: You follow a heavy trace of the Wyrm's taint, and find it leads to the cradle of a six-month-old child. While the child itself seems innocent, all signs point to the infant being Bane-possessed. What do you do?

LUCAS: I… don't know. I just… don't know.

WHITMAN: I make certain, then kill it.

[A very cold answer from Whitman in his usual flat tones, but deemed the correct one. Lucas looked ready to cry, clearly sickened by the sheer thought of it.]

MASTER: You discover a Black Spiral Dancer, and pursue it until it eventually seeks refuge in a heavily crowded nightclub. How do you deal with this situation?

[This question inspired a lot of debate. Were they with their pack or without? The Master asked them to give an answer to both situations. Neither of them came up with a satisfactory answer, although Lucas came close. He said he would wait out the Dancer. The Master replied: What if, in the meantime, the Dancer has called his pack for support? And so he stumbled there. *Both* of them replied that if the Dancer shifted into Crinos first, the Veil was already damaged and so they'd plow into combat, and worry about witnesses afterward.]

MASTER: So you would kill everyone in the nightclub?

WHITMAN: Only those not affected by the Delirium.

MASTER: A handy plan. Unfortunately, how would you tell?

WHITMAN: I'd find out… er, some way.

[Lucas was the same, although he was more humble and he admitted he didn't know how he would tell. Nobody won that round.]

MASTER: Would you slay one man, innocent or no, to save possibly hundreds?

WHITMAN: Yes. I believe in the greater good.

MASTER: Your question, Mr Lucas.

[Lucas knew exactly what this question was aimed at. He answered very quietly and near tears.]

LUCAS: It would depend on the situation. It's hard to know the answer when you're just discussing theory.

[Both answers were considered appropriate.]

MASTER: Would you kill someone you love if it would preserve everything you — and they — lived for and stood for?

WHITMAN: I would kill my own brother if need be.

[Another flat answer. The cold swiftness of this reply made even the Master of the Challenge blink. Whitman was fast cementing a reputation among the Glass Walkers as a cold and emotionless Garou.]

MASTER: Your question, Mr Lucas.

LUCAS: To be honest, I'm not sure if I could. If there was reason, I would understand that they had to die, but kill them myself? There's… emotional difficulty involved.

[Round to both, really. With the favor to Lucas.]

At this point, Lucas knew that he had challenged for the wrong reasons, yet when both disputants were asked if either would like to step down before the final decision was made, he shook his head quietly. He had noted the coldness of his alpha's answers, and while they made him efficient, he did not believe such an apparently cold-hearted person should be alpha.

So who do you think won? Well. As the Master announced that the floor was open for any final debate before her choice is made, the two witnesses from the sept to this challenge spoke their piece, listing their own thoughts on the answers both had given. During this, Whitman, annoyed at having his cold answers analysed and dug at, made the mistake of retorting that he has no respect for his pack, as they are "all too human."

As this sunk in, two angry pack members immediately stood and challenged him. They were out of line; this was still the middle of the first and official challenge. The Master bade them sit, and turned her eyes to Lucas, who had just been asked, almost mockingly, if he was sure he was Garou. His reply? No. He had no idea whether he should be here. Not when doing so seemed to deny the morality he had believed in up until this point.

The common consensus was that neither Lucas nor Whitman was a correct choice for the alphaship. One had drive, but no respect, either for his pack or life around him. One had respect, but no drive. The Master of the Challenge looked at them both blandly, turned to the beta of the pack, and nominated him alpha.

Whitman left the room in silence. Lucas acknowledged the wisdom of the decision. Neither won, but both had been given a lot to think about. The game shifted focus quite dramatically at that point; from "Rargh! Kill the Wyrm!" to "Are we so certain we're doing the right thing?"

And the raising of that question brought far more depth to the players, and the game, than I could have hoped for.

The moral of this particular story? Never forget the role of humanity in your games. Human morality and Garou morality are often at war, and the fact that neither is clearly right all of the time — perhaps even most of the time — can inspire some truly wonderful stories. There are repercussions to sociopathic acts of violence; whether from the surviving victims, law enforcement agencies or the perpetrator's own conscience. Don't be hesitant to act on them.

A Storytelling Game of Savage Horror

By Ethan Skemp

It's right there on the splash page of the rulebook. We cite it as the thing that differentiates **Werewolf** from the other World of Darkness roleplaying games — not "Personal Horror," not "Reality on the Brink," not "Passion and Horror," not "Modern Fantasy," not "Righteous Fury."

Of course, all those other themes, distilled down to their bare-bones mission statements, actually fit very nicely within **Werewolf**'s confines, **Werewolf** being the sprawling, versatile monstrosity of a game that it is. Personal horror? Of course; show me the werewolf that comes to his senses after going into the Thrall of the Wyrm that *isn't* undergoing personal horror, and I'll show you a player who's no good at roleplaying (or is choosing to play an utter psychopath very, very well). Reality on the Brink? Sure; the cosmic struggle of the Triat and the Garou's war to keep the Wyrm from being the one to rewrite the universe's rules would seem to fit that bill rather nicely. Passion and Horror? Naturally; the churning forces of Rage and Gnosis within a werewolf tend to imply that he'll feel passions on a scale that would frighten us humans. Modern Fantasy? Yes, if somewhat more obliquely; the techno-shamans of the Glass Walkers and the spirits of the urban Umbrascape qualify. And Righteous Fury? Well, there's no need for an example, is there?

So yes, **Werewolf** is versatile, and it can handle a wide variety of moods and themes. We knew that. (It's one of the reasons this book is a hardcover; if **Werewolf** were a simplistic hack-and-slasher, you'd be reading the **Werewolf Storytellers Pamphlet**.) But when trying to distill the essence of **Werewolf** down into a thimbleful of lycanthropic elixir, we come back to "A Storytelling Game of Savage Horror."

Why is that? The Garou are heroes, right? You get to crack jokes if you play a Ragabash or a Corax or a Nuwisha, or dress all sexy and provocative if you're a Bastet, yes? Tribes are driven by ideals like peace between peoples, honorable leadership, wisdom and enlightenment; where does the "savage horror" come in?

It's an easy answer. It comes in as soon as you say the word "werewolf."

The Garou are a fairly unique breed of werewolves, overall; they aren't "infected" by werewolf attacks, they aren't mindless animals when they change, they're not really at the mercy of the moon, and so on. Not only can they assume the werewolf form at will, they can even hold a rational dialogue when doing so (although admittedly, it's difficult) — something you never see in any werewolf movie except the comedies. In learning their vocabulary, their customs, their traditions, it's easy to start thinking of them exclusively as "Garou," and to stop using the word "werewolf" almost entirely.

If I may be so bold, this is a horrible mistake.

"Garou" is the werewolves' name for *themselves*. As your players learn to empathize with them more and more, they'll become more and more comfortable with that term — but by forgetting the "werewolf," they lose track of the fact that they're essentially playing monsters. Yes, monsters that are generally more humane and sympathetic than those you find in the average horror novel, but monsters nonetheless. But there *is* one person who needs to be willing to inject the "werewolf" back into the Garou, to play on the players' human sensibilities to show them the horrific side of the Garou's world. And yes, that person is you.

Step back outside the game and think back to before you ever picked up a White Wolf book. What did the word "werewolf" conjure up when you were younger? Why did you ever get interested in the concept in the first place? Odds are, the images that struck the deepest chord were of the near-immortal savage beast, the monster with the intelligence of the human and the morals of an animal. Yes, the concept had grown more harmless over the years by things like Fangface and *Drac Pack* and *Teen Wolf*, to say nothing of horrible SFX that wouldn't scare your cat, but there was still something deeper under all that, something frightening. The concept was still strong. You probably still respond well to it on an instinctive level, and so do your players — even if they've all but forgotten. But with a game of **Werewolf**, you can remember that visceral thrill — better, you can recreate it. And really, why wouldn't you want to?

And that brings us back around to "Savage Horror." Although this isn't the only theme that could be used to describe the Garou accurately, it is the underlying theme that, more than any other, describes the myth of the *werewolf*. The werewolf is the savage beast that wears human clothing — the unrelenting predator that is immune to pleas for mercy, an animal's fear of humans and even to bullets. It is a part of the wilderness that does not fear us humans, that can easily kill us — and that *hates* us. Not only does it knock us from our seat at the top of the food chain, it tears us into bloody chunks and cracks our bones for the marrow. Everything we've built, a werewolf can destroy, and it won't even care.

Use that. Use the savagery and horror of the werewolf myth to your benefit. When a character kills a human (for very good reasons, we're sure), work in a bit of description that likens the crunch of the victim's spine to a dog splintering a chicken bone. Play with slaughterhouse imagery — the way that corpses are littered on the ground like hunks of meat, the warm wash of blood that sinks into the earth. Emphasize that a werewolf's enemy is no more to it than a mouse is to a cat, or a cow is to a butcher. When a character frenzies, that's an ideal time to bring the savagery of the werewolf to center stage.

And by all means, don't restrict all this carnage to the player characters' doing! One of the cardinal rules of horror is that "anyone can die at any time"; the extrapolation is that in a game of savage horror, "anyone can die *horribly* at any time." If you want to have a respected elder or Kin slain by Black Spiral Dancers as a plot point, don't just let the players find a corpse with a Baneklaive wound in the back. Strongly consider having the corpse torn apart and littering the area, so blood-soaked and mangled that the characters are forced to carefully gather the remains just so they can identify *who's dead*. Not everyone horribly slain by a werewolf deserves it; that keeps them frightening.

It's the same principle in combat, particularly against "savage" opponents such as many fomori, Banes and certainly Black Spiral Dancers. Never describe a wound in terms of health levels alone — that royally undercuts the mood. Even a claw wound that does a mere health level of damage should soak the recipient's arm in blood and throb with pain. More severe wounds can tear muscle away from bone, splinter ribs, tear a fingernail or claw loose, rip loose a large patch of skin — the possibilities are limited only by your imagination. Yes, the idea is to make the players wince every now and again. That's what savage horror is all about.

(Although try to avoid making your descriptions of violence *too* florid. When you start describing skull smashing as "like exploding hairy watermelons full of spongy gray pulp," your players will indeed wince. But not in a good way.)

And don't forget to be egalitarian. If some of your players are playing less bloodthirsty Fera of other sorts, such as wisecracking Corax or courtly Kitsune, don't ease up on their behalf. Even if a Nuwisha doesn't have Rage, he's still a killing machine with the instincts of an animal — and coyotes aren't vegetarians. The Fera are part of the **Werewolf** world, and although the theme of an all-Fera game might vary somewhat from a traditional Garou chronicle, no shapeshifter is outside the war for Gaia. There are no civilians in the Apocalypse. This goes double for characters in crossover games such as mages or vampires — anyone who willingly enters the werewolves' world takes their lives in their own hands. No, you don't want to ruin your players' enjoyment of the game, and you shouldn't baptize every character in a rain of blood. But most people who sign up to play a World of Darkness game expect a little horror, and it can be very satisfying and cathartic for them to get it.

Used properly, the carnage and bloodshed of a werewolf story goes far beyond a violent vigilante story. The violence becomes not just a way of blowing off steam, but a way of reaching deep inside and playing on your players' — and your own — deep-seated emotions. A little horror keeps your players on the edges of their seats, and makes the games all the more memorable. Ultimately, the next time one of your player's characters makes a gruesome kill, tearing apart a foe with the ferocity of a rabid predator, that player might pause a bit, thinking "If I were in the World of Darkness, I'd be no more than meat to a werewolf."

And isn't that a good thing?

Index

main books

WEREWOLF: THE APOCALYPSE (REVISED)
WW3801
$29.95 U.S.

The core rulebook of the
game of Savage Horror. Hardcover.

WEREWOLF PLAYERS GUIDE SECOND EDITION
WW3108
$25.00 U.S.

All kinds of new rules and
Traits for Werewolf players.

WEREWOLF STORYTELLERS HANDBOOK (REVISED)
WW3804
$25.95 U.S.

All the secrets that Werewolf
Storytellers need to know.

tribe books

Tribebooks contain vital character information for players and Storytellers.

TRIBEBOOK: BLACK FURIES
(REVISED)
WW3851 $14.95 U.S.

TRIBEBOOK: BONE GNAWERS
(REVISED)
WW3852 $14.95 U.S.

TRIBEBOOK: CHILDREN OF GAIA
(REVISED)
WW3853 $14.95 U.S.

LITANY OF THE TRIBES VOLUME 2
WW3381 $20.00 U.S.
Combines the Get of Fenris, Fianna
and Glasswalkers Tribebooks.

LITANY OF THE TRIBES VOLUME 3
WW3382 $20.00 U.S.
Combines the Red Talons, Shadowlords
and Silent Striders Tribebooks.

LITANY OF THE TRIBES VOLUME 4
WW3383 $22.95 U.S.
Combines the Silver Fangs, Stargazers,
Uktena and Wendigo Tribebooks.

other supplements

ANANASI
WW3082 $17.95 U.S.
Rules for playing the shapechanging spider-people of the World of Darkness

**ART OF WEREWOLF:
THE APOCALYPSE**
WW3803 $14.95 U.S.
The lavishly illustrated art book that accompanied the Werewolf limited edition now available individually.

**AXIS MUNDI:
THE BOOK OF SPIRITS**
WW3067 $18.00 U.S.
Details Gaia's family of spirits, from mighty totems to the Naturae of trees, stones and rivers.

BASTET
WW3075 $18.00 U.S.
The secrets of the elusive werecats revealed.

BOOK OF THE WEAVER
WW3209 $19.95 U.S.
Learn the secrets of the most powerful member of the Triat, one of the greatest forces the Garou know.

BOOK OF THE WYLD
WW3113 $17.95 U.S.
Explore the source of all creation in this book detailing the Wyld's awesome power.

**BOOK OF THE WYRM
SECOND EDITION**
WW3109 $18.00 U.S.
The cosmic enemy of the Garou revealed.

**CHRONICLE OF
THE BLACK LABYRINTH**
WW3404 $12.95 U.S.
A compilation of Wyrm lore, collected from eyewitness accounts throughout the ages.

CORAX
WW3077 $15.00 U.S.
This Changing Breed Book details the society of the wereravens.

CROATAN SONG
WW3112 $17.95 U.S.
Werewolves in Pre-Columbian North America.

**FREAK LEGION: A PLAYERS
GUIDE TO FOMORI**
WW3066 $12.00 U.S.
Now you can play a fomor, courtesy of Pentex, Black Dog Game Factory and the Wyrm! For adults only.

GUARDIANS OF THE CAERNS
WW3212 $15.95 U.S.
The sourcebook about the secret lairs of werewolves.

GURAHL
WW3079 $17.95 U.S.
The werebears rise from their slumber in this Changing Breed Book.

**HENGEYOKAI:
SHAPESHIFTERS OF THE EAST**
WW3063 $20.00 U.S.
Witness — and play — the shapechangers of the Far East.

KINFOLK: UNSUNG HEROES
WW3074 $15.00 U.S.
Offers information for playing the mortal kin of Garou or even the kin of other Changing Breeds.

MOKOLÉ
WW3081 $19.95 U.S.
Details the werecrocodilians of the World of Darkness.

NAGAH
WW3084 $19.95 U.S.

NUWISHA
WW3076 $12.00 U.S.
Spotlights the werecoyotes, tricksters par excellence.

RAGE ACROSS EGYPT
WW3114 $17.95 U.S.

RAGE ACROSS THE HEAVENS
WW3110 $19.95 U.S.
A book about Garou prophecies and celestial influences, detailing the greater forces at work in the Umbral skies and providing many heavenly Gifts.

**RAGE ACROSS THE WORLD
VOLUME 1**
WW3069 $20.00 U.S.
Combines Caerns: Places of Power and Rage Across Russia.

**RAGE ACROSS THE WORLD
VOLUME 3**
WW3071 $18.00 U.S.
Combines Rage Across New York and Rage Across the Amazon.

RATKIN
WW3080 $19.95 U.S.
The Ratkin take their rightful place among the werebeasts with this Changing Breed Book.

ROKEA
WW3083 $17.95 U.S.
A complete reference to the savage and deadly weresharks.

THE SILVER RECORD
WW3210 $14.95 U.S.
The fabled account of Garou origins. Tradeback.

**SUBSIDIARIES:
A GUIDE TO PENTEX**
WW3211 $17.95 U.S.
The divisions of the Wyrm's industrial conglomerate revealed.

UMBRA (REVISED)
WW3111 $19.95 U.S.
A essential guide to the spirit world of the Garou.

WEREWOLF: THE DARK AGES
WW3800 $21.95 U.S.
Rule for playing medieval shapechangers. A crossover with Vampire: The Dark Ages.

**WEREWOLF CHRONICLES
VOLUME 1**
WW3207 $15.00 U.S.
Combines Werewolf: Rite of Passage and Valkenberg Foundation.

**WEREWOLF CHRONICLES
VOLUME 2**
WW3208 $15.00 U.S.
Combines Ways of the Wolf and Monkeywrench! Pentex.

A WORLD OF RAGE
WW3213 $19.95 U.S.
Updates players and Storytellers on the struggle of Garou across the globe.

**WEREWOLF STORYTELLERS
COMPANION**
WW3802 $14.95 U.S.
The essential screen and resource book for Werewolf Storytellers.

for more information visit us online:
www.white-wolf.com

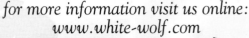

It is the Year of our Lord 1230.

This new age is a time of war.

A time to take up arms in the darkness
against those who would rob you
of your dark birthright.

Draw your sword,
hone your wits
and shore up your faith.

The time has come to join the War of Princes.

May 2002